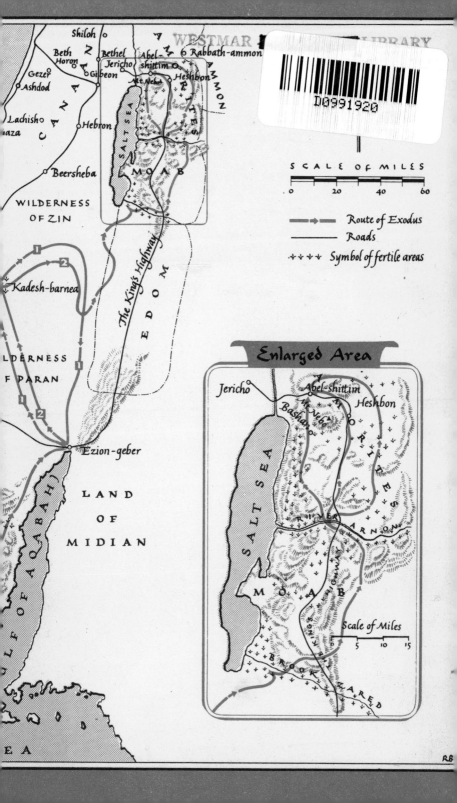

SCALE OF MILES

0   20   40   60

→ → → → Route of Exodus

——— Roads

✦ ✦ ✦ ✦ Symbol of fertile areas

Enlarged Area

Jericho

Abel-shittim

Bashan

Mt. Nebo

Heshbon

SALT SEA

ARNON

M O A B

BROOK

ZARED

Scale of Miles

5   10   15

Shiloh

Beth Horon

Bethel

Abel-shittim

Gezer

Jericho

Gibeon

Rabbath-ammon

Ashdod

Mt. Nebo

Heshbon

Lachish

Hebron

Gaza

SALT SEA

Beersheba

MOAB

WILDERNESS OF ZIN

CANAAN

AMMON

Kadesh-barnea

The King's Highway

EDOM

WILDERNESS OF PARAN

Ezion-geber

LAND OF MIDIAN

GULF OF AQABAH

RB

MOSES

SHOLEM ASCH

MOSES

TRANSLATED BY
MAURICE SAMUEL

G. P. Putnam's Sons, New York

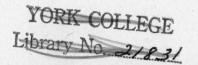

PART I

The event is the seed sown in the fields of time. The seed decays and is lost. That which blossoms from it is truth; for, as it is written: Truth shall spring out of the earth.

CHAPTER ONE

MANY and diverse were the reasons which impelled Rameses the Second to abandon the ancient royal capital, sanctified by many dynasties, namely the city of Thebes on the banks of the Nile, and to settle in Rameses, on the frontier road which led to the lands of the Asiatics.

Quite apart from the threat of the Asiatic countries, which in those days were surging forward and outward, with increasing pressure on Egypt's borders, quite apart from the need to keep an eye on that turbulent Eastern world, Rameses was dominated by a building mania; and from his earliest years he had been haunted by the dream of a new capital, with new temples and new palaces, and with a new name—his own. Goshen was to be the site of it, Goshen, the slave province in the Delta; and this resolution Rameses carried out over the protests of his high priest—the high priest of his father, the great god Ra, flesh of whose flesh he was.

And then again: The overseer of the imperial grain reserves, the mighty prince Pontiphos, a royal fanbearer, had drawn up a plan for the utilization of countless slaves in the erection of granary cities, where the grain of the fat years could be stored up for the lean years. And Pharaoh's chief architect, the mighty prince Nabara, likewise a royal fanbearer, had applied this building plan to the district of Goshen. This decision too had its contributory reasons: reasons of economy, for the slaves would not have to be transported to another province; and natural reasons, for the soil of Goshen afforded an abundant supply of the building material itself. The rich alluvial deposit which the Nile brought down to the Delta lent itself admirably to brickmaking, for it dried quickly in the sun. Moreover, the soil was rich in calk and lime, which, mixed with straw, furnished a strong building material. This the slaves would be able to produce locally and deliver without undue loss of time at the building sites.

Ever since the court of Rameses the Second had been transferred

3

to Rameses, the lower Delta, hard by Goshen, had become a favorite playground for Pharaoh and his entourage; for here they were able to hunt great birds with falcons, with arrows, and with curved wooden missiles, a sport to which they were passionately addicted.

When the Nile retreated to its natural limits after an overflow, it left behind a thick scum which remained for a long time in the covered pits and marshes which the sunlight seldom penetrated. Here, among the dense growths of reed and bamboo, there was a swarming of all kinds of creeping things, of fat-bellied frogs, of slimy, crawling lizards, of emerald colored Nilotic reptiles with the heads of land creatures—rich and tempting nourishment for every variety of bird, from the predatory falcon to the proud eagle, from the white and innocent dove to the black, repulsive carrioneater, the vulture.

The hunting of birds was so intimate a part of the court life that it was strictly forbidden to all but courtiers, even though in former times it had been the occupation of slaves.

It was forbidden also to the Prince Moses; surrounded with suspicion, tinged with mystery—because there were many who did not believe that he was in truth the son of the princess Bathiya, as the Hebrews were later to call her—he was rigidly excluded from the imperial suite whenever Pharaoh went out for a day's hunting in the Goshen Delta.

In the court all sorts of rumors were current concerning the strange Prince. The higher priesthood, which, gathered about the all-powerful high priest, formed the strongest caste, repeated furtively in its own ranks that there was an entry in the Book of the Royal Chronicles concerning the foreigner: he was the son of a Hebrew slave mother, and Pharaoh's daughter had found him, as a baby, in a little ark floating on the Nile. But this story was circulated in the strictest secrecy among the court priests; it was forbidden even so much as to mention it openly. Becknekos himself, the massive-chested, powerfully built high priest, with the great smooth-shaven head, Becknekos, who was universally known to regard the Prince with hostility and distrust, would however—both covertly and even half overtly—support the official version accepted by the court; this was the version which the Prince's mother, Bathiya, tenaciously defended, that she had borne the Prince exactly as the goddess Isis had borne the god Horus: in proof whereof, she said,

4

one had only to look upon his face, which, with its aquiline nose, so strongly recalled the falcon-face of the god Horus.

In any case, and for this reason or another, the young Prince was forbidden to approach the swamp channels, which stretched away like extended, withering arms from the Nile. This was known to every overseer of Pharaoh's household, and the prohibition was enforced with the strictest Egyptian discipline by the Prince's closest associates and guardians, as it had been ever since the court had been transferred to Rameses, hard by the slave province of Goshen.

Thus it came about that a death chill of terror descended on one of the eunuch overseers when, accompanying the young Prince on a morning ride, he saw the latter give his horse free rein, so that instead of turning toward the riverbank, as he had aways done, he suddenly galloped off along the downward slope which led to the district of Goshen. A dew of anguish broke out on the heavy white flesh of the eunuch and shone like pearls in the sunlight; his clean-shaven head reflected the dazzling rays as he strove with all his might to catch up with the galloping Prince.

"Son of Ra!" he gasped, in mortal panic. "Flesh of the god's flesh! Child of Isis! Spirit of Horus! Halt! Halt! Halt!" At last he managed to reach the Prince's side.

"I am going down there, to the swamps, to hunt the birds. The air is thick with them."

"In thy mother's name, child of Ra, spirit of the gods, not down there! The Delta is locked to thee, son-god of Horus; it is chained off, forbidden!"

"Why is it forbidden?" asked the Prince in agitation, and as always when he became agitated his speech was blocked; he barely managed to stammer the words, and his handsome face, with its slender, aquiline nose, reminiscent of the god Horus, took on a still deeper flush now that to the excitement of his spirit was added the excitement of the wild ride.

"Thou who hast imbibed wisdom from the all-knowing god Thoth, who cured thee of the wounds inflicted on thee by thine uncle, the god Set, thou knowest well that thy mother, the child of Ra, found thee—even as Isis found Horus—floating in the swamps of the Delta; even so did they find the dead body of thy noble father, Osiris, the god of the dead, whom thy wicked uncle, Set, slew out of jealousy for thy mother Isis. Down there thine uncle Set waits

5

in ambush for thee, thine uncle with whom thou art forever at war, to take revenge for thy father's death."

All this was familiar enough to the young Prince. He knew what the Egyptians believed him to be—a reincarnation of the god Horus. But he also knew that it was his "mother," Pharaoh's daughter, who had given currency to this belief, in line with the strange circumstances under which she had found him when he was a tiny child. Even in early years he had rejected this fable. He knew that what the priests, his enemies, whispered among themselves, was not merely inspired by malice: that he was the child of a Hebrew slave woman of Goshen, who had saved him from the decree of an earlier Pharaoh condemning to death all the male children of the Hebrews. She—this Hebrew slave woman, his real mother—had placed him in a little ark on the surface of the Nile, and there Pharaoh's daughter had found him. This was the true story of his origin. Yet how did he know it? It seemed to him that it was from his nurse's breast that he had absorbed the memory, together with the injunction never to forget it. He had been too young to retain the recollection of her actual words; too young also to remember her features. But the injunction had somehow become part of him. And there was something more: there was the secret messenger—if he could call a "messenger" someone who had never uttered a message, who had only haunted him—the messenger who could only have come, it seemed to him, from his own family: this was the mysterious girl—and she did, in fact, turn out to be his sister—who by hidden and devious ways found a kind of access to him even in Pharaoh's guarded and surrounded court.

His defiance of the overseer's authority, at this moment, had little to do with a desire to go hunting. What stirred him was the longing to visit, if only for once, the slave province, and to set eyes on his brothers, the slave builders of the city of Pithom, which lay not far from the hunting grounds. And it occurred to him that chance might lead him to his own, to a mother, a father, a brother.

He could never get rid of the idea that the tall, swarthy sunburned girl in the dress of an Egyptian villager, who so often managed to post herself at the gate of Pharaoh's court, was linked to him by blood. Sometimes she would eye him steadily, and sometimes, he thought, she would throw a significant glance at him. Even now, while he was riding toward the slave city, she was following him afar; he did not see her, but he could feel her gaze

6

on his back. And there welled up in him a hunger to meet with his own, to see his brothers at their labors, to taste the bitterness of their lives on his lips, to feel on his own body the sting of the overseer's lash.

Night after night he had been kept awake by this desire and had revolved plans for its fulfillment. He knew that hundreds of eyes watched him constantly, that every step of his was observed by visible and invisible overseers, most of them set on by the priesthood. And on this occasion, when he had drawn away a certain distance from his attendant, he had suddenly given his horse free rein, after heading it in the direction of Goshen. But he also knew that he would not carry it off easily. Humble slave though he was, the attendant had been authorized by the priests to call for help if need be and to bring the Prince back to the court even by force. The task before him, therefore, was to win the terrified attendant over to his plan; and he had decided to pit authority against authority, to play on the idolatrous feelings of the slave, to play them off against his instructions.

"Do the people of Egypt know that to me alone, the child of Isis, to me alone among Pharaoh's offspring has been entrusted the secret speech, the Ineffable Name of the god Ra, which my mother drew out of him when he was old and sick; yes, when my mother turned her witchcraft on him and poisoned him with the spittle of his own mouth? All the gates of the night are open before me. By means of the moonlight I penetrate all mysteries, and with the power of the Ineffable Name I work miracles."

The attendant almost fell off his horse. His enormous head started, his body trembled, and finally he fell rather than slid off his mount. He stretched himself out, face to earth, at the feet of the Prince's horse.

"Stand up and face me!" commanded Moses in a hard, metallic voice.

The attendant rose to his feet and stood with bowed head, not daring to look the Prince in the face; for it seemed to him that the fiery rays of Ra, when the god sent them blazing in the early morning over the waves of the Nile, were now streaming from the Prince; he felt the heat of them scorching his flesh.

And in truth a change had come over the Prince himself when he had spoken the words of conjuration. The rays did not issue from his face, but from his eyes. These had become two blazing

7

wells, and the amber shafts of light which darted from them and alighted on the flesh were like arrows of command, which burned whatever they touched. Invisible, they penetrated and wounded. The piercing quality of his gaze entered into the sound of his voice, and the sound of it was like the ringing of a hammer.

"Child of Ra, flesh of his own flesh!" The attendant trembled like a leaf in the wind, terrified lest one word uttered by the god would cause the earth to open and swallow him alive. "What is thy wish?"

"Mount thy horse and ride behind me. And whatever thou seest, whatever thou hearest, let it be buried in the tomb of thy heart!"

"Yes, child of Ra, flesh of his own flesh."

But when the attendant had mounted, he could not stir from the place. It was as though man and horse had both become petrified.

"Why dost thou not take thy place behind me?" asked Moses, in the same commanding, metallic voice.

The attendant shivered and panted. He saw before him the death which the god could bring upon him with a single utterance. Yet he did not stir. Still shivering, he babbled:

"Child of Ra! How shall I go away from the bank of the Nile when the scribe has entered in his report, 'Two horses, for the Prince and his attendant, to the river bank'?"

A soft smile touched the fine lips of the Prince. He thought: "Slavery is stronger than death."

He said: "In the scribe's report a fiery reed will enter the words, 'Two horses for the Prince Moses and his attendant, to the land of Goshen.'"

Only then was the overseer able to stir from the place. It was as though the Egyptian chains of discipline had fallen from his body.

As far as his eye could reach, Prince Moses saw a broad red-mud field stretching to the horizon. The field was covered with rows of workers, long, snakelike lines in measured rhythm. One could not, at first, make out separate persons; not because of the distance, but because each worker was so dependent on the mass of other workers that the individual was lost to the view, became submerged in the rhythmic chain.

From the dried swampland hardened in its channels came endless lines of slaves bearing on their naked shoulders wooden beams from each end of which hung two wicker baskets of equal weight. These, the carriers, brought the loam to the places where the treaders

8

waited. The treaders helped to unload the baskets, and the material was then mixed with picked straw. The treaders then stepped into the muddy loam, in which half their naked bodies were immersed, and trod out the material. When this part of the task was completed, other slaves lugged the ready material to the brickmakers, and these, with quick and skillful strokes, fashioned the large bricks. Other naked slaves then arranged the bricks in long lines, spacing them so that the sun could bake them.

At one end of the chain there was a high, square wall which served as a tally. The last two workers in the chain covered the front of the wall with the baked bricks. To one side of the wall, neatly poised on one knee, sat a scribe who entered the number of deposited bricks on a clay tablet. Wherever the wall was not covered, the shortage in the tally of bricks was at once revealed; and if it was not made good, punishment followed for the slaves.

The scribe at the end of each chain of slaves was an Egyptian; this could be seen at once from the shaven head, the shaven cheeks, and the shaven lips. His loincloth, too, was of a special form; made of fine Egyptian linen, it hung down like an apron. His naked body was Negro black, with broad back and muscular arms.

The slaves were Semites. One perceived it from the short black beards—some of them goat pointed—and the earlocks which hung down their cheeks. They too were naked, but their loincloths consisted of strips of coarse sackcloth strung around their loins. Nor did they wear their loincloths as ornaments, with knitted fringes, in the manner of the Egyptians; the cloths served merely to conceal their nakedness, and were therefore worn, not loose, but tied tight with strings and ribbons.

Their bodies showed the ribs and backbone starkly. In the blazing sunlight the black-scorched skin, wetted by the sweat of anguish and labor, glistened like copper. The faces were dumb and careworn, the lips thin, close locked, parched. But in those grim faces, with their long, hooked noses, the eyes blazed as if they were emitting from themselves all the accumulated bitterness and pain and rage of their owners. They did their work in dull silence; their motions and footsteps maintained a heavy rhythm under the threat of the whips, woven of river rushes, which were poised in the hands of the two Hebrew guards accompanying each line of slaves.

The failure to supply the full tally of bricks was charged not to individual workers but to the entire group, which would be pun-

9

ished by the imposition of night work and the diminution of the food allowance. This was why every line of slaves had its Hebrew guards to drive their brother-slaves on and to be responsible for them to the scribe. The scribes were responsible to the overseers, the overseers to the higher officers, and these to the commissioner of labor.

Thus, like a fanged snake, the slave chain of Egypt stretched from the swamps to the throne of Pharaoh.

Standing there, the young Prince saw the slave rings linked into each other until it seemed that the earth was covered with them. Naked, oppressed, stooping, with matted hair and beards, they stamped and wallowed in the slimy pits. When the eye finally became accustomed to the scene, the various details of the work became more evident. Then it was perceived that by no means all the slaves were engaged in the making of bricks; there were numbers of them harnessed to each other with long strands of rope. The endless succession of darkly lustrous bodies fused into a monstrous beast with multiple body, and countless arms and legs; at a given moment it leaned and pulled, with body, arms, and legs, at the gigantic stone to which it was harnessed. On the stone itself sat an Egyptian scribe; the heave and pull of the beast was timed by the rod which he held in his hand.

At first it had seemed to Moses that the chains of slaves at the brickmaking, and those that were harnessed to the huge stone were not composed of individual humans; they were like strings of ants crawling along a road, or like an infinitely extended centipede crawling over the hot sands of the desert. But the longer he gazed, the more clearly there were lifted out for him, from the fused masses of slave bodies, the component individuals and their faces. He began to distinguish separate persons, persons with their own heads, bodies, hands, feet; persons with their own, separate features, expressions, demands; eyes which glowered in black faces, penetrating the thick tangle of their overhanging eyebrows as with shafts of flame, menacing and forewarning; eyes which were extinguished, resigned, fixed expressionlessly on the distance; and eyes which were fixed in an unchanging side glance, like the eyes of obdurate donkeys, which endure the cruelest punishment but refuse to stir from their places.

He observed how, here and there, a body would define itself in the middle of the slave chain, would straighten out, would stretch, and remain standing in dumb, heavy contumacy under the burning lash of the overseer, until it collapsed and was pulled out of the line and shoved aside like dead vermin in the sand. He observed also, here and there, bodies which struggled in furious rebellion against the harness, and which tried to lift wild arms against their oppressors. But the vast majority of them endured in brutish torpor the burden of the harness and the sting of the lash.

Moses suddenly became aware that his hands were trembling, that he was shuddering from head to foot as though he were standing up against a tornado. A tide of bitterness rose in his heart. He was one of them! He had been born among them; his father, his mother, his brother were there. It was for their sake that he had put himself in danger, defying Pharaoh's command by coming to look on them. But he felt more than that: he had come to them because he had been called; someone was waiting here who would lead him to his family. But at this moment, as he gazed at the slave chains, he could not identify himself with them. Were these his brothers? How could that be? They were slaves, he was a prince of the household of Pharaoh. He was angry with himself for the feelings of distance and alienation, even of contempt, which these slaves awoke in him. The confusion in him increased. A sacred flame had been kindled in him, and his flesh quivered with fury; and this fury was directed not only at the overseers and at the system which was Pharaoh's, but at their victims, at the slaves. "Slaves! Slaves! Slaves! What are they to me?"

Then his eye fell on another scene. At a distance sat a number of women, with baskets of food and cruses of water. From time to time a group of slaves would be unharnessed, and the exhausted men, their bodies glittering with sweat and starred with drops of blood, would stagger, with their last energies, to the group of women.

The women would stand up and run toward the men, receive them tenderly, pass their hands over them to wipe the sweat from their streaming faces and bodies. They took off their headkerchiefs and placed them on the heads of the men, to shield them from the savage sunlight; they helped them on till they reached the place of rest. Some of the women made their men lie down in their laps, and with their tongues licked away the drops of their anguish; they lifted the cruses to the men's lips, and from their longing eyes looks of comfort and consolation were poured on the recumbent and tormented figures.

Moses caught from the distance the sound of the consoling words which issued from the lips of the women and caught more clearly the meaning of the words from the expression of the faces and eyes, as the women leaned over the men to shield them from the sun. The tenderness of the women moved him deeply. Yet there was something in this scene he could not understand. He drew closer to the group, and addressed himself to an overseer who was obviously timing the rest period of the slaves. He asked:

"Who are these women?"

"These are the wives of the slaves. They come here at the rest period of their men, and bring them food."

"Have slaves wives?" asked Moses.

"The Hebrew slaves cling to their families. We have made every effort to tear them out of their family groups, and to mix up their women; but we have not succeeded. The Hebrew women still stand by their husbands."

Moses stood motionless, a great joy in his heart. He stared with reawakened eyes and renewed feelings at the Hebrew families.

"Slaves which stand by their families are not slaves," he said to himself.

But with this thought his anger was rekindled; and it was as if the incandescent flame had darted from his heart to the extremity of his limbs.

Then he felt resting on him a pair of young eyes. They were eyes with which he was familiar; they belonged to the woman who had been following him many years, who had lingered for him at the gates of the palace or lurked in the shadows of the colonnades, because of whom he had taken the bold resolution to visit the slaves.

Now, turning, he lifted up his eyes to her. She was standing among a group of women who were occupied with their husbands, and her sensitive gaze was fixed on him. It was clear to him that she was trying to measure the effect which the scene had wrought on him; and it was clear, too, that she had measured it, for a look akin to bliss had stolen over her long, haggard, sunburned face.

Moses looked round and perceived the eunuch, his attendant, who, following him step by step, had at this moment become lost in the confused group of the resting slaves and their women. Spurred by the overwhelming impulse to see his parents, Moses sprang to

12

the woman's side, took her hand in a painful grip and said, almost as if in anger:

"Quick! Take me to my parents!"

She glided through the group, Moses following with rapid steps.

"How didst thou know that I would come today?"

"I have waited for thee every day. I knew one day thou wouldst come."

Moses spoke no more. He only hastened after the woman.

CHAPTER TWO

NOT far from the building site lay the slave camp. It consisted of light shelter tents, built of bamboo poles covered with palm leaves and mattresses of woven rushes. The life of the camp was all in the open, for most of the shelters were only three sided; only a few of them had flimsy doors of interlaced twigs.

The place was alive with movement. There were women at work in the little gardens which lay before the tents; others were occupied with housework, preparing the meals on the stone altar stoves from which rose mingled steam and smoke; still others carried jars of water on their heads or suspended from shoulder pieces, or were busy at the millstones grinding grain.

Moses paused from time to time at one of the tents, ignoring the impatience of his guide—Miriam, she had said she was called. He looked with eager eyes on the life about him, he noted the industriousness of the people. There were many children in the camp, of various ages, like flocks of fowl. But he observed that if there were any boys among the children they were kept out of sight— and he knew the reason.

But if he had not known the reason he would soon have learned it. For suddenly he heard a screaming of voices. Turning, he saw how a mother, of large and powerful build, with long, pendant breasts, was struggling and wrestling with Egyptian guards. He saw her clutching fiercely two terrified infants, which she held tightly to her body; screaming with wide-open mouth, her eyes filled with terror and fury, her hair flying in disorder, she fought off the men who were trying to drag the children away from her.

Other women left their work in the gardens or at the altar stoves, and came to her help. A furious battle developed between the women and the guards. The two threatened infants wailed at the top of their voices, and the mother fastened her teeth in the naked arm of a guard who had taken a grip on one of the infants and was pulling it away from her. Another guard snatched a short dagger from his

14

belt, and stabbed the infant which the mother was still holding firmly. A jet of blood covered the mother, child, and guard with crimson. And now the mother lost her strength; she only held the stabbed child to her breast, to cover up the wound. Meanwhile the guards had snatched away the other infant, and had made off with it, leaving the dying child in the mother's arms.

Moses had turned white. His lips quivered, and his hand sought the dagger at his girdle. But before he had drawn it, he felt the strong grip of Miriam's hand on his arm.

"Look well, and see everything, and be silent!" she said.

"Who are they?" asked Moses, though he knew the answer.

"Pharaoh's guards, who have come to look for the men-children which the Hebrew women have hidden from him."

"Yes, yes, I know it."

Miriam took him by the hand and led him away.

He heard a burst of laughter behind him; it was like the bursting of a stream of water through a dike. When he turned he saw the mother whose one child had been slaughtered, the other snatched away, standing with gaping mouth; her eyes glared out of her earth-black face, her hair was tumbled over her naked body. She held in her arms the dead child, and peal after peal of laughter came from her mouth.

A woman yelled after the disappearing guards:

"For every one you snatch away, we will have ten others."

"We will sow our seed like the sand on the seashore," another woman screamed from the entrance of her tent.

"Come, they are waiting for you," said Miriam; and Moses, starting from his trance, followed her silently.

They came at last to a corner of the camp where the shelters were no longer coverings of woven rushes on bamboo poles; here the walls were of Nile clay, and the palm leaves of the roofs were also covered with clay. The lots about the shelters were better tended; they were covered with rows of beans, with oats and barley, every growth sharply separated in its own bed. Near some of the huts there were little ponds, fed from the Nile, and on these ducks and other fowls swam about.

Finally Miriam led Moses to a hut of bamboo reeds sheltered by a bamboo grove. At the entrance, over which hung a woven rug, a family of three waited for him.

15

"This is your father Amram, your mother Jochebed, and your brother Aaron, Prince Moses," said Miriam.

Moses fixed his eyes on his mother's face and could not tear them away. It was a face plowed in every direction with lines and folds; the skin was burned and worked through and through. The throat was high and swollen. She returned his gaze from eyes with enormous whites netted with red veins; and the sockets of her eyes were red too. In her emotion she had drawn apart her twisted, swollen lips, and Moses saw the single tooth which still clung to her gums. He looked down at the work-weary arms, which were folded, as in embarrassment, and then at the bare feet, with the thick toes, crooked, like the roots of plants. A feeling of warmth stole through him. As if across a thick mist he recalled those features out of his earliest childhood, when he had lain at this woman's breast.

What he perceived more clearly in his mother's face, with its countless furrows gathered about the lips and eyes, was the agony of all the Hebrew mothers of Egypt, robbed of their children. In her hands he perceived the hands of all the Hebrew mothers who had ever struggled with demons for the lives of their little ones; in her glance, the last desperate glance which they threw after a disappearing child.

He bent down to her, and put his arms about her neck, in a gesture which she had not dared to make; and he kissed the salt tears which ran down her cheeks.

It was only when the greetings had ended that the Prince began, stammeringly:

"Who are you? Where do you come from? What is your origin?"

"We are Hebrews—that is our name; we are sprung from the father of our people, Abraham, who came from beyond the river. But we are also called Israel, the children of Israel, which is the name of another forefather of our people, who brought us here, to Egypt. We come from the lands which lie on the other side of the desert; and it is our hope that the spirit which revealed itself to our forefathers will one day take us back there."

"How is it that you are here, in Egypt?"

"A forefather of one of our tribes was once a ruler in Egypt. He was followed here by the forefathers of our other tribes. We came here as freemen. The forefathers of our tribes were men of

16

wide possessions and great wealth. But the Egyptians overwhelmed us and enslaved us."

Moses scrutinized the young man who was answering his questions. This was Aaron, his brother. He was tall, and well built; a black beard, cut straight in the Assyrian style, enclosed his long face. His hair hung down in carefully arranged curls, like the curls of one of Pharaoh's courtiers; they were even oiled. His dress was not that of a slave—the bare loincloth drawn tight about the middle—it was, instead, a white linen robe, adorned with black and violet stripes, which covered his body from throat to sandals. And Moses marked with astonishment that his brother answered him in Coptic, in the language of the learned, of the scribes and priests of Egypt, and not in one of the Semitic dialects current among the Asiatic slaves.

"How is it," he asked, "that you are not with the slaves at their labor? Do you replace the labor in the fields with another kind?"

"Our tribe," answered Aaron, "has retained from ancient times the privilege of freedom from slave labor because we are the priests and the guardians of the tradition of all the tribes."

"And does Pharaoh recognize the privileges of your tribe?"

"The privileges of our tribe are inscribed in the records of the laws of Egypt, and are sanctified by the tradition of the Pharaohs. These privileges were fought out by the tribe in the days when the Pharaohs fastened slavery on our people. We stood upon our priestly rights and refused to be drawn into the slave labor."

"But then," returned Moses, "if Pharaoh recognizes you as the priestly tribe among the Hebrews, then he must concede that the other tribes are not slaves either, for slaves have no priests. In Egypt only freemen are permitted to serve and worship the gods; it is forbidden to slaves. Slaves have no gods."

"All this we know," answered Aaron. "And this is our proof that the enslavement of our people never became part of the law of the land of Egypt. We did not enter this country as prisoners taken in war; we came hither as freemen, on the invitation of the Pharaoh. And this is why we are so zealous in defense of the privileges of our priesthood. We are the keepers of the birth records. Every child born to our people is entered on the rolls of its tribe; and our task is to preserve the purity of the families."

"Every child?" asked Moses. "Are men-children born to you whom Pharaoh's guards do not snatch away?"

"Didst thou not hear what the woman cried after the guard?" asked Miriam. " 'For every one you snatch away we will have ten others.' "

Aaron took her up. "We have secret places, caves dug out in the wilderness, where we conceal our children from Pharaoh's overseers. There they are brought up by the midwives and nurses. Miriam, here, is one of them. The children stay with the nurses until they are old enough to be taught the traditions and laws of our people by the elders and leaders, every child learning from the preceptors of his tribe. Through our overseers we then send them to the work, together with other members of their family. Sometimes Pharaoh's overseers recognize them as newcomers, grown-up children who were not delivered up at their birth. When this happens, the lad may be taken and bricked alive into the walls of a building. But very often we are able to bribe one of the overseers or scribes, and he averts his eyes. So we maintain our line."

"But for what purpose? To what end? In order that you may live out your lives in slavery?"

"The day of our redemption will come. And that is why we have sent for thee, brother. Our father and mother, like every man and woman in Israel, await the sign from God that the time of our enslavement is ended and the time of our enlargement here."

"How are these things known to you?"

"Our elders, the keepers of the tradition, have made the reckoning that soon we shall complete the four hundred years which the God of our fathers foreordained as the term of our slavery, when he made the covenant of faithfulness with our forefather Abraham."

"But did the gods make a covenant of faithfulness with us too?"

"Not the gods," returned Aaron, sharply. "The only living God, the ruler of our world."

"The only living God," mused Moses. "There was a Pharaoh among us, in Egypt, who wanted to replace all the gods by a single God. After his death they destroyed his temples and restored the old gods. Egypt does not desire living gods, only dead ones."

"I know it," answered Aaron. "But the God of our fathers is not an unknown living god, such as Pharaoh sought to introduce among the Egyptians. He is the one and only living God of Abraham, Isaac, and Jacob."

"And what is his name?" asked Moses.

18

"Why wouldst thou know his name? No one can compel our God with magic, through the use of his name, as Isis did with Ra."

"How come Isis and Ra to thee?"

"The priestly books of the Egyptians are not sealed to me," answered Aaron.

"Thou seemest indeed to have read them. But I asked not so much for God's name as for his identity. Is he a known God?"

"He is known to us through our forefathers."

"How so?"

"Our tradition, the customs of our forebears, the truths of our faith pass from generation to generation, and our elders keep watch over the generations and the faith."

"Who are they, your elders?"

"The elders of Israel, Levites, among whom thou art numbered. They dwell apart from us, in cave retreats which we have built for them, and they con and study the tradition which has been transmitted from the first generations, and they guard it in all its purity. From the older to the younger it passes undiminished. They know our origins. They know the lives of our patriarchs. They know the words of the covenant between God and our first forefather. They may even know the name of our God; but if they do, they guard the secret, for amongst us it is forbidden to utter the name."

"Lead me to them, brother Aaron. I would learn everything which is known, or which it is permitted to know, everything concerning the patriarchs, the tradition, the faith—everything."

"How then?" asked Aaron. "Wouldst thou remain with us?"

"I will wait with you for the redemption which our God promised to our forefather."

"And exchange Pharaoh's palace for our pitiful home and our bondage?" asked his mother, joyfully.

"But is not your poverty and your bondage my poverty and my bondage?" asked Moses, drawing nearer to his mother.

He observed that she was still standing with arms folded. He took her hands in his, and looked at them closely. The hands of all the Hebrew mothers whose men-children had been snatched away from them were here, in these twisted, rootlike fingers, which were lamentations made flesh. He put the fingers to his lips.

"Thou wilt be in mortal danger if thou stayest with us."

"More mortal was the danger when thou didst prepare the little ark and set me floating on the waters of the Nile. But the God of our fathers saved me."

Old Amram lifted his arms to heaven and stammered out the words: "I render thanks to Thee, God of our forefathers, that Thou didst make fast the bond between Thee and my son even in the remoteness of the house of Pharaoh."

"My brother," said Aaron, "hast thou forgotten that we are here in slavery? How wilt thou make shift in this place, after Pharaoh's palace?"

"You are in greater freedom here than I in Pharaoh's palace," answered Moses.

Silence fell on the other members of the family. They stared at each other, made speechless by the revelation of the imprisonment which Moses suffered in freedom.

"Is the daughter of Pharaoh good to thee?" his mother asked anxiously.

"My mother Bathiya is as dear to me as thou art, mother Jochebed. Has she not taken me to herself as a son? And not only on the first day, but on other days too, she has shielded me from evil and rescued me from death."

A wondering look came into the faces of Aaron and Miriam, to hear their brother speak thus; but the mother, in spite of the pang which his words sent through her, said humbly: "She drew thee out of the water, and gave thee the name Moses; she let me, thy mother, suckle thee, and she installed thee in her heart as her own son."

"She shielded me, as a lioness shields her whelps, from the hands of Becknekos, the high priest," added Moses.

Here Miriam spoke up—the most practical member of the family: "With all honor to our brother Moses, and if my words find favor with thee, my brother Aaron, it seems not wise to me that Moses should now, suddenly and without preparation, and without the knowledge of his mother, Pharaoh's daughter, leave the palace of Pharaoh. His footsteps are closely watched; the moment he is missed they will send out a thousand spies and guards. Becknekos has his spies amongst us, here in Goshen. They will come in search of him, and whether they find him or not, they will find the children we have hidden in the caves of the wilderness; we shall lose the children and their mothers. Let me counsel then, if I may, that Moses return to his mother in Pharaoh's palace, and confide to her

20

that he has found his people and his brothers, and that he would stay with them a while. She is full of goodness to thee, Moses, and she will let thee follow the call of thy heart and shield thee from thy enemies, as she has done till now."

Miriam's counsel prevailed, and Moses took leave of his father and mother, his sister and brother, embracing them and weeping on their necks. He returned to Pithom, and there he found his attendant and overseer, waiting with the horses.

When, on the road back, Moses descended into the swampy valley at the border of Goshen, he was surrounded by a terrified fluttering of countless wings. He had startled out of their hiding places the birds which nested in the reeds, and they rose in a cloud about the thunder of the galloping hoofs. Evening had fallen, and the sun was setting in a sky of blood-red waters, standing out against outlines of the single bamboo trees, which rose on a lonely little island. Suddenly he felt a blow at his breast, and reaching up from the reins his hand grasped a frightened dove, which had flown to him as if in search of protection. He did not know what the bird wanted, but as if by instinct he took it under his tunic and made it nestle against his naked flesh. Then, as suddenly, there came a burning sting at his arm. He glanced round and saw an infuriated falcon pecking at his arm with its sharp beak. This was it then: the falcon had been pursuing the dove and was now attacking the man who was protecting its victim.

Moses smiled and stretched out the arm with the falcon on it. He said, as if to himself:

"Bird of prey, thou hast my flesh; but the dove I shall not deliver."

And he continued to warm the fluttering, agitated dove against his breast; for it had become a sign to him.

CHAPTER THREE

I AM the god Ra; I am that which is alone.

I am the god Ra, in his first arising."

Whereof the interpretation is:

"The great god, who created himself, is the water. This is the heavenly sea, the father of the gods."

From earliest childhood, almost from the day he was brought into Pharaoh's house, from the time when he was weaned from his mother's breast, Moses had learned the dark sayings of the priests. The sun was the god Ra, who had made all things that were: "From his eyes came human kind, from his mouth, the gods."

Again and again they hammered into his mind that Ra was the god of the sun, the god of Egypt, and that Pharaoh was Ra personified, flesh of his own flesh. They taught him to sing magnificent hymns to Ra:

> "Thou art far, thy rays are upon the earth.
> Thou settest in the west,
> Earth becometh dark as death.
> Thou sustainest the son in the body of the mother.
> Thou comfortest him, that he weep not,
> Thou art the nurse in the body of the mother."

Every verse had its interpretation, which the pupil had to learn, repeating: "The Ra who created his own name."

The god Ra warmed with his light and rays not only the two lands of Egypt, but all the lands. He drew forth the green shoots from the earth, made all plants blossom, called out the buds on the trees—not only in the lands on the river Nile, but in all the lands on the face of the earth. His beams illumined and warmed friend and foe. The sun did not set when Pharaoh died; nor did it darken for the enemy when Pharaoh fought with a strange people. How can Ra be the creator of the world, if he is compelled, like the moon and the stars, to rise and set in his appointed times? How can Ra be the creator of the world if he is subject to the law which has somewhere been ordained for him? Isis obtains power over him by luring his name out of him. Apart from Ra there were many gods and goddesses who were envious of each other, who fought each other, poisoned each other.

Yet, with all their glorification of the sun and of light, the Egyptians worshiped night and death. The heavy shadow of the mighty god Osiris, into whose keeping every Pharaoh, every high courtier, passed at his death, lay thick upon the sun of Egypt. Every Pharaoh, every high officer, every high priest—others did not enter into consideration—spent all his life preparing for death, preparing his tomb, building his pyramid or cutting out a mausoleum in the rocks, accumulating the linens, the bonds, the unctions, the oils and wines and beer and bread, the furniture, and the chariot, which he was to take with him into the grave. Tens of thousands of slaves hewed at the rocks, dragged away the stones; thousands of others built, reared the pyramids. Engineers, architects, scribes, sculptors, painters, dancers, fencers, musicians, craftsmen in wood—all labored to prepare the graves, all were absorbed in producing the mummy wrappings, the vessels and the artifacts, which the dead man would take with him.

Osiris, king of eternity, ruler of the underworld, was as mighty as Ra. His temples occupied entire sections in Thebes and Memphis. Tens of thousands of slaves worked the fields which belonged to the temples, others guarded the produce which was stored in countless barns and granaries grouped about the temples. He, the god Osiris, even like Ammon-Ra, had not only his priests, but his singers, too, and even his harem, yes, his very wife, among the living.

Moses had from his earliest years felt a deep dislike for both Ra, the god of the sun, and Osiris, the god of night and death. All the priests knew, many others suspected, that the abandoned child, which Pharaoh's daughter had found, saying that she had received him as Isis received Osiris, in the swamps of the Delta, was of the children of the Hebrew slaves. And it was this Hebrew nature in him which revolted even in his youngest years against the gods of Egypt. His hatred of the god Osiris, to whom in particular his princess-mother sought to have him dedicated as a priest, was deeper than his hatred toward the other gods. He had a hatred of death; and his loathing for the gods of Egypt, and especially for the cult of the

23

dead, left a permanent impress upon his character and exerted a profound influence on the entire course of his life.

His mother, Pharaoh's daughter, was not only a priestess of Osiris, but, as the incarnation of Isis, she considered herself, and was acknowledged as, the wife of the god and the mistress of his harem. The harem was composed of the wives of the highest officials and priests. Their task was to play before the god on their harps, to tread the dance before him, and to help the goddess Isis seek out her beloved and lament his death.

Very often Bathiya would celebrate a private ritual before the god Osiris in the temple which she had in her palace. Then, as the goddess Isis, she wore horns on her head. She washed the god as a child is washed, anointed him with oils, dressed him in white robes and covered him with ornaments.

When Moses was young, she would often use him in the ceremonial as the young Horus. They put on his head the headcovering of a bird, and the Princess took him on her knee, and carried him, as Isis carried Horus in her lap, and gave him her breast to suck.

Moses remained a stranger in Pharaoh's court and from the first revolted in dislike against the rituals, and against the role of Horus which was imposed on him. Despite the strict prohibition of his preceptors and teachers, he tried even then to find a way to the Hebrew slaves, among whom his true parents were. He was drawn to them because he wanted to know the truth concerning his origin and bonds. This attitude did more than place him in a peculiar position at the court; it often put his life in danger.

In the years of his upbringing the way to his parents was completely closed to him. The alien child adopted by Pharaoh's daughter was officially recognized as a prince. Rameses the Second had been unfortunate in his offspring. Twelve sons of his had died, one had barely survived to follow him on the throne. And even though it was considered out of the question that the adopted son of the Princess should have any claim on the succession, the mere fact that there were few direct heirs made the status of the alien Prince —recognized as he was in the capacity of an actual son of the Princess—one of great importance. The high priests, and the sacerdotal circle as a whole, were the bitter enemies of the Egyptian Prince whose veins ran alien blood.

High though his status was at court, Moses was subjected to rigidly disciplined upbringing. According to the custom of the

Pharaonic court, adopted children were brought up together with princes of the blood—not in the court proper but in the military academy to which the sons of the highest families were likewise sent, irrespective of whether their careers were to lie in the army or in the priestly hierarchy.

The training in the academy was a harsh one. The cadet who was advanced to the first rank, that of "Captain of the Stable," began his classwork with the dawn and continued into the afternoon. The afternoon was devoted to athletics and military drill and maneuvers. The slightest infringement of discipline was punished with the lash. The Egyptians had a saying: "A boy has his ears behind; that is why he cannot hear except through his behind."

In the academy classroom the young Prince learned to read and write Coptic, and also mastered the secret script of the priesthood; the pictograph or hieroglyphic writing was taught only to those destined for the priestly career. They also learned the cuneiform script in use among the scribes; likewise the Semitic script of the Asiatic peoples, the Canaanites, the Hittites, the Syrians, against whom expeditions were frequently undertaken since the days of Rameses the First, the father of the reigning Pharaoh.

The curriculum included agriculture, law, and government; also astronomy, associated, naturally, with astrology, the divination of the future of individuals and of peoples, and exorcisms and magical remedies by means of the names of gods, by means of potions, and by means of fantastic decoctions, often of a filthy and revolting character; and there were elementary studies in anatomy and advanced studies in geometry, engineering, and architecture.

When the Prince was advanced to the rank of Captain of the Stable he renounced the title of Father of God, which he held as the consequence of his mother's intervention in the temple of Ammon in Rameses. To her chagrin, and the satisfaction of the priests, he elected a military career.

He took part in several expeditions which Pharaoh sent into the interior of Africa. The army crossed the continent westward and brought back hundreds of thousands of slaves, black and white, for field work. Moses went southwest into Abyssinia and distinguished himself at the capture of the capital, more by his ingenious strategy than by combative qualities.

Returning from the expedition, he was given the title of "Fan-bearer," to which he had a formal claim by virtue of his place at court. It was now his privilege to form part of Pharaoh's entourage at all formal receptions, and to stand, during these, immediately behind the throne. Thereby his prestige was greatly enhanced among the leaders of the court and his position against his enemies fortified.

But the young Prince, athletically built, iron framed, tall as a springing palm tree, pleasant to look on, highly protected at court as the adopted son of the beloved Princess, refused to take in marriage any of the daughters of the distinguished priestly families, which his mother proposed for him; he was indifferent to courtly honors, and very often he even failed to make use of his high privilege of standing immediately behind Pharaoh's throne in the company of the noblest Egyptians at formal receptions. He absented himself from great sacrificial and other ceremonials in the leading temples. He even avoided attendance in the morning processions to greet the sun, an extremely sacred ritual. And as against this he occupied himself with matters which gave currency to the suspicion that he was a disturber of the accepted order of things, an inciter of the lowest classes. He was regarded with hatred by the priests, and he alienated himself from his own circle, that which surrounded the Princess, at risk to his career and even to his life.

Because of his link with the Hebrew slave tribes of Goshen, he began to interest himself in the entire social system of Egypt.

It did not take him long to discover that his own, the Hebrew tribes, were but a small part of the slave body, an unimportant element in the general economy of Pharaoh's Egypt. So minor, indeed, was their proportion, that the scribes and temple chroniclers have not left an account of them; and no such account was chiseled into the stone documents for the later generations. They were considered simply as a tribe of brickmakers which had been consigned to the new granary city of Pithom, which Pharaoh was building in Goshen. True, they were unusually prolific, but Pharaoh's overseers had found a remedy: they killed off the sons. And against this, the Hebrew slaves exerted themselves with every ingenuity to save as many of the children as they could.

Pharaoh's army brought in slaves from near and distant countries beyond the deserts, Hittites and Ammonites, Canaanites and Moabites, Arabs from the desert and from lands about the Red Sea, Abyssinians from the south, black and white from everywhere. The entire body of Egypt was covered by the leprosy of slavery. Nor were the slaves exclusively foreigners, taken in battle or in raids;

there were native Egyptians among them. For that matter there were no free men in Egypt, except for Pharaoh, his opulent court, the upper priesthood, and the highest functionaries. And even courtiers, priests, and functionaries were so woven into the totalitarian system of the country that they were the slaves of Pharaoh. No peasant plowed the land, no gardener planted a tree, no shepherd fed his flocks, no carpenter made a table, for himself. Every product belonged to him that did not produce. All the wealth of Egypt, from the livestock and the crops to the finished handiwork of the craftsman, belonged to the state, or Pharaoh, or the temple. The craftsmen and laborers were paid from their own produce, according to their class and the value of their work. The difference between the skilled and unskilled worker consisted simply in the superior nourishment which the former received. The artist, the mason, the sculptor, the painter, the engineer, the scribe, the foreman—none of these worked of his own free will, but was driven to it by hunger. The slave overseer labored for his lord in exactly the same spirit as the slaves he drove, and there was a saying among the folk: The task of the scribe overseer is to whip the donkey on, that is, the simple laborer, but both of them are the slaves of the overlord god, the kingdom, which is Pharaoh.

The totalitarian system had become so sanctified by custom and education that the slightest reflection on it, whether by a member of the small group in power, or by one of the obscure masses, would have been regarded as a mixture of high treason and blasphemy. And in fact this way of life had established itself with such tacitness and completeness, that it never occurred to anyone to challenge it. In his wretched reed shelter the enslaved field laborer groaned that he was a donkey too heavily loaded and too lightly fed. The crushed masses gave expression to their sufferings in pathetic folk songs, tear filled and heavy hearted. They had not even a god before whom to pour out their sorrows, a faith to provide them with hope or courage. They had not even a law in which they might study what was permitted and what forbidden. In them the human species was degraded to the level of the brute, and it was on the brute level that the masses lived. The women had sexual intercourse with goats, the men with cattle; freaks and cripples were born; the cripples were thrown to the beasts, or else killed; those that grew up were destined to eternal drudgery.

Such was the state of Egypt as it revealed itself to the alien

Prince, Moses, when, as if touched by the finger of God, he was lifted to heights from which he could perceive the foulness and crime and evil in which the land was steeped. Reared in the Pharaonic court, he transcended the limits of his upbringing and was aware of that distinction between right and wrong to which all about him were blind. It was as though the alien in Moses had awakened, an alien not merely from another land or people, but from another world, where weights and measures were known for the evaluation of human deeds. The injustice which oppressed the land stung him; the voices of past generations sounded obscurely but powerfully in his blood.

As a slave in Pharaoh's household—as such he saw himself—he had no God to pray to, or place his hopes upon. The gods of Egypt had never been his gods—he had always felt for them a profound aversion; he hated their dead, mummylike forms, which filled all the temples and palaces of Egypt; and he hated above all the gods of the underworld: Osiris, Lord of Death, seated on his throne with the emblems of his rule in his hand—the crosier and the scourge—ready to judge the souls of the dead which were brought before him; Horus, his son, with the falcon-head, to whose service his princess-mother sought to dedicate Moses—the god who conducts the dead man before Osiris, takes out his heart, and weighs it. According to the judgment, the dead man was either transported to paradise, in the company of Osiris, or transformed into a black boar. Moses loathed this preoccupation with death, and all the paraphernalia that had grown around it, all the preparation for the other world which meant so much slavery, wretchedness, and tears in this world.

He could not conceal his feelings.

Next to slavery and the gods, Moses hated most the ritual of the dead. Queen Nefertori, wife of Rameses, was ill for a long time, and throughout her illness tens of thousands of slaves had been building her mausoleum in the Valley of the Kings. Other thousands had worked on the decoration and equipment of the tomb. The greatest artists of Egypt prepared the ceiling and the walls.

The ceiling was adorned with lapis lazuli; on the walls skillful painters depicted scenes from court life, and sculptors hewed out bas-reliefs in the rocks which the slaves had dragged from the remote desert and hollowed out the place for her coffin; about the stone reproduction of her mummy were grouped stone likenesses of the gods; unguent compounders, incense gatherers, linen spinners prepared the materials for the embalming of the mummy; exorcists presided over the preparations; and, along with all of these, master craftsmen, goldsmiths, woodworkers produced the furniture, the caskets, the tables, and the ornaments which the Queen would take into her tomb; while others worked on the baked meats, the oils, the fruits, the ducks, and the geese which would fill her tomb side by side with her favorite cats and dogs.

At the funeral the dead Queen and the reproductions of her mummy were set up in a posture of life at the entrance of the mausoleum; they were supported by priests in the masks of gods. Before the Queen defiled a long procession of slaves who carried into the tomb the tables and chairs, of wood and ivory, adorned with gold and lapis lazuli; the pavilion on which the Queen would rest, the beds and the linens, the salves, the perfumes, the jewels, and the chemises followed. Then came the slaves with the provisions, as if for a great banquet among the living, living fowl, woven baskets filled with bread and cakes, cruses of oil and wine, flower vases, even an ox and goats; finally, her two favorite dogs.

To the regular ceremonial of the funeral the priests added a most remarkable detail: at a certain moment the mummified Queen opened her mouth and emitted a long "o-h-h" of wonder and admiration. And when the chief priestess, in the garb of the goddess Isis, carried to the nose of the mummy the symbol of eternal life in the form of a bow—to signify that the goddess now reckoned the Queen as equal with the gods—a burst of artificial flame, the invention of the priest magicians, issued from the forehead of Isis, and shot like a rocket to heaven—a miracle manifest to all beholders.

The whole court felt exalted by this glorious sign that the Queen had been admitted among the gods as one of themselves, and had been crowned as the mother of the gods, like Isis.

It was on that occasion that a remark became current which was attributed to "the Stranger," as they called Moses in the priestly circle. It seemed that a slave, a scribe in Pharaoh's household, heard the Prince make it, and brought it to the ears of the priests; according to the report Moses had said to one of his entourage: "In Egypt the living work for the dead."

From that time on a host of spies followed Moses everywhere and listened to his every utterance.

It became known that "the Stranger" often consorted with slaves, spoke with them, evinced interest in their lot. He even permitted himself to touch slave bodies, an act which constituted defilement and disqualified him from taking part in the religious ritual in the temples, or even to set foot in them.

It even became known that with his own hand he had punished a scribe of Pharaoh's court because he had found him beating one of his slaves. It was true that the scribe himself was a slave, but he had been set in authority "over the laden donkey," and was therefore entitled to beat him if he thought it necessary. The sin of Moses, however, consisted chiefly in the fact that he, a fanbearer to Pharaoh, had used the hand devoted to his exalted function for the purpose of beating a slave. Apart from that, it was a grave misdemeanor for a noble courtier to punish a slave by direct action; a slave had to be punished by another slave; the lord only issued the order.

All of these transgressions on the part of Moses were duly brought before the highest, Becknekos.

Becknekos, the supreme high priest of the great god Ammon-Ra, was second in might to Pharaoh. He was supreme high priest not only of Ammon, but of all the gods, and his authority extended to all the temples and all the priests of Egypt.

He had reached this high position by gradual advancement, beginning his education, like all the sons of the ruling aristocracy, as a Captain of the Stable in the military academy. On graduating he had been given the title of Father of God and had proceeded through the various levels of the hierarchy; learning the secrets of his caste, he had in turn been a Veb, that is, a priest-actor, a priest-reader, a priest of purity, smelling and tasting the blood which was brought to the god, a priest-dresser, one whose task it was to robe the god Ammon; then the first assistant to the supreme high priest, and finally the supreme high priest of all the gods.

The wealth of Becknekos was beyond computation. The temple of Ammon alone had forty thousand slaves to work the temple lands. His agents collected tribute from many cities within and without Egypt's borders—cities which Pharaoh had deeded to the temples. The storehouses and granaries of the temples were filled to bursting with grain and manufactured products—bales of linen, alabaster utensils, utensils and instruments of bronze, jewels and ornaments, and countless vases and cruses of wine, honey, oil, and beer.

Thousands of trained slaves, managers, scribes, architects, engineers, painters, sculptors, workers in bronze and stone were the property of the temples. The priestly caste of Egypt was an empire within an empire, and its absolute ruler was the priest Becknekos.

In person the high priest was of mighty build, like one of the athletic figures of the gods chiseled out of Egyptian basalt. His huge head was cleanshaven, as was his face and the rest of his body. It was strictly forbidden to him to retain any hair, which might, the gods forbid, prove a nesting place for lice, or other parasites, whose presence would pollute him and unfit him for his sacred tasks. His enormous eyes, cold and pallid, were set in his vast naked face like the artificial eyes of a mummy model. Such was his appearance when he performed the ceremonial in the temple. In the court, however, he wore a thick, knotted black wig, woven like a helmet, and hanging down in folds over his ears and nape. On his massive naked chest he wore a corselet of beaten gold set with lapis lazuli and precious stones, covering him like a shield. An apron woven of the finest linen covered the lower part of his body.

Thus robed, and bearing in his hand his staff of office, the emblem of his high function, he entered the court one day and requested audience of Pharaoh.

At this audience he laid a charge against the alien Prince, who blasphemed against the gods, offended the spirits which were at peace in Osiris, defiled himself by contact with slaves, and moved them to rebellion against Pharaoh.

Moses had his good angel in Pharaoh's court—his princess-mother.

Rameses the Second had many daughters, for the female children of his concubines, unlike the males, did not perish in infancy. They lived in the harem attached to the court. Trained to dance and to play on the harp, they were Pharaoh's donative or gift daughters. When it became necessary to win the good will of an important priest, or reward a military leader for some extraordinary achievement in the field, or seal a pact with a powerful ruler of Syria or Mesopotamia who could not be defeated in battle, he was presented

31

with a daughter of Pharaoh, and acquired the title of "Pharaoh's Son-in-Law."

The daughters sat daily in the great hall of the harem; on their heads they wore wilting crowns, and their bodies were aquiver with the heat of the day. They sat in their transparent chemises of fine lawn, surrounded by naked girl slaves, who carried lotus flowers to their nostrils for refreshment, and sought to entertain them with dances to the accompaniment of harp players. It was thus that they spent their youthful years in the harem, the ornaments of Pharaoh's court, until the time came for them to be presented as an offering to one of his favorites, or as a reward for some great achievement, or as the ultimate ratification of a treaty.

Moses too had been offered one of Pharaoh's daughters when he had been promoted after his return from the Abyssinian expedition; but with the help of his mother he succeeded in evading the marriage. Bathiya felt that an indestructible bond of love held her to this child of alien birth. She endured with all patience and tenderness the difficulties, worries, and pangs which were created by the foreignness of his origin; and the more she had to endure for his sake, the more she loved him. It was beyond her to refuse him any request. She believed in his wisdom, his destiny, and his star; she believed that he had been born for great achievements, which the gods held in reserve for him, and she had been chosen to bring him up and protect him; it was from the gods themselves that this strange, mystical love came, which filled her breast and overflowed into the little one. She had neither the ability nor the inclination to scrutinize her feelings; she was only aware of this boundless love, this deep-channeled longing, toward the young life which had become a part of her.

Moses harbored for his foster mother a not dissimilar feeling. His devotion and his love for her had no connection with gratitude; his feelings sprang from deeper and more authentic sources. It was true that amidst the court throng which surrounded him with universal enmity, she alone afforded him a point of shelter and security; but he was aware, even more deeply, of something else—namely, that his still unrevealed destiny had called for her intervention. Like her, he believed that she had been ordained to become his adoptive mother. Her alabaster-tinted features, young, delicately cut, were dear and intimate to him, and he longed for them whenever he was separated from her. When, as a man, he would meet her after an absence, he would feel himself faltering in his resolution; his idea of leaving the house of Pharaoh—it had been with him for some time—dissolved in his feeling of devotion toward his mother. Her presence made him a child again. No, it was not simply a responsive adoration for the sorrows he had caused her by his strange and dangerous ways, for the complaints which she had to endure, for the isolation, even, which he forced upon her in her defense of him; it was something higher, something like a sacred and mystical presence which had come to him from another world. He began to see in her a messenger from the Spirit of his remote ancestors, the Spirit of the tribe to which he belonged and which had elected her to be his mother and protectress. And so the reverence which he felt for his origins was transferred in part to her, the stranger, who had become linked with his destiny.

When the Princess learned of the danger which threatened Moses as a consequence of the denunciation to Pharaoh by the high priest, she robed herself in her priestly garb, assumed the identity of the goddess Isis, and appeared before her father. With the full authority of her divine status she asserted that Moses was her child Horus, and that she would poison herself at the feet of the god Osiris if she were deprived of her one comfort in life, her son, Horus-Moses.

The vigor and fury of her intervention saved Moses from certain death; but he did not escape unscathed. He was stripped of every official function at the court and separated from its social life. He was deprived of all titles and privileges, but out of regard for his mother he was placed under the surveillance of a proved watchman, one of the temple eunuchs, who watched over him day and night.

CHAPTER FOUR

THE Princess whom Moses called mother had by now reached her fiftieth year, but the secret arts of the cosmeticians imparted to her the appearance of a girl barely in the twenties. Her slender body was always wrapped, like a mummy, in delicate linen. Her face was long and narrow, with oval-chiseled eyes. Her transparent skin, fine and translucent, was of the color of alabaster. The doctors had exerted themselves to the utmost in order that her features might retain that virginal aspect which was fitting to one who had dedicated her life to the gods; and the straight-cut nose, the thin lips, and the slender throat did indeed give her the appearance of a girl-child.

When Moses sent in, through her scribe-secretary, a request for an audience, she had only just returned from the ceremonial which, as priestess before the god Osiris, she celebrated every morning in the little temple attached to her quarters.

She had taken off the horned moon-crown which she wore as the goddess Isis. Her spirit was still exalted, filled with magnetism like the agitated amber stone, from the excitement of her ritual, from the anointing and robing of the god, from the bringing to him of lotus flowers, and from the singing of hymns before him. Her heart was still high with the sacred moment of contact with the lord of the underworld, her divine, beloved husband. Her emotions trembled on her face, and her eyes glowed and glittered with the ardor of her ecstasy. She felt herself to be uplifted and purified, as she always did after her ritual before the god.

She received Moses in the small, intimate boudoir next to her bathing and anointing rooms, where she loved to rest and prepare herself for divine services.

By contrast with the luxurious chambers and banqueting halls of the palace, with their countless lotus colonnades, the Princess's boudoir was a simple room, without columns, and with smooth, lofty walls. Only the ceiling was covered with decorations in red, yellow, and violet. The Princess reclined on a couch of carved wood set in ivory and ornamented with lapis lazuli. At her side stood a casket table of like materials and design.

On her heavy peruke, whose curls were interwoven with gold embroidery, she wore a diamond chaplet fronted by a falcon head. A collaret covered her high, slender throat. Her dress of lawn fell in many folds to her feet, which were placed on a footstool. Before her stood a naked slave girl, ministering to her with the perfume of a lotus flower.

When Moses presented himself with a deep inclination of the head, she dismissed the slave girl. She bade him seat himself on the couch, by her side, and taking his hand in hers she addressed him tenderly:

"Dear is thy face to me, my son, as the face of Horus is dear to the eyes of mother Isis. What hast thou to tell me which the gods have confided to thee?"

"I am thy servant, whom thou hast exalted to the rank of thy son. The stars of the night have seen the tenderness of the mother toward the son, and their testimony gives me the courage to lay my thoughts before thee. I went out to see my brothers, and I have looked on their bitter toil. I found my father and my mother among them."

A look of deep sorrow came over the face of the Princess. The skin took on a new pallor under the unguents, and her unformed breast trembled. She mastered herself and answered:

"I knew that one day thou wouldst find thy way to thy parents among the slaves of Goshen. It was not I who separated thee from them. I gave thee to thine own mother to be suckled when I found thee in the Nile as Isis found her son."

"I know it, mother; thou hast been gracious to me from the first hour of thy finding me. The gods have appointed thee to guard my steps from evil. How shall I thank thee for thy many kindnesses, great mother?" Moses stood up and bowed deeply before her.

"What wouldst thou do now, my son?"

"I would go to my brothers and be among them."

"One more drop in the ocean of Egypt's slavery?" she asked, anxiously.

"My brothers are not slaves, mother. Among them is the spirit of their God. They observe His laws, they remember the names and the deeds of their forefathers, and they live according to the

35

ancestral traditions, which are passed on from generation to generation."

"But in Egypt they are slaves."

"They live in the hope of redemption, according to the promise of their God. Those that live in the expectation of redemption are not slaves, mother. I want to be with them in their hope, and in their awaiting of redemption."

"Is it not enough for thee that thou art the son of Pharaoh's daughter, that thou shouldst be seeking another redemption? Wouldst thou exchange the given for the expected?"

"The given is alien to me. Thou hast exerted thyself in all thy love to fit me for the role which thou chosest for me from the first day. That role is not for me. The robe thou hast bestowed on me fell to pieces on me. The spirit of my parents has kept me a stranger in the house which thou hast built for me. I am not worthy of the grace which thou hast wrought with me, mother. I grew up a stranger at thy breast. I am like a tree that has been torn up by the roots and lies on alien soil. To thy gods, the gods thou hast given me, I do not belong, and my own gods I do not know. I must go to my brothers, and learn from them to know the spirit of their God. I want to know who my forefathers were. I want to be re-planted in the soil which is proper to my nature and my kind. It may be that I will find rest and support among my brothers."

Again the Princess fell into silent meditation, while she kept her dark eyes fixed on her son's face. Her look was filled with compassion and affection. The tremors which passed along her throat bore witness to her inner agitation. She stroked the hand she held, and spoke at last:

"My son, I know not whether thou wilt find rest and support among thy brothers; thou hast breathed too long an alien air. My heart trembles in me, my inmost parts lament in me for thy suffering. The gods have woven together like strands the veins of our hearts, and every sorrow of thine passes into my blood. I know how ill at ease thou art in the luxurious palaces of Pharaoh; but wilt thou be at ease in the slave tents of thy brothers? I know that thou hast remained a stranger to our gods; but will thine own gods become familiar to thee? Thou art like a plant which has been sustained for many years in an alien soil and an alien clime; wilt thou take root and flourish when thou wilt be set again in thine own soil? Thy roots have learned to take another nourishment; will they not shrivel and petrify in the hard earth of the slave country? Thou canst live a stranger among strangers, thou wilt not be able to live a stranger among thine own."

Now it was Moses who fell into meditation. His radiant, manly face darkened, his high, arched forehead became covered with wrinkles, and the luster of his eyes was eclipsed.

"I know, mother, that the danger is great. But I cannot renounce this step. The Spirit of my people has awakened in me a great love-thirst toward my brothers. Absent from them, I suffer more with them than if I were with them. I waken in the nights and cry out aloud, remembering their enslavement. Love and pity for my brothers eat at my flesh like the fangs of a lion. Always before me I see their bodies, covered with the dew of their agony, breaking under the weight of their burden. The lash that falls on them burns me with shame and pain. It is as though the God of my fathers had taken my heart and had made it into sponge to suck up their anguish. My body is too weak to bear this load of suffering; and perhaps, being among them, being at hand to witness their bitter labor, I will also share their hope, and wait with them for the redemption. Perhaps I will then find strength in greater measure than when I am alone, removed from them."

The Princess stretched out her hand to the eyes of her son, she gathered his tears with her finger tips and carried them to her lips.

Moses looked at her in wonderment.

"Mother, what dost thou?"

"Thy tears are the founts of that love with which the gods have fructified my body. When I found thee in thine ark among the reeds of the Nile, the same fountain of tears was opened. In that moment the goddess bade me drink the tears which would kindle in me my love to thee, my son. My destiny is bound up with thine, and whithersoever thou goest, I will be with thee. Go to thy brothers, and learn amongst them to know the strange and mighty Spirit which directs thy destiny. I feel, I know, that a Spirit issuing from unknown heavenly spheres, over which the influence of our gods does not extend, has thy ways in charge. He guides thy footsteps, as a pilot guides his ships; He forms thee, as the potter forms the vessel, to be an instrument in His hand. He has kept watch over thee since the day of thy birth. He has rescued thee from many perils; He has drawn thee out from between the teeth of the lions. He has struggled with our spirits and has overcome them. I know not whose that Spirit is, but I know that He is not mine. I am given to other authorities and other spheres; but I bow my head in awe

37

before His majesty. I know too that even I am an instrument in His hand, for the fulfillment of His purpose. For all that I have done, and do now, is by His command and His will; and I am obedient to His will. Go, my son, in the paths which the Spirit of thy forefathers has prepared for thee. He will shield thee from the dangers which lower upon thee, as He has done till now. He will shield thee from the hands of our gods, against our will, as He has shielded thee from the hands of our high priest; and when that Spirit will bid me help thee in thine appointed task, I shall obey even against our gods. For so I must, so I am commanded by the Spirit through the fire of love and devotion, which He kindled in my heart with the tears which I have drunk from thine eyes."

Moses could not remove his eyes from the face of the Princess. It was as though he could not recognize her. She had risen from the couch, she seemed to have grown taller, and her face was illumined by an inner light of sanctification. She was no longer to him the priestess of an alien god. She was like the prophetess of a God who was familiar to him, being his own.

The Princess clapped her hands. The high door of the boudoir swung open and there appeared in the doorway a young, powerful Negro girl, with rings in her ears and bracelets on her long arms. She was of unusual stature, with a mighty breast held in by a narrow red band. Her sex was covered with a short apron, and her belly and navel were bare. She prostrated herself in the doorway of the boudoir.

"Fiha! Take the Prince, put him in the dress of a slave, and let him out through the secret door of the temple of Isis. Then conduct him to the fields of the brickmakers in the slave city of Goshen. Thou art responsible for his life and his well-being. Thou wilt be with him as long as he has need of thee; thou wilt do all that thou hast to do, and thou wilt refrain from doing that which thou must not do."

"As thou sayest, great mother," murmured the Negress.

"Go, my son, whithersoever the Spirit of thy people leads thee," said the Princess.

Moses bowed his head before her. "Mother!"

She drew near to him, and for the last time took her son's head in her long, slender arms.

"Mother! My Spirit will be thy Spirit too."

"When thou findest Him, come and speak to me of Him."

"Yes, mother."

38

CHAPTER FIVE

LIKE a panting and thirsty hart, which, after many tribulations, draws near the clear spring, and in its onrush pays no attention to the thorns and brambles which lacerate its skin, having but one thought: to reach the source of living waters; so Moses gave no heed to the petty ambitions which filled those who were closest to him, and had but one longing, one impulse: to learn to know, ever more intimately, ever more thoroughly, his own people.

The traditions of the tribes were transmitted by the elders of Israel from generation to generation. The "elders" did not consist merely of the aged; there were young people among them, too. Among the tribes there always went on a search for young people whom God had blessed with wisdom and understanding, and they were assigned to the cave where the elders of Israel sat. For it was desired that the tradition should be renewed for preservation in the fresh young minds of the latest generation. But the most important among the elders were, in fact, the old men.

One of them was blind. He was the ancient Uziel, before whom every one was silently attentive when he recited the acts and the generations of the forefathers. Tall of form, pale of countenance, with a thin gray beard, he seemed to have focused his eyes irrevocably on the far distance, as though he could see there, beyond the reach of the gaze of others, the sources of his knowledge of the beginnings. The others sat around him, Amram, Yizhar, Hebron, some young people, children of Yizhar, drinking in his speech, and repeating what they heard.

It was said of the ancient Uziel that he was so old that he could remember the generation which had followed Joseph, the days when the Ibrim, the Hebrews, still lived as freemen in Goshen; but this was something of an exaggeration. Uziel, though himself never a slave, had been born when the tribes were already enslaved. In any case, he was certainly considered the most aged of the elders, so

39

that it was through him that the traditions of the generations had flowed.

Uziel was held in high honor by the sages. At the time when Moses came to know him, he was already feeble with age. He was no longer able to move. He always lay in a bedding of tender white sheepskins, and they fed him on milk, like an infant. For all that, his memory was so fresh, and when he rehearsed the tradition he did it with so much vividness, that one would have thought he had once seen, with those eyes which were now closed in everlasting night, the things of which he told; and one would have thought he had closed his eyes of his own free will, in order that he might retain unimpaired every detail of those far-off events and persons.

Uziel's was the final authority when there was dispute or uncertainty regarding some incident of the past, some custom handed down from the patriarchs, some name in the genealogical tables, some expression used by the fathers. For not only incidents, revelations, and customs were considered important; important too were the tongue and the words which had been transmitted through the previous generations. They attached much weight to the uniformity of the tradition and saw to it that every one of the elders was letter perfect in the phrases and expressions and even words in which the record was transmitted. The ancient had never been known to add or to subtract from the tradition, not by so much as a word, no matter how often he rehearsed it.

With old Uziel Moses sat hearing and repeating all that he heard concerning the lives of the forefathers from the very first day; and the words were graven into his heart as with a stylus of steel.

There Moses learned that a Spirit, whom they looked on as the God of their forefathers, and who concealed Himself behind an unspoken Name, had created heaven and earth; had brought order into the *tohu-va-vohu,* the primeval chaos; had set the sun and moon and stars in the heavens; had populated the earth with all manner of beasts and birds; had filled the oceans with fish and creeping things. And this He had done not in playfulness, and not out of caprice, but with a purpose. And this purpose was goodness, which is justice. For from the very first day of the creation, the Spirit had made the distinction between good and evil, between justice and sinfulness; and He weighed and measured all His creatures, their behavior and their deeds, according to whether they were good or evil, just or sinful. He brought the flood upon the

40

earth—Moses had learned of the flood in the Babylonian scripts, which were conned in the military school—again not in caprice or playfulness, but because His creation, man and animal, had declined from the purpose of creation, the purpose of good and evil; and He had chosen a few individuals of all the species, and saved them from the flood, in order to make a new beginning.

From the outset, then, the Spirit had taken the world of His creation under His special tutelage and providence. He did not abandon it to its own devices even in the days when He was still unknown to the children of man. He kept watch over those who fulfilled His intentions and conducted themselves in righteousness; to them He was gracious. Those that digressed from His intentions and practiced unrighteousness, He punished and destroyed. Till the day came when He was discovered by the first one, the father of this people, Abraham, who was called the Ibri, the Hebrew, because the word signified that he had come from beyond the river, and was a stranger in the land where he had settled.

The father of the tribes was the first among the children of men to discover that there was but one Spirit, the only Spirit, who was the creator of everything in heaven and on the earth. The Spirit revealed himself to the father, and made a covenant with him and with his offspring throughout all the generations to be. The Spirit became their God, the one and only God of the people which sprang from Abraham. It was to be a chosen people, and it took upon itself the fulfillment of all the laws and commandments and customs which God appointed for it, so that it might be an example of righteousness and truthfulness to all the other peoples of the world.

And this people, which was to multiply, and to become in number like the stars in heaven, and like the sands on the seashore, was to issue from Abraham, who was as yet childless at the time of the promise. The one and only God had, moreover, set apart for this people one of the lands of the earth which He had created. He marked out the boundaries of the land; the people was to enter the land and dwell there in righteousness and justice, and this would be the service of the people before Him. From that time on God had taken under His shelter the destiny of the people.

Having recognized and accepted the one and only Spirit as his God, Abraham became utterly obedient to Him, and was unquestioning in his obedience. He sought no reasons and asked for no purpose. He believed in Him, and believed that whatever He did

41

was as it should be and served the good. He did not even question Him when He revealed that Abraham's children would be strangers in a strange land, subject to a strange people, oppressed for four hundred years before they would attain their peoplehood.

And Abraham, the father of all the tribes, having made this covenant with the unknown God, was prepared, at His command, to offer as a sacrifice on the altar his one recompense, the son begotten in his old age, the evidence of the fulfillment of the covenant. Never questioning the command, never knowing the reason for it, uncomplaining, he led his son Isaac, in whom the promise was incorporated, to the sacrifice, to be a burnt offering. Thus Abraham had with a thousand mouths nourished himself at the sources of the unknown, in order that he might conjure out of it the one known, the Spirit of eternal being; and having found Him, he surrendered himself to Him unconditionally. Not for the sake of the future, not for the sake of his posterity, did Abraham make this bond, but for the achievement of his own oneness with the Spirit. Abraham dissolved in the Spirit because in Him and with Him was the eternal life without form and without content. And the Spirit did not desire a sacrifice by the death of Abraham's son, but rather a sacrifice in the life of his son, as He desired it of all the sons and daughters who were to issue from Abraham. The manner of their conduct, the sanctity of their lives—this was to be the sacrifice.

And suddenly Moses perceived the contrast between the Spirit of Abraham and the gods of Egypt. The Spirit which had appeared to Abraham was not a spirit of the dead. He was not an Osiris, the god of eternal night, with whom Pharaoh became one in death; He was not Ra, with whom Pharaoh became one in the upgoing of the sun. He was the God of eternal being, of creation, of becoming, of life, of all that there was, of all presentness. One mighty presentness was in him, that of all the worlds. For all the worlds, all that is —sun, stars, night, the known, and the unknown—were part of His creation. In Him was locked he for whom creation was ordained— man. And by the covenant which Abraham made with the Spirit, a covenant was created among all his descendants, to serve the Spirit, not with death, but with the conduct of their life.

Every one of the slave brothers of Moses, as he saw them trampling out with naked feet the slimy earth, to make bricks for Pharaoh, was part of Abraham's great cognition. His brothers were the covenant with the Spirit, in form and content. In them lived the promise of the Spirit. And with the promise was woven into their blood and marrow the hope of the future, the hope of all being, for they were life.

No, not the slaves of Pharaoh were these, the children of Joseph, as the Egyptians called them—and as they were glad to hear themselves called, for their descent from the savior of Egypt was their one claim on the Egyptians. In those tormented bodies, under the rope and the lash, flowed the blood of Abraham, of him who had been the first to uncover the eternal Spirit of being. Every one of them had been bound on Isaac's altar, and every one was ready to bring his future as an offering to the Spirit. Every one was a descendant of him who had been first to walk in the ways of the Spirit. And though their bodies were covered with the scars of the lash, in them lived the covenant, the promise, and the hope of man in God.

But Moses was, before everything else, a man of practical realities. He had an eye for everything about him and soon became familiar with his environment. He grasped easily the complete structure of the slave system, which held his brothers in its chains. It was a system with a rigid code which resisted the slightest change, and to his pain and shame Moses soon discovered that his own brothers in slavery, and even members of his own tribe, carried no little share of responsibility in the perpetuation of the system. They contributed to the enslavement of the tribes in the functions of slave overseers and slave officials. They negotiated with the Egyptian authorities as to the number of Hebrew slaves needed for some specific piece of work, and they decided among themselves who were to be the overseers for it. They assumed the responsibility for the delivery of provisions to the workers; and they collected the produce from Hebrews who, in return, were accorded the privilege of working their own plots of land.

Moses discovered, moreover, that by no means all of the Bnai Israel were condemned to the hideous tasks of the brick kilns. This was, in fact, only the lowest category of brute labor. A considerable number had been assigned to the superior crafts. The Egyptians were a calculating people; they were not the kind to indulge the luxury of hatred at the expense of usable talents. Wherever a young slave exhibited intelligence and skill, he was apprenticed to some master craftsman and trained to serve the Egyptians in a higher capacity.

43

Hard by the mud fields, where the bricks were baked, Moses found the work tents of the stonemasons: open booths set in the hot sand, with curtains of palm leaves to keep off the scorching rays of sunlight. Row after row of naked backs bent over the stone blocks; row after row of skilled slave hands holding the bronze adzes and the wooden mallets; and over every row of laborers, the inevitable overseers, lash in hand, maintaining the rhythm of the work. In other booths the shaped blocks were polished—again row after row of sweating bodies in rhythmic motion, this time over the finished stone, which acquired the smoothness and luster of marble. And in yet other booths a superior craftsmanship was applied to the chiseling of decorative stone figures, gods and beasts and men, for the adornment of the temples.

And every slave, whether unskilled laborer or trained craftsman, whether treading out the clay for bricks and dragging the basalt blocks, or cutting with delicate chisel the images of gods and men, was equally exposed to the lash. In this respect there were no gradations; and there were no gradations in the state of slavery, which was complete, immitigable, and irrevocable. From the day of its birth the child, if only allowed to live, belonged to Pharaoh. Even pregnant women were fastened to the looms in the tents which stood in the adjoining fields. Linens and coverings and shrouds—there was never an end to the demand for these for the living and the dead of Egypt.

When Moses first saw the long rows of weavers' tents, it seemed to him that the bodies of the women and the looms that they worked had become single machines. The sticks of the overseers maintained a rapid, steadfast rhythm on little drums, and the feet of the workers maintained the same rhythm on the treadles, their hands maintained the same rhythm in shooting the shuttle across the frame. Wherever a hand or foot fell out of rhythm, the lash descended. Limbs and muscles were kept at the highest bearable tension, without pause or relaxation; and side by side with the mothers, under the same drive, at the same speed, worked the girl-children.

But the mud fields, the stoneworkers, and the weaving tents did not exhaust the varieties of slave labor imposed on the Bnai Israel. Moses soon learned that there were many Hebrew slaves "loaned out" to wealthy Egyptians. Their work might be of the coarser kind, in field or garden, fishing, or tending cattle; or of the more delicate kind, calling for superior craftsmanship.

And as Moses also discovered, the Bnai Israel were bondsmen not only to Pharaoh, but to the Hebrew overseers, Korah, Dathan, and Abiram, who had the authority to hire out the Hebrew slaves for every kind of work, as laborers, or as managers of estates, as scribes and as bookkeepers, as art weavers, mixers of ointments, gold- and silversmiths. And thus it came about that while the life of every son of Israel belonged to Pharaoh, his talents and his knowledge were at the disposal of Korah and other Hebrew overseers, to do with as they saw fit.

More than by their enslavement to the Egyptians, Moses was cut to the quick daily and hourly by the enslavement of the Bnai Israel to overseers and oppressors of their own blood. The web of slavery had been cast with infinite cunning over the tribes: the appointment of Hebrew overseers over Hebrew slaves subjected one part of the people to another. The heart of Moses bled for the weak and the helpless and flamed with anger against the oppressors—not least those of his own people; and he made an unuttered bond with himself to cast in his lot with the clay treaders and brick bakers, and not with the prominent men of his own privileged tribe of Levi.

At one time Amram, the father of Moses, had become so crushed by the long slavery that he had ceased to believe in the promise which God had given the patriarchs; and faith in the promise was the only force which sustained the tribes and kept alive in them the spark of life.

Amram, while in his prime, had refused to bring any more children into a world in slavery. To what end create new lives? In order that the fish of the Nile might have more food? But as against Amram, his daughter Miriam, who was like a torch of revolt, carried the blazing word of hope from tent to tent among the tribes; and she wrought also in her own tent, so that in later years she restored to her father his lost faith. And then, when the youngest child was born in the house of Amram, after a lapse of years, the reborn faith became stronger still because of the marvelous events which followed: this youngest one was saved from the jaws of the fishes in miraculous fashion. Pharaoh's daughter found him and brought him into her father's court, to rear him as her own child. Herein Amram saw the beginning of the redemption, and he believed that the child had been born for a great purpose.

The miraculous rescue of Moses roused to renewed hope of redemption all of the members of the household and inspired the oldest son, Aaron, who had been born before the dread edict that condemned the men-children, to prepare himself for the high role which would be his in the fullness of time: he chose for himself the high priesthood, having an eye to the important position which the priests occupied in the life of the Egyptians. He devoted himself to a study of the ritual of the Egyptian priests and learned their prayers, hymns, and conjurations. Following the custom of the Egyptian priests, he developed a fastidious physical purity and harmony; he robed himself in robes of shimmering white; he anointed his hair and his beard, which he did not shave off in accordance with Egyptian practice, but permitted to grow after the manner of the tribes; he improved his diction and enriched his speech with high religious symbols. And for the priesthood he prepared not only himself, but his two oldest sons, Nadab and Abihu; and he trained them to be his assistants in the eminent position which he expected to occupy.

But Aaron was so absorbed in the maintaining of the living tradition of the patriarchs among the tribes, and in strengthening the hope of the impending redemption, that he lost sight of the individual living Hebrew. No doubt he knew of the torment and privation which the slaves endured, but he had grown so completely into the regime of slavery, was so accustomed to it, that he accepted it as being in the nature of things. Not only did he fail to oppose, to protest against, the sons of Korah and the others who dealt with the Hebrews as if they had been beasts rather than human beings; he was even of the opinion that as long as the slaves were in exile to the Egyptians, the exile had to be accepted for what it was. But Moses, reared a freeman in Pharaoh's court, could not reconcile himself to the savagery of the slave regime. He perceived that, while his brother continued to assert the tradition, and to prepare himself for the priesthood, the individual Hebrew was rotting away in the lime pits of Egypt. It seemed to him that if this continued for a little while longer there would be no one to liberate and no one for whom to prepare the priesthood. But most he was embittered by the Hebrew overseers and guards whom Pharaoh's officers had set over the slaves. More than once Moses tried to consider, together with his brother, the condition of the Hebrew slaves, the indifference of the sons of Levi to the sufferings of their brothers, and the conduct of the sons of Korah and of the others who lent

46

their help to Pharaoh in the strengthening of the slavery. But the answer always was:

"As long as the Spirit of our fathers comes not to us, and does not redeem us from bondage, as He promised our forefathers, even so long we must believe that our time is not yet come."

"Dost thou not rather believe, my brother, that only those who will to be redeemed will be redeemed? For only those that are sons of freedom in their hearts can become sons of freedom in reality. You who ratify the conditions as they are bring slavery into the hearts of the Jews."

"What wouldst thou have us do? Rise in rebellion against Pharaoh? Knowest thou not, my brother, that those who revolt against our bondage in Egypt revolt likewise against the Spirit of our forefathers, who foretold our bondage?"

"Meanest thou thereby, my brother, that it is the will of the Spirit of our forefathers, the Spirit of Abraham, Isaac, and Jacob, that their descendants shall be bondmen in Egypt, and live a life of slavery? And how, my brother, does thy imagination forevision the redemption?"

"The redemption?" repeated Aaron, and gravely stroked his long, well-tended black beard. "The redemption will come when the Spirit of our forefathers will soften the heart of Pharaoh, making him see that he has treated us unjustly, that we are not the descendants of prisoners of war, slaves by conquest, but the descendants of freemen who were invited into Egypt by the Pharaoh himself, and by his vice-regent, Joseph. Then he will restore to us the rights which we enjoyed in the first days—the rights we of the tribe of Levi still enjoy—and he will permit us to worship our own God in freedom, or he will assign us a place in the wilderness, and there we will have our sanctuary, and there bring sacrifice to the Spirit of our forefathers."

Moses became white with anger, and his speech left him as it always did in moments of great agitation. He trembled like a reed in the wilderness, but he exerted himself to overcome his anger and to conceal his contempt for the slavery, which stagnated in the hearts of those who were nearest him, in his own environment.

"And perhaps thou thyself art destined to soften the heart of Pharaoh. God appointed Pharaoh's daughter to be thy mother and protectress. Is this not a sign that thou art the chosen one, the one who, through the daughter, will make mild the heart of the father,

47

so that he will restore to us the rights which were ours before they enslaved us? And is not this the reason why we have sent for thee?"

"Is it thus that the Spirit of Abraham, Isaac, and Jacob deals with his enemies? With supplication and submission?" asked Moses, astounded.

"Hast thou a better way with Pharaoh, king of Egypt?"

"I? No! But the Spirit of our fathers? Yes! With a mighty hand and an outstretched arm!" cried Moses, and he lifted a closed fist to heaven.

Now it was Aaron who became pale. He bowed his head before his brother. For the first time he saw as it were rays of light issuing from the eyes of Moses.

The one outstanding person in the environment of Moses who could not make peace with the concept of slavery was his sister Miriam, the lofty, lean woman who was almost like a skeleton covered with a darkly sunburned skin of a leathery consistency. In that haggard form burned a sacred flame which gave her no rest but drove her to ceaseless activity. She was never still. She knew every one of the families; she visited them in their tents; she was familiar with all their struggles and needs and sorrows. Here she would help a mother conceal her little man-child, and then smuggle him past the guards and overseers to a place of security; there she would sit with a bereaved mother who had just lost a son, and comfort and strengthen her; elsewhere she would take over in the tent of a sick woman, prepare the wretched meal for the slave husband, and carry it to him in the field. She knew also the secret tribulations of all the women, of the trials they endured at the hands of the abominable Egyptian overseers, who were for ever forcing themselves on the Hebrew women during the absence of their husbands at slave labor.

It was from Miriam that Moses first heard of the savage overseer Aharnes, and of his vile treatment of the Hebrew mothers.

The Egyptian overseers had made it their objective to wipe out the purity of the family life, which reigned among the Hebrews, to demoralize them in order that they might be better slaves. The other slaves, the non-Hebrews, knew nothing of family bonds; and the intention of the overseers was to bring down to the same level the Hebrews, whom the most crushing labor had not been able to reduce to that condition. More than all others, the overseer Aharnes was devoted to this purpose, bringing to his beastliness the determina-

48

tion to advance his reputation as a slave master. It was not enough for him to enter the tents of the Hebrews and to attack the women; he wanted to break their obstinate resistance, to make them submissive and willing. He knew well enough the faithfulness of the Hebrew women, the love which reigned in the Hebrew families; he knew of the purity which was observed, the tenderness with which the Hebrew women received their husbands when they came plodding home in the night, broken with their labors. With Aharnes it was a point to make even bitterer the lot of the men, to poison them against their wives, and perhaps to make them complacent in the hope that their burdens would be lightened.

Aharnes the overseer was especially concerned with the family of Phineas, son of Dosi, of the tribe of Benjamin. He had thrown an eye on the beautiful woman, Shalmut, he had seen her when she tended her husband during the meal respite, he had observed with what gentleness and love she ministered to him, wiping the sweat away from his face. And his lust was aroused.

One evening Aharnes appeared on the threshold of the tent of Phineas ben Dosi. He demanded that Shalmut give herself to him there and then, in the presence of her husband, and without physical compulsion. If she refused, her husband would be taken from the stone dragging and put among the mud-treaders, a work altogether beyond the strength of a man of his age. Husband and wife were determined, however, to endure all torments rather than defile the purity of their family life; and from that time on Aharnes the overseer set himself to make things unendurable for Phineas ben Dosi. Not only did he place him among the treaders of clay, but he delighted in watching for the moment when Phineas, on the point of collapse, paused to cool his burning feet; then he would fling himself with the lash on the panting slave. Aharnes was waiting for the hour when Phineas ben Dosi would in fact collapse in the clay, to be trodden underfoot by the other brutalized laborers.

When Miriam recited this story to Moses, the latter asked:

"And what will happen to her, to Shalmut?"

"She will follow her husband into death, and not permit herself to be defiled by the heathen. She has told me this herself, and has begged me to look after her son, who is in one of the caves with the other men-children."

Moses ground between his teeth the point of the beard which he had grown since the time he had come to join his brothers in

Goshen. He stood motionless a while. Then he unbound the blue band which covered his apron, and threw it from him. He stood now only in the loin apron, the dress of the slave.

"Thou throwest from thee the band of the tribe of Levi?" cried Miriam, in terror. "The overseer will take thee for one of slaves and drag thee away to the work."

"That is what I want. Let me not take advantage of the privileges which Pharaoh has conferred upon the tribe of Levi. Let me be one of *them.*"

"How wilt thou help thy brothers if thou art become a slave like them? Are slaves lacking in Egypt?"

"Not them would I help, but myself. I want to be one of them, nothing more," answered Moses.

CHAPTER SIX

WITH the thick cluster of black hair on his head, with the black beard which surrounded his face like a granite frieze, with his powerful neck and his broad shoulders, and his arms like two hammers, Moses looked like a slave giant when he reported to one of the Hebrew overseers at the mud pits.

"From what tribe?" asked the Hebrew overseer, looking at the unfamiliar form and face out of his narrow eyes set in the long face which the pointed yellow beard made even longer.

"I came to take the place of the ailing Phineas ben Dosi, whose feet are swollen with labor, and who cannot work any more," said Moses, not answering the overseer's question.

In the mud pit one of the naked figures, which were treading the slimy mass, the leanest and most wretched of the figures, straightened, and a face streaming with sweat was lifted in astonishment. Who had uttered his name?

"I have not received permission from the brick foreman, Aharnes, to free Phineas ben Dosi from his work," answered the Hebrew overseer.

"I have come to free him, overseer. The count of bricks will be made good," said Moses.

"My orders are to keep Phineas ben Dosi in the mud pit, and to see that he does not stop from work even for a moment."

"I will take his place." With one leap Moses was already in the pit. He lifted the frail, bony Hebrew, who almost broke in his grip, and set him on the rim of the pit. Then he sprang back and took his place in the chain of treaders.

"No, no! That cannot be! Thou canst not! It is forbidden!" shouted the overseer. He ran over to the panting Phineas ben Dosi where he lay in the sand, and began to whip him with his overseer's lash. "Back into the pit!"

The voice of Moses came from the pit like the roar of a lion: "Villain! Why strikest thou thy brother?"

51

The yellow-bearded Hebrew turned and saw a pair of eyes that shot fire; he saw a hand lifted toward him like a mighty hammer. Mortal terror seized him at the sight of the blazing eyes and the threatening hammer. He stepped back from the half-dead Phineas.

Moses entered the chain of the other nine Hebrew slaves at the mud treading, and imitated them. They worked rhythmically, as in a dance, kneading with their feet the heavy slime which had been unloaded at the bottom of the pit. From time to time quantities of sand dust, mixed with straw, dried leaves, and chips of wood, were emptied into the slime, to give hardness to the material from which the bricks would be formed. Before long Moses began to feel a burning in his feet, as if there were a fire under the bottom of the pit, heating the clayey mass. Now and again he felt a sharp stab, when a splinter pierced his flesh. But the physical pain, which grew with every minute, was washed away in his deep inner contentment. He was doing something which he needed to do, and the spiritual satisfaction overbore the burning pain in his limbs. He exerted himself to work conscientiously, steadily, not pausing when the others did, so that he might do his full share in providing the tally expected from his gang.

Suddenly he felt a nervous tremor pass through the naked, sweat-drenched bodies of his companions. They shrank together, their feet took up a faster rhythm, and a hot wave of terror passed over them, bringing out a heavier dew of sweat. The overseer on the rim of the pit also became nervous, and he began to drive the slaves with renewed fury. His whip flew over the heads of the workers, but he did not dare to let it descend on the bodies; terror of the giant who had joined the chain held back his hand.

"Faster! Faster! One, two! One, two! The right down, the left up!" he yelled at the slaves in the mud pit, and drops of fear formed on his forehead.

A moment later Moses saw the man whose appearance had thrown slaves and overseer into the same agitation. On the rim of the pit stood a tall Egyptian. He was naked but for his loincloth. His head was shaven; on his breast hung a chain from which was suspended a small metal shield; in his hand he carried a bamboo rod with a copper load. He bent over the edge of the pit, and his round gray eyes, naked, rimless, with the brows shaven like his head, passed intently over the slaves. He turned with a growl on the shivering overseer.

"I do not see Phineas. Has he fallen into the mud?"

"No, overseer set by Pharaoh. His place has been taken by another."

"At whose command?"

The overseer trembled and panted, but could not utter a word.

"At whose command?" repeated the Egyptian furiously.

The overseer pointed at Moses. Covered with slime to the waist Moses looked up from the pit with an imperious glance.

"On the command of a slave?" roared the Egyptian. "Give him the lash!"

His feet buckling under him, the overseer approached the pit. As he lifted his hand, he felt the eyes of Moses light on him, and his hand fell again, as if suddenly paralyzed.

"Overseer set by Pharaoh, he is not a slave," stammered the Hebrew with mounting terror.

"He is not a slave? He is not a slave? That will be seen in a moment."

The Egyptian stepped closer to the rim of the pit and lifted the loaded bamboo rod over the head of Moses. Out of the slime rose the upper half of the body of a giant; under the high forehead two eyes shot fire at the overseer.

The outstretched arm of the Egyptian, holding the bamboo rod, also became motionless, and remained in mid-air, as if it had been petrified.

"Not a slave? Who then is he? Who is he?" the Egyptian yelled, and the rod came down on the head of the Hebrew overseer.

"Overseer set by Pharaoh, Pharaoh will lose nothing. In the place of a sick and feeble worker thou hast a strong and healthy one. The tally of bricks will not be diminished. Why beatest thou a faithful servant of Pharaoh, who is guiltless?" called Moses from the pit.

"Who art thou, that darest to instruct an overseer set by Pharaoh? All of you are Pharaoh's slaves, all of you belong to the great king, the sick and the healthy, the feeble and the strong. Drive the idler back into the pit!" the Egyptian commanded.

The Hebrew overseer poured out his bitterness and fear on the wretched Phineas, who lay half buried in the sand and did not stir. The blows which he had received from the Egyptian he now paid out in double and triple measure on the sick body at his feet.

53

"Back to the pit, idler, malingerer! Thou art lazy, not sick. Back to the clay!" yelled the Hebrew overseer.

"Why beatest thou thy brother?" shouted Moses. "Seest thou not he is sick, that his limbs are covered with wounds? Have I not taken his place? Am I not doing his work?"

"Thou wilt work, and he will work too. All of you are Pharaoh's slaves," cried the Egyptian, and added his blows to those of the Hebrew overseer.

Barely had Phineas ben Dosi managed to crawl into the pit when Moses lifted him in his arms tenderly, as a mother lifts a child; and holding him thus he began to tread the mud.

"Let him down! Let him work!"

"He cannot work. He cannot stand on his feet."

"Then let him fall and be trodden into the mud. Into the mud with him! I, Pharaoh's overseer, command it," yelled the Egyptian at the other slaves.

But when they saw the fury in the eyes of Moses the slaves in the pit were as terrified as the overseer outside.

Moses carried the sick, wilting body of Phineas out of the pit, laid it tenderly on the sand, and said imperiously:

"Here he will stay and rest. I will work for him." And he re-entered the pit.

Phineas lay motionless, as if all life had departed from his body.

"I fear that he cannot work," said the Hebrew overseer to the Egyptian.

"If he is not good for work, he is good for something else," and bending over he brought down the copper-loaded rod on the Hebrew's head with all his strength. The body started spasmodically, then fell back lifeless.

"Here!" cried the Egyptian. "Here is straw for your bricks!" And with his rod he rolled the dead body down into the slimy mud.

The body sank and disappeared under the feet of the mud treaders. Moses sprang out of the pit. His fists were clenched, the veins had started out on his throat. His face was white, but his eyes blazed. He approached the Egyptian, who began to breathe heavily; the tall figure shrank, as if it were already overwhelmed by the giant confronting it. It trembled like a leaf.

"If thou art one of us, take pity on thy brothers. If thou slayest the Egyptian we shall all share the fate of Phineas ben Dosi," whimpered the Hebrew overseer to Moses.

Moses thrust the point of his beard between his grinding teeth, and departed with great footsteps.

"Who is he?" asked the Egyptian of the Hebrew overseer.

"We do not know who he is. But he is not of the slaves."

"How knowest thou?"

"He speaks and acts like a son of freedom."

"Whoever he be, he is a rebel. Report at once to Dathan and Abiram that a dangerous agitator has appeared among the slaves and stirs them up against Pharaoh. Let them find out who he is and take the proper measures against him. All of you shall be responsible for his deeds."

CHAPTER SEVEN

MOSES sat on the threshold of his father Amram's hut, and his sister Miriam tended the wounds and blisters which the hot clay had brought out on his legs. His brother Aaron, who had already learned of the incident at the pit, was reproaching him for his dangerous and irresponsible behavior.

"Are we short of slaves that thou shouldst have come out of Pharaoh's court to add to their number? This step of thine has imperiled the status of the whole tribe of Levi, for should Pharaoh learn that one of the Bnai Levi has renounced his privileges and has of his own free will entered the clay pits, to labor under a Hebrew slave overseer, he may demand the same renunciation from all of us, and then, God forbid, we shall lose the privilege which we have defended so long and so obstinately. That, my brother, will be the reward of thy action! Our brothers of the other tribes will not be helped thereby, but thou wilt bring the curse of Egypt on thy own tribe."

"I know not who the tribe of Levi is and know not by what right it claims a destiny different from that of its brother tribes. I only know that the Spirit which appeared to our forefather Abraham is a God of justice and judgment. From the elders of Israel I have learned that the Spirit which created the world, the Spirit of Abraham, Isaac, and Jacob, sent a flood upon the earth, to destroy the sinners. He rained destruction on Sodom and Gomorrah for the same reason. But from the flood He saved Noah; and on the supplication of our father Abraham He would have spared Sodom and Gomorrah, had there been but five righteous men in the cities. From all this I learn that the God of Abraham, Isaac, and Jacob is a God not only of righteousness and justice, but also of compassion and forgiveness. We cannot fathom the secret reason why He keeps the children of Abraham in subjection to Pharaoh, why He permits the evildoers to torment the children of His friend. But we must believe that if He is a God of righteousness and justice—and He is

56

that—then injustice is hateful to Him. From the window of heaven He looks down, He beholds what Pharaoh's servants do to the children of His friend Abraham, and He is with them in their tribulation. He will reward tenfold those that help His people, and He will take vengeance on the tormentors; for though He is merciful and forgiving, He is also the God of vengeance and punishment."

Aaron's anger faded before the faith which Moses displayed. He was caught up in the passion of distress which poured from his brother's lips; and once again he started back from the hot light which blazed up in his brother's eyes. He answered, in a milder voice:

"Yes, all this will come to pass when the Spirit of our fathers will have mercy on us, and will deliver us from Egypt according to His promise. Until then we must bear the yoke of bondage, we must suffer and be silent."

"But how can one be silent when the eyes see what mine have seen?" asked Moses, and covered his face with his hands.

"Thou knowest better than another what happens to slaves of Pharaoh who rise in revolt against him," said Aaron.

"I?"

"Wert thou not one of Pharaoh's warriors, who helped to bring nations under the yoke?"

Moses was silent for some time, and the color ebbed from his face. His eyes sank to the ground, and he answered humbly:

"Yes, my brother Aaron. Thou hast reminded me of my guilt and my shame. In my ignorance I helped Pharaoh extend his dominion over other peoples, until the Spirit of my fathers taught me to feel for the soul of the slave in the enslavement of my brothers, till He taught me the taste of slavery on my own flesh."

"No one must learn of that, brother Moses," said Aaron. "The thing must be concealed not only from Pharaoh's overseers, but likewise from our own tribes. Above all, Dathan and Abiram must not hear of it. It were best that thou return to Pharaoh's court. There Pharaoh's daughter is thy protectress. There wait a while until the Spirit of our forefathers will reveal Himself to us; then thou wilt be a greater help to us in Pharaoh's court than thou canst be here, where thou art a slave among slaves."

"For me the way to Pharaoh's court is barred forever," answered Moses. "My place is among my brothers."

"Among the slaves neither thy freedom nor even thy life is

assured. Go, hide thyself among the elders of Israel, so that it will not be discovered who thou wert. There, in the cave of the elders, study the tradition, and find comfort in the promise of the eternal Spirit."

Later Aaron took his sister Miriam aside, and said to her, secretly: "Take thy brother and conceal him, and let no one know of his hiding place; his life is in danger."

But Moses refused to go into concealment. On the contrary, he showed himself more and more among the slaves. He helped the carriers with their burden, he yoked himself in the ropes of the stone haulers, he dug side by side with the clay diggers. As if he wanted to taste every variety of slavery, he appeared in every field, mingled with the brickmakers and the masons, with the canal diggers on the banks of the Nile, and with the hewers of the rocks in the hills.

No one knew who he was; and yet all, overseers no less than slaves, recognized in him the son of freedom. His appearance alone proclaimed him as such, for he stood out among the Hebrew slaves, with their bodies withered by hunger and labor, like a giant among pygmies. His powerful, majestic head towered above them; and more imposing than his physical appearance was the light which darted from his eyes, the light which lay on his free, open face. In the loincloth of a slave, without a symbol of authority, he commanded both among the slaves and among the overseers, Hebrew and Egyptian alike. He was taken for a secret overseer, an agent of the court of Pharaoh in slave disguise, sent to acquaint himself with the conduct of the slaves and of the overseers. Both the tormentors and the tormented trembled before him and obeyed him.

In order not to implicate his own family, and also that he might learn more of the life of his brothers, he left his father's house and settled among the slaves. The only one who still maintained contact with him was again his sister Miriam. Heedless of her brother Aaron's instructions and warnings, she found a tent for Moses among the slave fieldworkers. She tended to his needs, she helped him to penetrate more intimately into the ways of the slaves. And from her he learned also of the subsequent fate of the woman Shalmut, the widow of Phineas ben Dosi, of the tribe of Benjamin.

After the murder of her husband, the Egyptian Aharnes took her away from the field and made her work among the men slaves,

58

carrying baskets of trodden clay to the brickmakers. This labor, beyond her strength, broke her back and twisted her hips out of shape. But her will was neither broken nor twisted, and she would not surrender to the Egyptian. Finally the Egyptian came to her tent and violated her in the presence of beholders. Unable to endure the shame, Shalmut threw herself into the pit where her husband had been done to death and died as he had done.

When Moses heard of these things he fell into a long silence. His head dropped to his breast, and only the violent working of his thick eyebrows betrayed the storm which raged in him.

Miriam continued: "But the villain is not content with this victim. He is pursuing other women; he is breaking into other homes. The cry of the Hebrew mothers goes up from our tents."

Moses lifted his head.

"When does this wild beast go out on the hunt?"

"Whenever the hunger moves him. He watches among the women at their work, or when they come to their men in the pits, chooses his victim, pursues without pity until he has his way. Sometimes he enters a tent in the daytime, when the husband is at work; sometimes he enters when the husband is there. Whenever he appears in the camp terror falls on the tents, and no woman is safe from the abomination."

"Is there no one who can stay this villain?"

"Who shall do it? Who can stand up to him even with a word? We are delivered into his hands, we, our lives, and our honor."

"There is still One, and that is the Spirit who appeared to our fathers. He looks down from heaven and nothing is hidden from him. He has set a boundary to evil—thus far and no further! He has prepared the day of reward for the righteous and the day of vengeance against the wicked, as he did with Sodom and Gomorrah," said Moses.

As Abraham recognized the true God among the chaos of the false idols which surrounded him, so Moses had perceived the spirit of righteousness in the sea of unrighteousness which had surrounded him in Pharaoh's court. He had been brought up in a world which knew of no weights and measures for right and wrong, for good and evil, which knew only of the division between the privileged and the unprivileged, the oppressor and the oppressed; out of this darkness of Egyptian bondage he had conjured up the bright perception of justice. And now every sin he encountered was like a stumbling stone in his path—it had to be removed; every crooked deed had to be made straight. When he encountered a villainous act it was as though fire had been applied to his flesh, his rage started up, and his nerves and muscles became taut in preparation for the act of restitution. But he held down with steely discipline the impulse of his rage, knowing of the danger which threatened anyone who protested against injustice in Egypt.

He had known of it in Pharaoh's court; but there he had had a great protectress, his mother. Here, among his own, he had to hold his fury in check; he had to see and hear and be silent. Not he alone would be in danger, but those he sought to help. "If thou slayest the Egyptian we shall all share the fate of Phineas ben Dosi," the Hebrew overseer had whimpered. The words had remained with him, and they were a rein on his passion.

Now, hearing of the threat which the Egyptian had suspended over the Hebrew mothers, he felt the rein snap in him. A lash was laid upon him, driving him, commanding him, compelling him to action, to be the protector of the unprotected.

He took up his stand, like the appointed instrument of justice, among the Hebrew tents, to wait for the next appearance of the abomination. He lingered there day and night, unceasingly.

Then he saw the Egyptian approaching with great stride from the region of the pits. Night had fallen, but he recognized the man in the brilliant starlight. He was carrying the copper-loaded bamboo rod with which he had smashed the head of Phineas ben Dosi; in that rod of death Moses saw the symbol of the power which the Egyptian wielded over the life and death of his brothers.

He left the shadow of the tent where he had stationed himself and went out to encounter the Egyptian.

"Whither goest thou, Egyptian?"

The man lifted his eyes and cast an astounded look at him who dared to address him thus.

"Who art thou that questionest one of Pharaoh's overseers?"

"Pharaoh set thee as an overseer over the work of the Hebrews —their work, and nothing more. But this is not a working hour, nor is this a field of work. What seekest thou among the tents of the Hebrews?"

For a moment the Egyptian was speechless with amazement. He stared closely at Moses, and recognized him.

"What? Art thou not the slave who once dared to hinder me in my service to Pharaoh? My men have long been seeking thee. It is well that thou hast fallen into my hands."

The Egyptian thrust out a hand to seize Moses, but Moses threw him off.

"Pharaoh made thee an overseer over the bodies of the Hebrews, not over their souls. No one has given thee the right to defile the women of the Hebrews. Be gone, and leave the Hebrew women in peace."

"Slave! Impudent Hebrew slave! Wilt thou tell an overseer of Pharaoh what his rights are, wilt thou command him to leave a place? Down!" And with this he swung up the loaded rod.

On the instant, with the unforgotten swiftness and skill of his gymnasium days, Moses twisted the rod into his own grip, and he dealt with the Egyptian as the Egyptian had dealt with Phineas ben Dosi.

Moses looked around on every side. No living soul had seen him strike down the villain. The night was silent and brilliant. He lifted the Egyptian's body, placed it on his shoulders, and carried it far away from the tents of the Hebrews to the rim of the wilderness. There, with the help of the Egyptian's rod, he dug a hollow in the sand; into it he threw the body, and after it the bloody rod. With hands and feet he covered them up, hiding forever the last traces of the abomination which had hung for so long a deadly danger over the Hebrew encampment.

CHAPTER EIGHT

THE province of Goshen in the Delta, where Joseph had settled his brothers and their families at the time of their coming to Egypt, was among the fattest and most fruitful in the land. Thousands of streamlets issued from the Nile in the season of the floods and filled the ditches and canals dug in the pitch-black earth. The soil was interpenetrated with the rich alluvial slime brought down by the river, and the swift ripening of all growths, of grains, vegetables, and flax, under the sun which blazed unclouded at all seasons, made possible a rich double harvest every year.

Apart from the abundance of planted things, the ditches and canals, which threaded the beds and meadows nourished, with their inexhaustible supply of frogs, worms, and water lizards, countless flocks of geese, ducks, and other fowl; and all year round there was rich pasture for the fat cattle.

The first generations of Hebrews, who were protected by the great name of Joseph, lived in plenty. Some, the immediate relatives of Joseph, and many members of the tribe of Levi, which rapidly achieved the place of leadership, even became wealthy, accumulating large landed possessions. In addition to hired laborers, they began after a time to employ slaves, in the manner of the Egyptians; these they bought in the slave markets, which Pharaoh's armies supplied with prisoners of war taken among the many conquered Asiatic peoples. Later they even acquired dominion over a part of the poorer tribes, who were compelled to apply for help to the richer and more energetic. Thus they at last drew into slavery not only aliens, but many of their own brothers who, unable to pay their debts, sold themselves into slavery just as Egyptians did under the same circumstances.

The rapid increase in the rich landowning and cattle-breeding class among the Hebrews was one of the causes—though not the most important one—which led to the enslavement of the tribes in Egypt. The Egyptians were stung to envy and hatred of the aliens, who were isolated in their manners and customs from the natives, who did not recognize their gods, did not pay the tax to the temples; envy and hatred were followed by fear of the separatism of the Hebrews. The Egyptians began to cast about for means to diminish the wealth and power of the tribes. The enslavement did not take place at once, but step by step, beginning with the poorest who had fallen into the hands of the rich. The Egyptians confiscated first the inheritance of the less privileged tribes, those that were descended from Jacob's servant wives, for the nonpayment of taxes and of other debts. According to Egyptian law, the owners were requisitioned together with the forfeited land. In any case, robbed of their land, the debtors had no alternative but to enter the service of the new owners.

But not all of them surrendered immediately to enslavement. There were families which rose in revolt. Others abandoned Egypt and settled on the borders of the land Canaan.

The most obstinate resistance was put forth, among the tribes, by the children of Levi. They refused to surrender the rights which they had enjoyed in the days of Joseph. More vigorous than the others, firmly grounded in the tradition, proud of their forefather Levi who had defended, sword in hand, the honor of Jacob, they had become, soon after Joseph's death, the leaders of the tribes. Pharaoh's advisers were quick to see that it would be easier to maintain dominion over the alien Hebrews—with their traditions of the forefathers, their belief in a strange God, their recollection of freedom—through their own instruments than through foreign instruments. The government of the Hebrews was therefore placed in the hands of the tribe of Levi; and through the tribe of Levi the Egyptians introduced the system of slavery which finally engulfed the tribes. But the privileges enjoyed by the Levites did not extend to the safety of their sons.

Among the strongest and richest families of the Bnai Levi, ranking—in the matter of prestige—after Amram, the father of Moses and Aaron, was that of Korah, the son of Yizhar, the brother of Amram.

Korah was at this time in the prime of life, of great physical strength and imposing appearance. His rule over the tribes was one of terror. He had considerable possessions in land, sheep, and cattle, which he had inherited from his father Yizhar. In contrast to his brother Amram, who had refused to work hand in hand with the Egyptians in the imposition of the slave system, and whose possessions the Egyptians had therefore confiscated, the younger Yizhar had been eager in his offer of help. To him, among others, was entrusted the task of supplying the Jewish overseers for the slaves of Goshen, of assigning the count of workers for the various tasks, such as the treading of the clay, the baking of bricks, the digging of canals, the carrying of burdens. And Pharaoh rewarded the faithfulness of Yizhar, not only permitting him to hold fast to his inherited possessions, but adding thereto the confiscated possessions of rebellious Hebrews. The wealth accumulated by Yizhar became the portion of his son Korah.

In the great house built of bricks in the Egyptian style, beneath the yellow-chalked columns, which sustained the wooden ceiling of the lofty main hall, were assembled the Bnai Levi. Only the older generation was absent. Amram was too feeble to attend; he remained in his hut. Yizhar was no longer alive, and old Hebron and Uziel were in the secret cave of the elders of Israel, studying the tradition. Those occupied with the business of the slaves belonged exclusively to the younger generation. Chief among them, and their spokesman, was Korah.

He sat at the head of the assembly, on a carved stool, which was a sort of throne. Although only in the forties, he seemed, because of his massive build, to be older. He was thickset; his bull throat was covered by a gray-black beard curled and twisted in the Assyrian style. A colored robe covered his body to the knees. A chain hung over his breast, and his short, fat fingers were adorned with gold rings.

Opposite him sat Aaron, who also wore a colored robe which left one of his shoulders bare. There was a tradition that the sons of Jacob wore colored robes when they came to Egypt, and the Bnai Levi covered themselves with colored stuffs in order that they might be distinguished from the other tribes.

All of the assembled, among them Korah's brothers, Nepheg and Zichri, and the sons of Uziel, Mishal, Aliphzin, and Sitri, were similarly robed, and all wore the metal badge of their tribe on their bosoms. The younger generation, among them Korah's sons, Amir, Elkanah, and Abiasaph, who, with their massive chests and their curled beards, resembled their father, stood ranged behind their uncles. Among them were also the brothers Dathan and Abiram, two of the younger overseers. Though they were not of

64

the tribe of Levi, but Reubenites, their position gave them the right to attend the gathering. They too wore plaques on their chests and carried carved bamboo rods set with copper rings, the insignia of their superior rank in the slave hierarchy.

Before this grave assembly stood Moses. His breast was bare, without the shield of his tribe; his loins were covered with the white cloth of the slave class; his heavy locks and his thick beard hung down wildly, as if he had only just left his labors in a clay pit. And this was indeed the case. The Bnai Levi had summoned him to the assembly, and he had come before them from his slave labor.

"Moses, son of Amram!" Korah turned on him his narrow eyes sunk in fatty folds, and lifted his harsh voice, tinged at this moment with a mixture of anger and sorrow. "Moses, son of Amram! Our brother! When the Spirit of our fathers manifested His goodness to thee, and brought thee into the court of Pharaoh under the protection of Pharaoh's daughter, it was our hope that He was preparing in thee a second Joseph, who was to arise for our brothers in slavery. So we believed all these years, and we saw in thee a second defender, a second helper of the helpless. How our hearts swelled with gladness when we heard of the greatness achieved by one of our blood in the service of Pharaoh! In thy destiny we saw a sign from the hand of the Spirit, that the time of the redemption was close upon us. And the elders of Israel, they who know the destined hour, told us that the period of our agony was approaching fulfillment. Then it was that we sent for thee. And it was our belief that thou wert the elected and chosen one and that through thee the Spirit would restore us to our place in Pharaoh's government, would re-endow us with the rights which were ours in the days of Joseph. Thine it would be to move the heart of Pharaoh to deal graciously with us, so that we might live in peace and happiness, as in the days of old. But what is this that thou hast done? Instead of freeing thy brothers, thou hast thyself become a slave; instead of lifting up our heads, thou has brought down new dangers up them, thou hast brought upon the brothers of thy tribe the threat of slavery. All of us are under suspicion of rebellion against Pharaoh because thou stirrest the hearts of our brothers against their bondage, and since thy coming among us we have fallen so low in the eyes of Pharaoh's servants. Thou hast carried matters so far that thou hast dared to lay a hand on one of

Pharaoh's overseers when he stood on duty at his post. And now there has come to us an order to deliver the rebel, the inspirer of revolt, to the security guard. We are held responsible as a whole for the deeds of the one. Dathan and Abiram, produce the order which you have received from Pharaoh's chief overseer."

Dathan and Abiram, the sons of Eliab, came out from behind Korah's chair and stood before him. They laid their rods at his feet in token of submissiveness, and the elder of them, Dathan, took out from his girdle a papyrus covered with script and, with an obeisance, declared in a loud voice:

"Korah ben Yizhar, this is the script which we have received from Pharaoh's great overseer of the third order. Dathan son of Eliab hereby delivers the script into the hands of Korah ben Yizhar."

Korah took the script in one hand and, pointing to it with the other, cried: "Here is the command to discover the rebel who threatened one of Pharaoh's overseers and to deliver him to the security guard before the change of the moon."

"Paltiel, the Hebrew overseer, recognized and identified Moses ben Amram, and declares that he is the man who stood up against Pharaoh's overseer and threatened him with death," declared Nadab. "The Hebrew overseer is here to testify. Shall I call him in, Korah ben Yizhar?"

"No need to call him!" said Moses, interposing with a gesture. "I it was who stood up against Pharaoh's overseer and lifted up my hand upon him. Before my eyes this Egyptian slaughtered a soul in Israel, one of my brothers. Not for the fulfillment of a law, and not in line with his duty as overseer, but out of wickedness and the corruption of his heart, for he lusted after the man's wife. If there is any guilt in my hands, take me and deliver me to the security guard. I stand in submission before you."

"Moses ben Amram! We are not judges appointed by Pharaoh to weigh right and wrong. Pharaoh has his servants and judges. It is not for us to say what an overseer may or may not do. This thou knowest full well. Nor is it our intention, God forbid, to deliver thee into the hands of Pharaoh. Thou art our brother, our flesh and blood. We have but one prayer and supplication to thee: leave the fields of the slaves and return to Pharaoh's court. Pharaoh's daughter has taken thee as her son, and thou art indeed a son to her. She has shielded thee from thine enemies till now, and she will

66

shield thee from now on. When thou art under her shield, none will dare to persecute thee. And who knows if thou wilt not yet, with the help of thy mother, obtain a lightening of the burden for thy brothers? Great things were destined for thee by the Spirit of our fathers. Through thee the redemption may yet come. Moses ben Amram, such is the decision of the elders of thy tribe, and to this decision thou art bound to submit."

"Korah ben Yizhar! Not through my hands, and not through flesh and blood can the redemption come, but through the one and only living Spirit who appeared to our forefathers and bound them to him in the bond of an everlasting covenant. His heart wakens for every injustice, and His eye beholds every unrighteous deed. He has seen our suffering and shame, and He will hasten to our help when the hour comes for the fulfillment of His will. Only His hand can avail us, and only through Him will the redemption be true and complete. Who am I, that you should repose in me the hope of the afflicted? In the past I did not know my brothers; and now that I know them I am one of them, a slave among slaves. I am with them in their need and their pain; with them I will wait for the redemption. The mud pit by day, the naked tent of my brothers by night; these are for me Pharaoh's house."

There was silence among the men surrounding Korah ben Yizhar. The man himself had turned gray, the fatty sacs about his eyes had become limp, and his eyes sank deeper into their beds. He stared at Dathan and Abiram, and they stared back at him, and no word broke the silence.

Then finally Aaron rose and addressed himself to Moses:

"Moses, my brother, too long hast thou been a freeman to be able to understand the soul of the bondman. The son of freedom when thirsty may slake his thirst with water; the bondman must learn to drink his very thirst. The doubled backbone and the broken spirit of the slave are his armor and his weapons. We cannot be as free in our wishes as thou. We too know the weights and measures of right and wrong. But we must forget them. We too would like to make a stand against Pharaoh's servants; but we must renounce the desire, because in our slavery we have security. Go away from us, brother Moses. If thou wilt not return to Pharaoh's court, find thyself another home."

"My home is among my brothers in their need, brother Aaron."

"But if thou desirest to live in the home of thy brothers, thou must put on the broken bearing of a slave. A freeman among slaves brings danger upon himself and death upon his brothers."

Moses meditated for a space, and then, in the broken voice of one who prays, he said: "Brother Aaron, I will be a slave, even as they are slaves."

"Thou wilt not be able to suffer it, brother Moses. Seest thou not that it is beyond thee even now? Go away from us, brother Moses, before it is too late."

"I will seek to humble my spirit, bend my backbone to the slavery, if only I may be with them," said Moses in a supplicating tone.

"Thou wilt not achieve it, brother Moses. The God of our fathers will not let thee. One of us must be free!" answered Aaron.

"Ah, I must be with them—I must," said Moses, as if to himself.

"We have done our duty. We have warned thee betimes," said Korah, and rose from his chair.

He could not become one of them. In spite of his efforts to harness himself in slavery, to bear the yoke exactly like his brothers, to be of them as he was with them, without distinction of any kind, he could not tame his free spirit. It was as though the Spirit of his forefathers had Himself struck the spark in his heart, so that it might glow more and more brightly and in the end kindle the light of freedom. But if this was so, he must remain among them, and remind them daily and hourly that they were sons of freedom, children of Abraham, Isaac, and Jacob, to whom the Spirit had promised redemption. He must remain among them whatever the dangers he courted.

But had he the right to be a son of freedom among slaves? Had he the right to make even heavier the yoke of their bondage? That he was indeed a stumbling block in the way of the tribes of Israel, even as Aaron had said, soon became obvious to him. A harsher discipline was instituted over the Hebrew slaves; Egyptian and Hebrew overseers alike became more demanding. The hours of work were lengthened; the workers were driven from their tents while the stars were still in full luster, they were kept at their work till the stars returned. They had less and less opportunity to work the little gardens which adjoined the shelters. There was no rest for them, or for their wives. The latter too were drawn into the work, compelled to carry the crushing burden of mud-filled baskets on

68

their heads. They could no longer work in the dwellings, prepare the meals for their husbands, bring them their food into the fields.

Moses also observed that the Hebrew overseers had become harder and more brutal than the Egyptian. They were in a frenzy to get more and more work out of the tormented bodies of their brothers; and in Moses there arose a bitterer anger against the Hebrew overseers than against the Egyptian. But he put forth a great effort to overcome his rage and not to betray his instinct for freedom. But he did not long endure it.

He could not but perceive that he had been the cause of the deterioration in the condition of his brothers. He could no longer show himself among the slaves. Whenever he approached a group and offered his help, either in the lifting of a heavy load, or to break with a spade an obstinate piece of soil, the slaves turned from him in terror and drew away from him. They saw in him a stranger, one who did not belong to their world—one who belonged rather to the world of the enemy, a disguised Egyptian. And Moses himself caught, behind his back, the words of the Hebrew slaves:

"There goes the disguised Egyptian, whom Pharaoh sent to spy upon us."

"Since he appeared in our midst the overseers have doubled their lashes."

Moses would have liked to turn with the cry: "I am a brother of yours! I slew the Egyptian for your sake!" But he held his peace, driving his sorrow back into the recesses of his heart. He understood too well the sources of their fear—namely, his own kind, Korah, Dathan, Abiram, Aaron's sons, Nadab and Abiah. They were assiduous in the spreading of evil reports against him; they were making him hateful in the eyes of the slaves, hoping that he would be forced to go away.

He observed that Aaron too kept away from him; all, all remained at a distance and whispered behind his back. He felt, too, that he was being followed by secret emissaries. The moment he arrived amidst a group of laborers, a man would appear in their midst, rod in hand, and drive them away, crying: "Back to your work! Do not listen to him! He is not one of us!"

His sister Miriam was the only one who did not abandon him. She guarded his secret retreat among her slave friends, and she tended to his needs. She said to him one day:

"I do not know the meaning of it, but in Korah's house there are forever assemblies to deal with thee. Beware of the sons of Aaron."

"I know it. Theirs are the secret emissaries who dog my footsteps and who spread an evil report of me among the Hebrews."

Once he came to the mud pit where, some time before, he had taken the place of Phineas ben Dosi. He happened to arrive at the very moment when the two Hebrew guards, Dathan and Abiram, were beating a Hebrew treader who had fallen in exhaustion at the rim of the pit. The leather thongs of their whips cut into the flesh of the half-dead slave, and streams of blood ran from the ripped veins.

"Back to the pit, back to your labor, lazy dog's body," they howled.

A shattering rage awakened in Moses, and he forgot his resolution. He gave no thought to the danger he ran, he only felt the unbearable sting of injustice, the shame of a brother's brutality to a brother. Driven by a power he could not master, he sprang to Dathan's side, and with one gesture twisted the man's arms behind his back. The little yellow, evil face of the Hebrew slave driver swam in front of him.

"Villain! Why smitest thou thy brother? Wouldst thou fling him into the pit, to be trodden into the mud, as the Egyptian overseer did with another Hebrew laborer?"

"Who hast made thee a lord and judge over us? Wouldst thou slay me, as thou slewest the Egyptian?"

Moses released the overseer and strode away.

Now he understood. Now he saw beyond the shadow of a doubt that the lot of the Hebrews had been harder because of him.

That evening Miriam brought him a message from Aaron.

"Get thee gone from Goshen without delay. Thy life is in danger. Dathan and Abiram are conspiring against thee. Thou hast made our lot heavier than ever it was before!"

Now, at long last, he resolved to leave Goshen.

The land of Goshen was close locked. On one side lay the Great Sea, on the other, Egypt. The only place to which Moses could flee from Pharaoh's borders was the wilderness of Shur, which lay beyond the Sea of Reeds. Now the Sea of Reeds was not the Red Sea, which lay farther away, about the peninsula of Sinai. It was a vast red swamp of wild reeds and bamboo growths which ran along the length of Goshen and divided it from the wilderness of Shur. Inlets of the Great Sea penetrated the land of Goshen, filling a series of lagoons over a wide area and emptying finally through the slimy flatlands of the Delta into the great Lake Marah, the Lake of Bitter Waters. Thence, through natural canals and ditches, the waters flowed into the Red Sea. The Sea of Reeds was shallow; in many places it could be forded on foot, though there was great danger of being sucked into the scummy swamp—a fate which had overtaken many refugees, together with their baggage and their cattle. Also in the swamps they were surrounded by dangerous snakes and crocodiles. Only those who were thoroughly acquainted with the area knew the few paths by which a traveler on foot could cross in safety. To Moses the Sea of Reeds was an unknown world; but this much he knew, that it was beset with danger. But it was the only avenue by which he could escape from Pharaoh's guards and his own brothers.

So, beset by his own, he was rescued by his alien mother, Pharaoh's daughter.

Fiha, the servant girl of Bathiya the Princess, came to him with a message, finding him in his hiding place with the help of Miriam: "Pharaoh's sword hangs close over thee, sharpened by the hands of thy brothers."

"Here," said Fiha, "are the Egyptian clothes sent thee by thy mother. Put them on, and get thee gone from here. Pharaoh's guards are approaching."

"The doors are locked before me," said Moses.

"I know a door through the Sea of Reeds to the wilderness of Shur."

"Thou knowest well the Sea of Reeds?"

"I come from that region, and I know all its paths. Get thee ready and hasten with me; there is no time."

Moses put on the Egyptian clothes, went to take leave of his parents, and embraced his sister Miriam. And the son upon whom so many hopes had been laid vanished, and left his nearest in loneliness.

All night long Fiha led Moses through the slimy paths of the Sea of Reeds, and in the morning they came to the wilderness of Shur.

"Return to my mother, tell her that I have listened to her words,

71

that I have become a stranger among strangers rather than remain a stranger among my own."

But Fiha did not move. She fixed her eyes on Moses, and they shone with supplication and submission.

"What is thy desire, Fiha?"

"I, too, am of princely rank, the daughter of a royal house; my people, like thine, has been enslaved by Pharaoh; and like thee I cannot bear to look on the suffering of my people. Take me with thee, my lord, and let me be thy servant."

"I am neither prince nor lord. I am about to become a stranger in a strange land."

"But with thee goes the great hope of liberation; and I would share that hope for my own people."

"Return, Fiha. There is nothing I can give thee. Hope thou mayest have, like every one of us, if thou believest in the great Spirit who will come to the help of the weak and tormented."

"The Spirit of thy fathers?"

"He can become thy Spirit too, for He is the Spirit of all who believe in Him."

CHAPTER NINE

MOSES now found himself in the midst of another sea—the sea of the desert. He did not know which direction to take, nor did it matter much to him. The sandy wilderness, heaped into hillocks by the wind, stretched uniformly away from him, without a single point to tempt the eye or awaken the will.

He knew that the nearest path was the caravan route lying along the shore of the Great Sea and leading to the land of the Philistines, or the land of Canaan, whence his forefathers had come to Egypt. This latter was the land of promise, the land given to Abraham, Isaac, and Jacob as an inheritance for their posterity. But at this moment Moses felt himself altogether estranged from the promise, as if having no part in it. True, he was no longer linked with Egypt; but neither was he linked with his brothers. For it seemed to him that he who could not be with his brothers in slavery, could not be with them in redemption either. And what had he to do with alien Canaanites, whose land his brothers would someday inherit?

He was in the midst of the wilderness without a brother and without a God. He had long ago, almost in his childhood years, rejected the gods of the Egyptians; and the Spirit of his fathers he had not found; or rather, he had found Him and lost Him again. For Moses now felt himself estranged not only from his brothers, but also from the Spirit of his forefathers.

He had conceived and perceived that Spirit as the spirit of justice, the essence of righteousness which he had sought all his life. The manner in which He had created the world, the manner in which He directed the destinies of persons and peoples, had but one purpose—the institution of the reign of righteousness. To this end He had punished the wicked and rewarded the just, without respect of persons, making no distinction between the mighty and the weak, whether it was a Pharaoh, king of Egypt, or the servant woman Hagar, whom His friend Abraham had wronged.

The ideal of the God of righteousness, whom he had made one

73

with the Spirit of his fathers, had so filled him with love and adoration that he could not admit even the thought of an imperfection in His deeds. Yet before his eyes stood the frightful reality of Egypt. The Spirit heard the cry of the oppressed going up from the soil of Egypt: Why was He silent? Why did He not hasten to their help? Why did He not redeem the sufferers? Why had He not dealt with the Egyptians as He had dealt with Sodom and Gomorrah? How could He look on while the children of his friend, with whom He had made an everlasting covenant, were trampled daily underfoot by the clay treaders and their bones bricked into the buildings of the Egyptians?

Nor could Moses understand the idea of the four hundred years of slavery. Did the price of their election as God's chosen people have to be paid in torment and slavery? Was it necessary for them to be purified in such a blazing limekiln? He could not understand the reason for their suffering.

Moses was in essence a simple man with one obsessive feeling— the distinction between right and wrong. He saw on the one side bondage, suffering, oppression; on the other, dominion, sin, and wickedness. He saw that the wicked, in the lust of power, had overwhelmed their weaker brothers, harnessed them like beasts of burden, condemned them to eternal labor—and there was none to take the part of the oppressed and to punish the oppressor, as had happened once upon a time in the days of his forefather Abraham.

What were those things then, in the far-off past? Were they but dreams born of longing and hope in the midst of despair? Was it possible that there had never been a promise given by an invisible Spirit, that there had never been a covenant with the forefathers, that it was all a vision, an illusory sweetening of the bitterness of slavery? Moses shrank from the notion to which his own bitterness had driven him. No; slaves did not nourish hopes of a redemption. These were not slaves. The promise of the Spirit was real; it lived among them and gave form to their lives. The promise was as strong as if it had been renewed daily. The Spirit of the forefathers lived in their midst and renewed the covenant daily. This alone could explain their election. They clung to the hope; in it they strengthened their patience and endurance.

Sunk in these meditations, Moses strode forward through the desert. Though he had no objective before him, he knew quite well where he was. He was not unacquainted with the desert country,

74

though his expeditions had taken him southward, to Ethiopia, not eastward to the Asiatic countries. He was well provisioned—to this his mother had seen through Fiha—carrying, besides food, several pursefuls of silver pieces of the weight of shekels, which were a universal currency. He knew at what point he had issued into the wilderness of Shur and where the oasis city of Kadesh-barnea lay, this side of Edom. And after some aimless wandering he turned his footsteps in that direction.

In his boyhood days, when he had studied the cuneiform scripts in the military academy, he had become acquainted with the laws of Babylon and particularly with those which governed the relations of lord and slave. His early preoccupation with the problems of good and evil, right and wrong had awakened his interest in law, and in the laws of Babylon he had perceived a certain measure of justice. He had discovered in them infinitely more sympathy with the condition of the poor and the widowed than in the laws of Egypt, which set no limit on the brutality of its slavery. But in Egypt he had not found the opportunity to make a thorough study of the Babylonian code. The relations between Egypt and Babylonia were hostile; even trade between the two lands had been suspended. They lived in eternal rivalry, each seeking to swallow up the lands and peoples occupying the wide area which separated them, each in fear that the booty would fall to the other. Thus Moses had become acquainted only with fragments of the Babylonian code, and he had long nurtured the secret wish to visit Babylonia and to make a study of its laws. During his days at the court the enmity between the lands had made this impossible; now, a wanderer in the wilderness, he began to think of his old intentions and revolved in his mind the plan to pass through Edom and across the Arabian desert to Babylon.

A thin trickle of Egyptian caravans crossed the wilderness of Shur. The interior caravan route, as distinguished from the sea-coast route, lay in the wilderness of Paran, a direct link between the city of Memphis and the peninsula of Sinai. Along here, too, lay the road to the Arabian desert through the little oasis town of Ezion-geber, at the tip of the eastern arm of the Red Sea.

The place where Moses now found himself was a desolation. After leaving the townlet of Succoth, through which Fiha had led him in the swamplands, he had not encountered a living soul. Nor did he know of an oasis, in the khan of which he might find shelter for the coming night. To Kadesh-barnea in the wilderness of Sin was a week's journey. It was therefore pointless to march on after evening had fallen; and Moses prepared himself to pass the night where he was.

With sunset a cool wind sprang up. A thick dew fell like a veil on the desert sand. Moses felt the chill, and he wrapped himself in the white woolen mantle which Fiha had brought him and sat down in a hollow which the wind had left between two hillocks of sand. He opened the bundle of food which he had carried at the end of his stick, and the gourd of water which was tied to his belt, and began to eat.

Night followed sunset suddenly, and when Moses stretched himself out in the hollow, the stars were already at full brightness. Moses looked up at the stars, and he remembered hearing the elders of Israel tell the marvelous story of the father of all the tribes: how he had been on the road to Haran when night overtook him, how he had lain down to sleep on the bare ground, how he had seen in a dream a ladder stretching from earth to heaven and angels of the Lord going up and down. Moses understood now the meaning of the dream. There was a link between heaven and earth; man was not abandoned to blind chance, like the beast of the field, but stood in eternal contact with his Creator, who directed the ways of the world through the angels ascending and descending the ladder between heaven and earth. By the light of the stars falling on the desert sands, Moses too perceived the angels, the messengers between the depths and heights. It was as though he could actually touch the bond between man and his Creator and could hear the voice of the Spirit who addressed Jacob: "I am the Spirit of Abraham and the Spirit of Isaac."

The heart of Moses was filled with awe before the Spirit of his forefathers. Like Jacob he had left his father's house, and like Jacob he felt the Spirit of his forefathers accompanying him. Like Jacob, too, he wanted to pray to Him, call Him by His name, stretch out a hand to Him, become one with Him. But he could not find utterance at first. He did not know His place, did not know any prescribed hymn of His. He was familiar only with the hymns and prayers of the gods of Egypt. These he had learned to hate, and he could not address the Spirit of his forefathers with the words used by the Egyptians to address Ra. He sought a bond with the Spirit of his forefathers through a hymn and a name belonging to Him alone, and not to some idol. He desired to belong to Him, to be entered under His providence, as his forefathers, Abraham, Isaac, and Jacob, had been, as their children in Egypt were.

He rose, knelt in the sand, and lifted his face and arms to the starset sky:

"To Thee, whose name and place I know not; to Thee, who art about me, though I see Thee not; to Thee, who didst appear to my fathers, to Abraham, Isaac, and Jacob, to Thee I lift my voice. I know not Thy ways, and know not Thy righteousness. But I believe in the promise Thou gavest to my fathers, and I know that Thou knowest all that is done to the children of Thy friend. Thou seest their suffering and hearest their groaning, and Thou wilt fulfill Thy promise and redeem them from bondage. Wheresoever I come, let me not forget the pain of my brothers. Keep strong the bond betweeen them and me. And when the hour will come and Thou wilt hasten from Thy dwelling place with Thy heavenly hosts to their liberation, liberate me too, God of my fathers, thrust me not away from Thy people, let my portion be with them."

In the morning, as Moses strode through the wilderness of Shur, he heard a voice behind him:

"Thou who wanderest afoot! Thou who wanderest afoot! Thou art not on the right path."

Turning, Moses saw a man riding after him on an ass. When the traveler had drawn near, Moses looked at him in astonishment.

The rider was covered with scarves and rags, which covered not only his body, but his face too. Only his eyes were barely visible, actually only one eye, for the other was missing. From the place where the eye had been red drops fell. But if the rider showed no human face, the ass did, and its large eyes were fixed on Moses. From the man's rag-covered body depended idols and figurines of clay, in the forms of beasts and creeping things; and from the saddlebags protruded clay tablets and rolls of papyri. From the ass, too, hung many idols, the largest being in the shape of a mummified cat swinging from the ass's neck.

"How knowest thou, stranger, my path and purpose?" asked Moses. "And that with covered eyes?"

"Does a seer need eyes to see what is happening on the road? My ass sees for me. She belonged to my enemy in another generation. I cast a spell on her, and made her my ass. Now she is my eye and my mouth for all that is revealed; that which is unrevealed I see with my spirit."

"And what is it that I seek, stranger?" asked Moses.

"Thou fleest from a great evil, and thou hast set out to find righteousness."

"Who has told thee this, seer?"

"My spirit, which lives in my blind eye. Thou art not the dress thou wearest. Thy robe is of the finest Egyptian wool, and the purses at thy belt are crammed with silver pieces of the full weight, which makes them current coin in all lands. Thou hast no beast under thee to carry the worthy body clad in so dignified a robe. Nor hast thou a guard at thy side to watch over the treasure at thy belt against robbers and highwaymen. Thou hast no servant to relieve thy shoulders from the heavy burden of thy provisions. A perfume of good oils comes out of thy bundle to my nostrils through the thick covering on my face. All tells me, stranger, that thy departure was hasty and secret. Who can it be that flees with so much possession? A thief? No, a thief strides not so openly in the light of day. A high-placed servant of Pharaoh's, an intimate of the king, a royal official, who has fallen into disgrace at court? Does he, persecuted by enemies, set forth to seek righteousness elsewhere? However this may be, thou needest the help of the gods on this dangerous path. I have for thee here a string of sacred scorpions. The god's name is carved on them, and I give it thee in secret"—the stranger lowered his voice—"I heard the name of the god from the lips of the great priest in the temple; and I carved it on the scorpions. He will be the bondman of thy will. Thou wilt be able to command him as I command my ass, who is nothing more nor less than a prisoner-god. One of thy purses of silver, and the name of the god is thine."

"Gods who can be made prisoner and sold for silver to be my protectors? No, stranger. I am on my way to seek Him who cannot be taken prisoner and cannot be bought like a slave. The God I seek is the God who created the heavens and the earth and all that is in them. And He rules over them in righteousness, for He is a God of righteousness."

"What was it I said?" And the seer slapped himself delightedly on the stomach. "The dress is an Egyptian dress, the body belongs to Pharaoh, for it is of the Bnai Joseph. But in vain do they wait for the great God to come and deliver them. Like father, like son. Joseph was a dreamer, and the Hebrew slaves are dreamers too."

"Slaves do not dream," Moses exclaimed.

"In vain, in vain! The great God will not come. The great God sits a prisoner on the fiery mountain of Sinai. He could not get along with people; He was always demanding righteousness. And when that was not forthcoming, there He was with His punishments—a flood, or fire from heaven. He could manage neither with men nor with gods, because of His unspeakable jealousy. So the gods made a league against Him. They conjured His name out of Him, and by means of it conjured Him down from heaven to earth; now He is kept a prisoner on the fiery mountain, Sinai. At night you can hear His voice lamenting among the peaks. And Abraham's grandchildren are still enslaved by Pharaoh and go on waiting for His coming. In vain, in vain, they wait in vain. The great God with whom Abraham closed his covenant is no more."

"Like gods, like seers! Falseness dwells in their hearts, lies upon their lips, deceit in their hands. Not out of this stuff of your gods is the God of Abraham fashioned, that He can be tamed and taken prisoner. The God of Abraham is the God of righteousness. Righteousness may disappear for a while, but it lives forever, for righteousness is truth."

"*Ai-i, ai-i, ai-i,* that is exactly what I say. The God of Abraham was in truth the God of righteousness, and that is why He could not dwell under one roof with gods or men. Righteousness is too high a price to pay for a god. Therefore you wait in vain for righteousness to come and liberate you. The God of righteousness sits in chains. I tell thee, thou wilt do better to make a bond with the home gods, the gods of the earth, who know the nature of men, their demands and needs. Here, for instance, a little scorpion-god like this, which thou canst buy for ten silver shekels, will be a far greater help to thee in thy need than the God of righteousness. He will shield thee from the evil eye and conceal thee from Pharaoh's servants. And for a whole purseful of silver thou canst obtain from me the god of the sacred calf, who will strengthen thy loins and increase thy fruitfulness. A stranger with strong loins and great fruitfulness is a welcome guest in every house where there are daughters."

But Moses no longer heard the babbling of the blind seer. He had changed direction and was hastening on with rapid strides. Instead of Kadesh-barnea he chose Ezion-geber as his objective and plunged again into the interior of the wilderness of Shur. He hoped

79

thus to throw off the track the pursuers which Pharaoh must have sent after him.

The strange encounter left Moses heavyhearted. He did not know who the man was, but he was acquainted with the type—wild prophets of wild gods who wandered from land to land selling their idols. The entire area from Egypt to Babylon was covered by a sinister shadow of magic and idol worship. It flowed heavily out of Egypt and spread darkness in all directions where human beings were to be found. Reptiles and repulsive animals, mummies of cats and crocodiles had dominion over man. Dead gods were their law, and the earth was filled with black demons and superstitions. God had locked Himself away in heaven and had turned His face from the earth, leaving His creation to chance and accident. No trace seemed to be left of a divine providence in the affairs of humankind. All restraints had been loosened, all boundaries leveled; man, beast, and creeping thing mingled, to become one family, earthy and formless.

The only people which still retained a spark of heavenly light was in bondage to idolators. The memory and tradition of a one and only living God was struggling fitfully in a flood of slavery and debasement. Abraham's covenant was a mockery among the nations. The recollection of a higher Spirit was passing away. Blind souls in a black world! The one people still endowed with sight was enslaved, as though, God forbid, the reptile gods had risen against the higher God and held Him prisoner while they ruled the world undisturbed.

But everything in Moses revolted against this vision of mankind. He could not admit that the world had been condemned to eternal darkness and man to extinction. He who had created the world had done so with a higher purpose, and had pointed everything toward it. There was law, order, and meaning in His creation. There recurred to Moses a notion which had started up in him when he had considered the Egyptian worship of the sun as a god. The sun was not a creator, and had no power over the destiny of the world. It had not even a will of its own. It was only one of many created instruments and behaved in accordance with the ordered procedures prescribed for it by the Creator. And like the sun were all the other created things, integrated into the system of His rule. Great Egypt, with its opulence and power, was the slave of a slave. Thus it was with all peoples and all persons who did not acknowledge the one living God, and worshiped instead one of His creations. And thus the only sons of freedom were precisely Pharaoh's slaves, the children of Abraham, among whom still lived the perception of divinity, and who waited for the fulfillment of God's righteousness. And even though He delayed His coming, they did not lose their faith and trust in Him. They were free in the midst of slavery because they accepted Judge and judgment.

"O God of Abraham, Isaac, and Jacob, the one living God of my fathers, let my portion be among the slaves of Egypt. Hold me bound to Thee. Let me see Thy light, and let me not be swallowed up in the darkness which covers the earth," prayed Moses, again and again.

Ezion-geber, where Moses arrived after long wandering, was, he soon perceived, a dangerous place for him. It was the gathering point of caravans which passed between Egypt and Arabia and a way station for the expeditions which Pharaoh sent into the Asiatic countries. It was also the Red Sea port which served as base for Pharaoh's fleet. Moses made his stay in Ezion-geber brief. He was in constant fear of being recognized by an emissary of Pharaoh. Leaving Ezion-geber, he turned toward the left, not into the Arabian desert but toward the wilderness of Midian, which lay toward the other fork of the Red Sea; and after a day and a night of wandering he reached the oasis city of Midian.

As was the custom with all strangers coming to a new place, he paused by the well which lay outside the city and sat down to wait till the inhabitants would come for water, in the hope that one would invite him to be his guest.

It was still early in the day. The first rays of the sun were beginning to suck up the dew on the grass. The site pleased Moses. He observed the little clay huts which stood in the shadow of the date palms; he was refreshed by the plots of green which stretched from the water springs, and his eyes found rest after the sustained heat of the desert sands.

He recalled his forefather Jacob, the stories of whose life he had heard so eagerly from the lips of the elders. He saw before him Jacob sitting by the wells of Haran on the day of his arrival. There came into his mind the prayer which Jacob had uttered in Beth-el and the vow he had taken, that if God would be with him in the way he was going and would give him bread to eat and raiment to put on, so he might come again to his father's house in peace, then the Lord should be his God. He too, Moses, had left his father's house. No, he had never known his father's house. But he had left his brothers, and his heart longed for them, as the heart of Jacob longed for Isaac. And like Jacob he now prayed to keep him in the way he was going. For himself he asked no more than Jacob had asked—bread to eat and raiment to put on: no kingdom and no dominion—only the crust of the simple worker, and a garb for his nakedness. He also asked God to bring him back in peace to his father's house, that he might be together again with his brothers. In freedom. Or even in slavery.

Sitting thus, and meditating on Jacob and on all that had chanced with him, by the wells of Haran, Moses suddenly saw Rachel approaching. He recognized her! She was the tallest among the group of sisters. This was she, leading her flock, carrying the cruse on her shoulder, with proud and free motion. Her black locks fell about her shoulders, and her neck was a strong white tower. Her steps were measured and slow, and all her being was in rhythm with her footsteps. Behind the flock came her sisters, driving the sheep before them; the sheep followed slowly after the tallest sister, in the rhythm of her footsteps.

Moses felt an impulse to approach the well and draw water into the trough for Rachel's sheep; but he reconsidered: he was a stranger in this place. She who was approaching was not his kin, as Rachel had been Jacob's. He was a stranger to the Rachel who was approaching. He could not fall upon her neck and say that he was of her blood. His blood was in Egypt, among the slaves of Pharaoh. He remained motionless, therefore, and watched how the seven maidens drew water from the well and poured it into the narrow stone trough. The thirsty sheep pushed their way to the fresh, brimming water; the maidens stood by and stroked the white heads of the sheep.

And as Moses sat there, rejoicing in the picture, which filled his heart with good will to all men, as he thought of the foresight of Providence, and of the waters which flowed for all men, a sudden tumult broke into his mood. A band of wild shepherds, a lifting of raw hands, a shouting and threatening—and the sheep were being driven away from the trough. Staves and whips flew among the peaceful animals, which but a moment ago had been drinking their fill innocently. The sheep scattered in panic, and with them the young women, who tried frantically and helplessly to keep them together.

Moses forgot that he was a stranger here, forgot that Pharaoh's emissaries might be drawing close, that anyone might arrest him and hand him over. The instinct of outraged justice took command of him, the passion to protect the oppressed. His anger flared up against the wild band of shepherd men, and in an instant he was among them. His stature, his blazing eyes, his commanding voice were enough to terrify the cowardly attackers.

"You! Women in men's garb! Wild desert goats! Would you take to yourselves the water which gentle women's hands have collected with so much labor? The water belongs to those who draw it. Begone from here with your flocks! Begone from the trough!"

"We hear you, lord!" babbled the shepherds.

Moses helped to collect the scattered sheep, to bring them back to the trough under the hands of the maidens.

When the sheep had drunk their fill, Moses said: "Go home in peace to your father. I will remain here and see that the shepherds do not follow and molest you."

The young women obeyed.

CHAPTER TEN

THE daughters of Jethro the priest found Moses as they had left him, seated by the well, when they came to bring him to their home on their father's command. Leaning on his staff, he was sunk so deep in meditation that he did not observe the seven maidens drawing near. The oldest of them lifted her voice and said:

"My lord, our father Jethro sent us for thee. If we have found grace in thy eyes, rise and come with us and eat bread with us under our father's roof."

Moses rose and accompanied them.

The priest of Midian, with shaven head and face and eyebrows, came out to greet him.

"Blessed be thy coming under my roof. My daughters have told me how thou didst take their part and defend them against the brawling shepherd men at the well. Moreover, thou didst help them to water the sheep. Thou didst not ask for payment or recompense, and thou didst shield them against further molestation. I sent my daughters for thee. Stay with us a while and eat bread with us." Jethro made an obeisance before Moses. After him came his son, Hobab, brown skinned and sunburned, and made obeisance likewise. Then followed the daughters, from Zipporah, the eldest, to the youngest, and all of them bowed before him.

"I am too little for the kindnesses you show me. I did only that which is accepted as right, protecting the weak from the strong, and it calls for neither recompense nor thanks."

"Thou didst that which is accepted as right?" repeated Jethro in some astonishment. "It is not an accepted thing in our land, to take the part of the weaker against the stronger. May I then know the name of the thrice-blessed land whence thou comest? It is not Egypt, however thy dress testify."

"It is an accepted thing among my people."

"Thy people!" exclaimed Jethro. "Art thou not, then, of the people of Abraham the Hebrew?"

Moses started back in amazement.

"Whence knowest thou of Abraham the Hebrew? And why dost thou number me of his people?"

"Whence do I know of Abraham the Hebrew? But who among us does not know of him? Our fathers and our forefathers have told us of him, and in our chronicles it is written that he was a friend of the great Spirit. From childhood days on we have heard of his hospitality. Our fathers held him up before us as an example. And thou must be of his people for thou dost act according to his precepts. Did he not take the part of Lot, his nephew, fighting against Chedorlaomer to free the oppressed peoples? And was he not blessed therefor by Melchizedek, the first priest of the high Spirit? Did he not even take the part of the wicked people of Sodom? Oh, we know well the name of Abraham the Hebrew, and his people. Art thou indeed, then, of the stock of Abraham?"

"I am of it—and am not of it. The descendants of Abraham are slaves in Egypt, but I grew up as one of Pharaoh's sons. My brothers knead mud and bake bricks; I am free. I am neither a slave nor a son of freedom. I could not remain in the court of Pharaoh, neither could I be among my brothers. I could not remain a freeman among slaves. I saw their suffering and their need, and my hands obeyed the dictates of my free spirit. I could not help them, and I placed my own life in danger. I was driven away both by the tormentors and the tormented—I am in flight from both."

"Among us thou wilt find shelter from both. Our place lies deep in the desert, far from the main road, under the shadow of Sinai. Hither the emissaries of Pharaoh will not penetrate—and still less the lamentations of thy brothers. God has not blessed the womb of my wife with many men-children. A single son is my heir, and I cannot expect much from him. He is not formed to be a priest, neither is his inclination toward it. Hobab is a son of the desert, expert in herbs and plants; and though this is good for the art of healing, it is not good for priestly service. Priestly service, to begin with, calls for a lofty figure, a man powerful of build, with strong hands, great eyes, a radiant countenance; a man with a mighty voice—such a man as thou art, whose frown inspires terror. The people hereabouts thirst for help and counsel; and even though we are in the heart of the wilderness, there is not a little coming and going of the needy. There is much want and much sickness; also women seek a cure for their own barrenness and for the barren-

85

ness of their cattle. There are plagues and visitations. And all appeal
to the gods for help, all believe that the priest can cure any evil,
can obtain the intervention of the gods for every misfortune. Our
local knowledge is small, and new sources there are none, for we
are remote from the world. Thou couldst be a mighty help to us,
fresh as thou art from Egypt, knowing, I doubt not, the secrets
of the magic of Egyptian temples, and schooled in Egypt's schools.
Perhaps thou knowest, too, the remedies of thy forefathers. It
is said that among Joseph's children the tradition is well guarded.
All of these things could be of use, and thou couldst be a mighty
help."

"Priest of Midian, gladly would I stay with thee, but thy helper
in the priesthood I cannot be. My people knows but one Spirit, the
great Spirit of our forefathers. There are no others. Before Him
magic is an abomination. If thou wouldst have me stay with thee,
it can be under one condition only. Shepherds were my forefathers,
and I too would be a shepherd. I will keep thy sheep."

"Ah, it had slipped my mind that thy Spirit is a jealous Spirit.
Did not thy forefather Abraham destroy the idols of his father
Terah? All of us would serve the one great Spirit if we but knew
how. He is without name and without place; and gods must have
both. Men must have something they can see, something they can
touch with their hands, in order to know what they are about. Let
it be as thou sayest. Whatever thou art, it is well to have thee here,
with thy great presence, where men are few and women many.
Tell me, shepherd, what shall be thy reward?"

"One of my forefathers came, like me, to a strange place. Like
me, he had none but the Spirit of his fathers to accompany him
in his way. Like me, he brought with him no gold and little silver,
no sheep and no cattle; only the labor of his two hands. And when
he saw the woman he loved, he engaged himself to serve for her
seven hard years. As I sat by the well I meditated on my forefather
Jacob and I prayed in my heart to the Spirit that He might decide
my ways and be with me among strangers as he was with Jacob.
And as I sat so meditating, thy daughters came with the sheep, and
I saw Zipporah, thy eldest daughter, as Jacob saw Rachel. And my
soul was straightway bound to hers. Like a sister she was in my
eyes, as Rachel was in the eyes of Jacob. Give me thy daughter
Zipporah to wife, and I will serve thee seven years."

"Not even seven days wilt thou serve. Like a son thou wert to

86

me when I set eyes on thee. My daughter is thine, and the sheep are thine. Shepherds make good seers; so, at least, men think." And as if speaking to himself, Jethro added: "That will serve me in my priestly craft, too." He turned to his son. "Go, Hobab, prepare a rich wedding feast, and call together the people. A son has come to Jethro the priest—a child of Abraham. What is thy name? I have not asked till now, thinking thou wouldst not trust a stranger. Now that thou art my son, tell me thy name."

"My name is Moses."

"That I knew when thou toldest me who thou wert. What is thy concealed name, thy secret name, behind which thou hidest thyself?"

"I have no other name. My name is Moses."

"It is not well for a man to have but one name. It is easy to work magic on him when he has no secret name for his concealment. As a sign of my faith in thee, my son, I will entrust thee with the secret of my hidden name. I have many names, but the name which I carry for my family, my family name—" here Jethro stepped over to Moses and murmured in his ear—"is Reuel. For others I am Jethro, or Jether, but for thee from now on I am Reuel. Thou too must have a secret name. When one will seek to work magic on thee by thy name Moses, he will not reach thee, for thou wilt be hidden in thy secret name, which none will know but those of thy family whom thou hast entrusted. And I will call thee—" and Jethro approached Moses again and began to whisper in his ear the ritual of the conferring of a secret name.

While Jethro conducted the ritual Moses looked about him and saw the many idols and images, and the instruments of magic, which filled the house. He remembered that in the house of Laban, too, where Jacob sojourned, there were many teraphim, and he said to himself: "The Spirit of my fathers wills that in this, too, my lot shall be like that of Jacob our forefather, that I should live among teraphim, but that I should believe in Him and be faithful to Him."

The driving off of the wild shepherd men by which Moses signalized his appearance had made a deep impression not only in Jethro's household, but among all the inhabitants of Midian.

Midian was a little island oasis in the great sea of the desert; it had good pasturage and many wells. The shepherds whom Moses had driven off belonged to a tribe which lived on the rim of the wilderness, hard by Midian. They envied the Midianites their pastures, and even more their wells. They had always been a trouble to the Midianites, and many were the attacks they had made on the wells and on the flocks. The dwellers in the oasis were in constant terror of a general attack, in which they might be driven permanently from their happy fields. There was a scarcity of men in Midian, and the danger from the wilderness increased from year to year. The Midianites had even been compelled to use their women for the tending of sheep and cattle, to the derision of the surrounding tribes.

The action of the stranger—obviously an Egyptian—in dispersing the band of young shepherds who had molested Jethro's daughters at the well awakened the fear of the shepherd tribe, as it aroused the admiration of the Midianites. Rumors began to go about concerning the Egyptian to whom Jethro the priest had so hastily given his daughter and entrusted his sheep. He was a giant, not a man; his mere glance, sharp as a spear, had overwhelmed the shepherds, and they had fallen in the dust at his feet. Moreover, he was mighty in magic, having studied with the priests of Egypt. The stories concerning him became more and more fantastic. It was told that he knew the names of the gods and that by incantation he could make the sick well, the well sick, the dead alive. The more the legends grew concerning the Egyptian giant, who had taken to wife the daughter of Jethro, the higher rose the prestige of the priest of Midian. It was believed that, armed now with the skill and knowledge of his Egyptian son-in-law, he had acquired new cures, new medicines, new incantations, and all manner of magic powers, for which Egypt was so famous.

Jethro was not only the priest of Midian, but likewise the healer, the judge, the mediator, the helper in difficult times, and the counselor in all that happened to the families and clans of Midian. Moses observed the people who came to the priest, listened to the problems which they submitted to him, heard their troubles, and pondered the advice which Jethro gave them. Jethro believed in all the gods and sought to satisfy each visitor under the god in which he believed. He distributed amulets and magic formulas; he also distributed medicinal oils, unguents, and incense, which had curative powers. He was deeply versed in the lore of medicinal plants, having received the traditions of the priesthood.

This lore was a growth of many generations, and it had been spread in the first instance by the wandering seers who were skilled in primitive medicines. The desert dwellers suffered widely from eye and skin diseases, brought on by the hot winds and the scarcity of water. The priest could tell from the symptoms on the skin which diseases were curable, which incurable, and which infectious. The carriers of infectious diseases were carefully segregated; there were also primitive hygienic regulations for the population as a whole and strict dietary laws which forbade the eating of certain animals and certain fish, the flesh of which was believed to be harmful. All these regulations and prohibitions were enforced as a religious ritual, attributed to direct divine command.

The Midianites came to Jethro with all kinds of disputes and claims and transgressions; there were quarrels between neighbors, family quarrels, thefts, robberies, and slayings. The Midianites had a primitive code which incorporated a rough sense of desert justice. In the first line were the seven fundamental laws, which, according to the accepted view, had come down from the time of Noah; and these laws had been sanctified by all the desert tribes. In contradistinction to the Egyptians, the Midianites were most scrupulous in whatever pertained to the integrity and purity of the family; and physical intimacy was forbidden between close relatives as between man and beast—intimacies which were common among the Egyptians.

All these laws, or, as they might better be called, usages, which Jethro had introduced to the Midianites, were ascribed to Noah, which was only a way of saying that they were very old, that they had always existed, like laws of nature. But they had become sanctified because they were, in addition, regarded as commandments issued by Abraham, whom many of the desert tribes were proud to claim as their ancestor, either through his son Ishmael or his grandson Esau. Abraham, Ishmael, Esau—they were accepted as heroes who had lived in the remotest past.

There were many legends dealing with the lives of the heroes, their habits, customs, and behavior. Abraham's hospitality became a commandment and a sacred duty among many desert tribes. Some of the tribes laid special emphasis on the commandment to honor father and mother, and this too must have come down to them from the forefathers of the Hebrews. There were on the other hand tribes in which the rights of primogeniture were practically unlimited: when the father became so old that he could not defend himself against the eldest son, the latter killed him and inherited his wives and possessions.

Thus, side by side with good usages, there existed among the tribes usages which were primordially savage and cruel. Among some of the tribes there had emerged a humane attitude toward slaves and strangers; among others the attitude was one of ruthlessness and brutality. But the good and the bad usages were accepted as being equally right and proper. There was no external standard of justice. Antiquity of wont and custom and behavior decided everything, and all judgment was made accordingly. It was as though man, like his gods, had been smitten with blindness and could not distinguish between the right and the wrong.

Of the heart of Moses it might be said that it was like a moral filter, which separated good from evil. Observing closely the life about him, he studied with attentive ear and eye all the manners and usages of the tribes, their laws and their judgments. He recognized beyond any shadow of a doubt the customs which flowed from the undefiled well of his forefathers and which were touched with the grace of the high God whom they had served. He recognized in these customs the will of God, His love of man, and His concern over him. He recognized the hand of the mighty One; and his faith was renewed that the God of his fathers kept watch over mankind; and even if one did not feel His hand ruling the world, if, in fact, the power of wickedness seemed to have dominion, yet the truth was that God's kingdom would be renewed in the appointed time. He believed in the covenant with the forefathers and in the promise made to them; and with all the vehemence of his nature he loved the good and hated the evil and clung to the notion of righteousness as the sole hope of rescue in the stormy sea of being.

Moses lived a lonely life, a life apart, in Jethro's house. In spite of the high tribute which was paid to him everywhere, he was a stranger to his wife. In Jethro's house it was known of course that he was of the Bnai Joseph, who were slaves in Goshen. But there the knowledge was not a discredit to him. The Bnai Joseph had never really been regarded as slaves. They were known to be of noble descent, and the memory of Joseph, who had been the vice-regent of a Pharaoh, still lived among the tribes. Widespread, too, was the report that the Bnai Joseph awaited redemption; this, together with their descent from Abraham, gave them standing in the eyes of the people, despite their present status. It was also known in Jethro's household that Moses himself had never been a slave in Goshen, but had been brought up in Pharaoh's court, and educated in the academies of Egypt. There he had studied, among other subjects, agriculture, in which he had acquired wide knowledge; and from him the tribes learned to let their fields lie fallow at regular intervals, in order that they might recover their fertility.

With all this, a certain darkness, a suggestion of mystery, surrounded the personality of Moses, and he did little to dispel it. It was not that he deliberately kept apart, by no means, for he helped his father-in-law to advise the many people who came to him in their distress. But he would not recognize, let alone acknowledge, their idols, and this was an astonishing thing, for it was regarded as self-understood that any stranger who came to settle in a new place should accept the local gods. He, however, did not participate in their festivals. With his natural openness and his ardor he even permitted himself to express contempt for the orgiastic ceremonies with which one of the gods was worshiped, ceremonies in which the young abandoned themselves to indiscriminate sexual license under a sacred tree. And when Zipporah bore him his first son, and wanted to tattoo the body of the little one with the family emblems, as the custom was for the oldest sons, Moses set his face rigidly against it.

He did not worship the local gods, nor did he observe any ritual for his own God. He seemed to conduct himself as though he alone among all the people stood outside the protection of a god.

And thus, too, Moses himself sometimes felt. He saw himself an isolated figure between heaven and earth, and he belonged to no one either in heaven or on earth. His brothers in Goshen had driven him away, and doubtless they had already forgotten him; perhaps they had forgotten, too, the God of their fathers. And he himself —alone among people—was consumed with a vain longing for the Highest, for the God Who had once appeared to Abraham, to be a light and a guide to man. But since that time thick darkness had descended on the earth, and in that darkness Moses walked, seeking the light.

Meanwhile he tended the sheep of his father-in-law. The shepherd's calling was not considered a lowly one. On the contrary, it was regarded as a form of religious worship. The shepherd who spent his days and nights in loneliness, with his flocks, wandering the wilderness, was close to the gods. Often the shepherd was regarded as a seer, and men came to him for counsel. He had knowledge of cures, and he was looked upon as a holy man. Often fathers of tribes, priests, and even rulers gave up their high status and withdrew as shepherds into the solitudes of the wilderness.

Moses too regarded the tending of sheep as a holy work, because the forefathers of Israel, Abraham, Isaac, and Jacob, had all been shepherds. The forefather of his own tribe, Levi, had tended, together with his brothers, the sheep of their father Jacob. And Moses took to his work earnestly and diligently.

Nor was the tending of sheep in the wilderness a simple work; and Moses had to apply himself with much attention in order to master it. One had to become intimate with the secrets of the wilderness; one had to learn how to seek out the hidden places, the little green valleys toward which water flowed and where dew accumulated, nourishing the grass, or where a desert spring burst out between rocks. But once Moses had acquired this skill, he was of great help to his brother-in-law, the young Hobab.

Hobab was a lithe, bronze-skinned lad with a head of thick, crisp-curled hair, a face and forehead tattooed with the family emblems, and ears set with rings. He knew the wilderness of Midian as if it were the courtyard of his father's house. He would disappear into it for days at a stretch and return with strange specimens of cactus plants, wild reeds, leaves of myrrh and camphor, from which his father Jethro pressed the juices for his medicines. When Moses first went out into the wilderness, Hobab accompanied him and gave him his first experience in the mysteries of wilderness life, and showed him the concealed green strips in the tiny valleys between towering hills. Here the sun never penetrated, and the thick dews of the night lingered through the days, accumulating, providing rich nourishment for the sheep. Hobab knew which cactus roots and palm leaves retained water, which plants were sweet to the palate, and which were bitter and poisonous. He guided Moses to concealed caverns where he could find shelter for himself and the sheep during sandstorms. Moses learned industriously and mastered the nature of the wilderness; he learned, too, how even in the wilderness God had planted life and had supplied it with the nourishment it needed.

Carrying with him the bundle of dried cheeses and flat-baked cakes, which his wife Zipporah prepared for him, with the water gourds hanging at his girdle, Moses tended Jethro's sheep. He studied anxiously the ways of his charges. These dumb brutes, to whom God had vouchsafed no means of defense, were entirely dependent on the grace of the shepherd, as man was entirely dependent on the grace of God. Moses set himself to learn perfectly the shepherd's calling. He sought to understand all the needs of the sheep, to recognize when it bleated for thirst and when it bleated for hunger. He took care of the young which the sheep dropped in the sand; he learned to forefeel the coming of storms and to lead his flock to shelter. He became expert in the finding of the green retreats and the accumulations of water; and always he compared the dependence of sheep upon man to man's dependence upon God.

It often happened that Moses observed a restlessness in the flock and could not discover the cause. The sheep set up a tumultous bleating, and he sought in vain for the reason. Their foolish eyes were filled with terror, they ran together in panic, and Moses could not perceive the danger which revealed itself to them at a distance. In time he learned that when this happened, the faint smell of a jackal had reached the nostrils of the sheep. Somewhere in the vicinity the beast of prey was lurking, waiting for the night. Or perhaps they had caught sight of the glitter of the jackal's eyes, somewhere between two rocks. But the shepherd had smelled nothing, seen nothing.

It happened once that Moses, hearing the agitated bleating of the flock, did not recognize in it the note of terror and supplication which proclaimed the nearness of danger. He, their shepherd and protector, had covered himself with his white woolen mantle and had fallen asleep under the stars. He was awakened by the bleating and did not know its meaning. When he arose at last, he found that a jackal had broken into the flock. He drove the beast off, but he was too late to save the sheep, which the marauder dragged away into the night. Bitterly he reproached himself with his heedlessness and blindness, and he felt crushed and humbled before the dumb charges whom he had failed in their need.

"What manner of shepherd am I, who do not understand the lamentations of my charges?" he asked himself.

From that time on he no longer lay down to sleep in the night, but stood guard until the morning, staff in hand.

On another occasion he saw a young lamb break away from the flock and run off alone, against the nature of sheep.

Moses hastened after the lamb, but it was unusually lively and he could not catch up with it. Finally he came upon it in a narrow pass between two rocks. There it stood, and as Moses was about to chase it back to the flock, he saw that the lamb had its muzzle close to the soil and was licking avidly at the moisture which oozed up from between the rocks.

Moses was filled with shame, and he waited, saying:

"Thou wert thirsty, and wentest to seek water, and I chased thee impatiently. Poor, tired little creature!" And he lifted the sheep on his shoulders and carried it back to the flock. "Spirit of my fathers, let me be a good shepherd to my sheep, as my forefathers were to theirs," he prayed.

CHAPTER ELEVEN

SOME years had now passed since Moses had settled with Jethro and tended his sheep in the wilderness. He had grown accustomed to the shepherd's calling, and his heart was in it. The solitary life in the desert places, where he could be alone with his thoughts, where he could meditate on his brothers and unite his spirit with the Spirit of his fathers, accorded with his mood.

He was completely at home in the wilderness now, knew all the oases, the green retreats, the occasional clusters of date palms, the gathering places of water. He wandered far afield with his flock in search of pasture and sometimes disappeared for weeks at a time. He had learned to nourish himself on sugar cane and on lichen flowerets, which grew on rocks like moss and which the dew left behind like a hoar deposit. Dried and rubbed into a paste, they could be baked into sweet, tasty cakes.

Wrapped in his shepherd's mantle, he would stand or sit by his flock through the night and look up into the stars for a sign from the eternal Spirit in which his faith was rooted. But sometimes, when his thoughts wandered to his brothers and he remembered their bitter bondage, he would reproach himself and ask himself how he could sit here in freedom, secure under the open sky, while their blood was being shed by Pharaoh's slave drivers.

Had he done well to leave his brothers and to save his own life? Was it just that he alone among his people should have exacted retribution for the evil done them? Had he been right in slaying the Egyptian? Who was he that he should have taken it upon himself to kill a man and thus endanger his own life and the life of his brothers? Perhaps that Hebrew overseer had spoken only the truth when he had asked: "Who has made thee a judge?"

But his self-searching always reached the same conclusion: he could not find any guilt in himself for what he had done.

"The wickedness of the overseer made me a judge," he said to himself. "Could I look on calmly when he slew a soul in Israel, out of his evil desire and the wickedness of his heart? I was the witness of his wickedness and thus had the right to judge him and to execute sentence. Only he who has seen with his own eyes the act of wickedness has the right to punish the doer of wickedness. I did not dare to ignore the abomination in silence for the sake of my own safety. Better to suffer for righteousness than to become enslaved to unrighteousness. This sentence against the Egyptian I myself had to execute, because I myself had been the witness of his evil-doing."

Wandering with his sheep in the remote, solitary, desert places, far from men and the habitations of men, Moses felt with all his senses the Spirit of his fathers and found fulfillment in Him. He sought Him and found Him, not in the heavens, not among the stars, not in the sun or moon, or in any of His creations, as the idol worshipers did. He felt Him in the whole being of the world, through His ways and attributes. The Spirit had not only created the heavens and the earth and all that was in them: He ruled and directed them in the order of His will. Not for a single instant was his direction withdrawn from any part of the world or from any of its inhabitants. He had instituted law and judgment for all their deeds and the measure for good and evil. He judged the world and all that He had created, according to the law and the measure, which were righteousness. All that was righteous and good was with Him and of Him; all that was unrighteous and evil was against Him, against His will and His order, and therefore had to be destroyed from off the earth.

And He would keep His covenant, and fulfill His promise to redeem Israel, but not through cowardly ways, by supplication and mendicancy, not through a second Joseph, as the Bnai Levi and his brother Aaron believed. No, not through self-abasement and flattering petition, but through judgment and justice. And though redemption lingered, and Pharaoh wallowed in sin, in murder, and robbery, shedding the blood of Israel daily, God would surely appear and demand an accounting for every soul, blood for blood, life for life. He would demand and exact payment from the Egyptians for every day of bitter labor which they had exacted from the Bnai Joseph. His righteousness would blaze up like a new sun in the heavens, and all that lived would see that a Judge ruled the world. He was terrible in His vengeance, as He was glorious in His graciousness. And the hearts of the evildoers would melt with terror of the God of Israel, and they would cast away their idols and images like broken potsherds, and they would besiege the tents of Israel to seek out Him who kept His promise to the fathers and dealt out righteousness to the strong and weak alike. Then only one Spirit would have dominion over the earth, and there would be one measure of righteousness.

Under the hot sunlight by day, under the starlight of the cold desert nights, standing by his flock, Moses nurtured the vision of a just God of Israel and sheltered it deep in his heart. And the vision gave him the strength to endure the anguish of his meditations on the slavery of his brothers, confirming his faith in the coming of the redemption.

From time to time he returned from the wilderness to his father-in-law Jethro in Midian, to his wife Zipporah, and to the two children she had borne him. On one such occasion Jethro made a tally of the flock, went through it, and picked out the lambs which had been born during the last sojourn in the wilderness. These he set apart for Moses, to constitute the beginning of his own flock.

"Thou hast thine own children now," he said. "It is time for thee to build thine own house and to guard thine own sheep."

"My house will be with the Bnai Israel, when the Spirit of our fathers will redeem them from the bondage of Egypt. While they are enslaved to Pharaoh and have no home, I have no home either, for wherein am I better than they?"

"But they are in exile and thou art at home. Thy home is there where thy wife and children are."

"My home is where my husband is," interposed Zipporah. "If my husband's home is with the slavery of his brothers, my home is with them too."

Jethro, in whom a feeling for order and justice was deep rooted, was pleased by his daughter's words.

"It is the way of the world," he said, "that a wife shall cleave to her husband and that they shall become one flesh. But thy husband's place is no longer among his brothers in Egypt. Nor did he ever belong to them. He was a stranger among them, and he is a stranger among us here, too. Has he not named his older son Gershom, which signifies 'a stranger in a strange land'? But a man must belong to a place. He cannot forever remain between two worlds. It is time for thee, Moses, to decide to whom thou belongest, to them or to us."

Moses had no answer, for he recognized the truth in Jethro's words; he was a stranger wandering between two worlds.

"I know that thy heart is with thy brothers in Egypt. Thou art not here with us, thou seest not thine own children. Thou thinkest only of thy brothers," said Zipporah, when she was alone with Moses. "If thou goest to them, take me with thee. I would be one of them."

"In Egypt? In slavery?"

"I would rather be there, in slavery, with thee, than here in freedom without thee."

"I cannot go to my brothers in slavery. Thou hast heard what thy father said. He spoke the truth."

"Like thee, I believe in the great Spirit who will come to redeem them. Let us go to Egypt and there wait for the redemption with thy brothers."

"I do not belong to them, and the redemption is not for me. I remain outside."

"Why? Art thou not one of them?"

"Only he who can suffer as they suffer, and in the midst of suffering remain strong in faith, can await redemption. I fled from them, I shook off their sufferings."

"Dost thou not suffer more than they? Have I not heard thee groaning in the night, like a wounded animal? Know I not that thy heart is twisted with anguish when thou rememberest the slavery of thy brothers? Double are thy sufferings, for thou sufferest with them and thou sufferest for them."

"No, Zipporah, I cannot go to them. God has afflicted me with a free heart and a rebellious will. I must remain far from them. From afar I must hear their lamentation, and from afar I shall have to hear their jubilation when the hour of their deliverance comes. For only those who have been with the children of Abraham in their Egyptian bondage will have their share in the redemption— and not those who fled from it."

Returning once with his flock from the wilderness, Moses found visitors in Jethro's home. It sometimes happened that wandering priests and seers stayed with Jethro as his guests or paused to exchange with him amulets, teraphim, herbs, or instruments of magic. Some of the visitors now with his father-in-law Moses had already encountered in the neighborhood. Among them was the blind seer who had stopped him in the wilderness of Shur; and on this occasion he was the chief speaker in the little gathering.

"It cannot be otherwise," he declared, "than that the high Spirit of Abraham has thrown a spell on the Hebrew slaves, to prevent them from casting Him off, no matter what calamities are visited upon them. For now there is a new affliction; and every day Pharaoh takes a number of their children in order to bathe in their blood. They say that a kind of leprosy has smitten him, and the doctors have told him that he can be cured only by bathing in the blood of children. So every day they see their children dragged off to the slaughter—and still they believe that the Spirit will come to redeem them from the hand of Pharaoh. In former times, in the days of an older Pharaoh, it was the custom to cast the bones of dead slaves into the mud pits, to make the bricks firmer. Today they take young children and brick them, still living, into the walls. The voice of the children cries out from the walls—and their Spirit sits, a prisoner, among the thorns of the fire mountain, and His voice is heard, too, lamenting for the sufferings of His believers, whom He cannot help."

"I, too, know of this," said another seer. "Shepherds who have led their sheep by night near the fire mountain have heard a voice among the thorns, a human voice, lamenting, but with such power that trees are uprooted and crags are split and fall into the abyss with a noise like thunder. Such is the power of the voice which cries out of the fire mountain. Most assuredly a spirit is locked in the stony walls of the hills. When the shepherds find out that they are near the mountain, they hasten away with their flocks."

"It is the gods who have seized the supreme Spirit of Abraham and keep Him a prisoner there, so that He may not issue forth and free the children of Abraham. They are afraid, the gods, that if the children of Abraham are freed from slavery they will spread the name and laws of their Spirit among the peoples of the world, and all the peoples will turn from the gods and worship Him. It would mean the death of the gods if the promise to Abraham were fulfilled."

"And we, too, know. We have it from our fathers. The high God of Abraham is a God of jealousy and vengeance, and he will not tolerate other gods at his side. They say that the first condition he laid upon Abraham was, that his children should have no other gods beside Him, and Him alone they were to serve. The gods are in danger, and they are filled with fear lest the children of Abraham escape into freedom and spread the worship of their God everywhere."

"Not the gods alone are in danger, and not they alone are filled with fear. Equally threatened and terrified are all the priests and seers of the gods."

"The children of Abraham shall never be freed. We will not have it."

"No, Pharaoh will never let them go."

"The priests of Egypt would not permit it. They know the meaning of it."

"We must use every method to win the Hebrew slaves away from their supreme Spirit. We must let them know that the Spirit which made the convenant with Abraham is a prisoner of the gods who have also made a covenant—a covenant against Him, that He shall never be freed. Let the Hebrew slaves accept our gods, or the gods of Egypt. Then Pharaoh will make lighter their yoke. Only thus will we be able to wipe out the memory of the supreme Spirit from off the earth. For if His followers will cast Him off, He will be forgotten," said the blind seer.

"The children of Abraham will never cast off their Spirit. I know them. For Him they will endure all sufferings, and they will go down into the grave carrying thither their faith in Him. I fear that thy plan to spread the story of the imprisoned God is a vain one," said Jethro to the blind seer. "They will laugh thee to scorn. They know well that no one can take prisoner the Spirit of their father Abraham. This is certain."

"If it be so, then we must see to it that the children of Abraham perish in Egypt. We must make it clear to the priests of Egypt, and they in turn must make it clear to Pharaoh, that not the gods of Egypt alone, but all the gods of all the peoples desire the death of the Hebrews, so that with them may perish the memory of their Spirit from among the living. For His memory lives only among the Hebrews, and only from their mouths can the peoples hear of His being," said another seer.

"Not only among the Hebrews lives the Spirit of Abraham, but in all His creation. If Pharaoh were to wipe out not only the children of Israel, but all the children of men, he still would not destroy the memory of the one living God. His glory and praise will be uttered by all creation. Heaven and earth will testify that he is the one and only Spirit who created them, and they will carry His name till the last day," cried out Moses from his corner.

"They said that of the god Aton, whom Amenhotep, fourth of his name, installed in Tel el Amarna, after he had removed all the gods of Egypt and forbidden their worship. You remember how they sang to the god: 'Thou art the father and mother of all that thou hast created'? And where is he now? His name dare not be mentioned, his temples are desolate in Tel el Amarna, and no memorial of him survives. That is the fate of every god who tries to do away with the other gods. His place is the fire mountain, where he is chained to the crags," said one of the seers.

"To whom dost thou compare the living God of Abraham? To one of his creatures. Who was Aton and who is he? The same as Ammon-Ra, whom he drove out—the sun, whom all of you worship. The sun is only one of the creations of the great Spirit. He has many suns, which you have never seen. And all are the creation of His hands," said Moses.

"Who is that?" asked the blind seer in astonishment, rolling his eye round the room. "That voice is familiar. Is this not the man I met once, years ago, on my way in the desert? They told me of him in Egypt. He moved the Hebrew slaves to revolt and slew one of Pharaoh's overseers. The guards are still in search of him. Is it not the same man?"

"That is my son-in-law, Moses. He is of the Hebrews," said Jethro.

The dark reports of the new persecutions in Egypt threw the soul of Moses into a turmoil, and he found no rest. It became impossible for him to return to the wilderness with Jethro's sheep. He could not understand the meaning of it all. Was it, then, possible that what the magician had said was true, that the false gods had overcome the God of Abraham, and that He had gone under, like Aton? No, no, it could not be. All his feelings declared that the God of Abraham lived and was in the midst of life. He saw it in a hundred ways. God lived in the memory of his brothers, the slaves; He lived in the order of the world, in the rising and setting of the sun, in the procession of the stars. Moses saw Him in the tiniest of the plants that blossomed in the desert, he felt Him in the dumb pleading of the sheep, in the clinging to each other of mothers and children, in all the manifestations of His creation. The eye of the Creator was never withdrawn, and His compassion flowed over everything.

But if this was so, why was He silent? Why did He endure the suffering of His friend's children, whose bodies were thrown into the clay pits, or built into the walls of Pharaoh's treasure cities? How long, how long? Why did He not appear, why did He not bring order among men as He had brought it into the rest of creation?

His heart was bruised by the shame that had been done to the Spirit of Abraham when they placed Him on a level with the idolatry of Aton. Pharaoh Amenhotep, the fourth of that name, had indeed established Aton when he revolted against Ammon-Ra, destroying the temples of the latter, suppressing his name, and seeking to wipe him out from the memory of the Egyptians. Then Amenhotep had gone on to suppress all the other gods, declaring Aton to be the only god of Egypt: he had left the capital of the former Pharaohs and had gone downstream with the Nile to found himself a new city among the crags and to dedicate it to the new god. Tel el Amarna became the center of the new faith. No other god dared be mentioned beside him who was the giver of life, the father and mother of Pharaoh, Aton. And now the city Tel el Amarna was a desolation. No human foot trod it, and no one uttered the name of Aton. The later Pharaohs, beginning with Amenhotep's son-in-law, the young Tutankhamen, had dethroned Aton and restored the dominion of Ammon-Ra and all the other gods. Pharaoh became once again the god Ra, flesh of his flesh, and the hierarchy of the gods flourished again.

The worship of Aton lasted no longer than the reign of the Pharaoh who had exalted him. Nothing was left of him now but the ruins which were once the city of Tel el Amarna. Moses had seen them; he knew the desolate temples; he knew the image which had been Aton—an image of the sun with many radiating hands, which went out to the four corners of the earth.

A sacred anger was kindled in Moses. Deep as his love was for his brothers, bitter as was his suffering with them, deeper was his love for the Spirit of Abraham, bitterer his suffering for the indignity heaped upon Him. To him that Spirit had become his heaven and earth, his refuge, possession, and life fulfillment. Uprooted from his kind, sundered both from Pharaoh's court and his own brothers, far removed from his father and mother, he had made the Spirit of Abraham his all. He was the foundation of his being, physical and spiritual; there was no one for him but that Spirit whose name he did not know, nor where to seek Him. That strange, unknown, concealed and yet intimate, only revealed Spirit had become his personal possession.

A great zeal burned in him, a compound of pain and fury for the humiliations offered to the Spirit. Jethro's house became intolerable to him, because of the offense which had been committed in it. He went out into the field, fell on his knees, spread out his arms to heaven and lifted his voice with the cry of a wounded lion:

"Spirit of Abraham, how long wilt Thou be silent? See to whom they have compared Thee!"

CHAPTER TWELVE

AGAIN a torment of restlessness had taken hold of Moses. The faith which had been his in the loneliness of the desert fled from him. There, in the desert, while pasturing his sheep, he had been able to pray to the Spirit of Abraham, whose name he had not been able to call upon. In the stillness, under the stars of the desert, when he stood sentinel over the sheep, he had made up his own name for Him. He had looked at the sheep huddling together under the great singing heavens, seeking protection; he had felt God's grace resting on creation; and in his heart he had named Him the God of grace and mercy.

He knew then, with all his senses, that the God of grace and mercy suffered with His people and with all sufferers. He suffered for the evil which man inflicted on man, and He was with His people in its wretchedness. The blood of the young ones immured in the bricks of Pharaoh's great palaces and storehouses went up to Him—and yet He was silent.

There was a reason for His silence. He had appointed a time, and the time was at hand. It flowed closer and closer, like the flowing of a stream, and it would flow until the reservoir of patience was exhausted.

He could not sojourn any more in the wilderness; nor could he stay in Jethro's house. He therefore gathered his flock, said farewell to the household, and set out across the wilderness to Eziongeber, at the end of the eastern arm of the Red Sea.

It was as if a voice within him had said clearly: "Go by way of the mountains of Sinai."

Far off, from the summits of the sandhills of Midian, Moses could descry the crags of Sinai. The first flash of the morning sun, the departing rays of the setting sun, touched the copper-colored peaks and slopes with fire and imparted a pearly shimmer to their snowcaps. The reflection of the crags glimmered over all the expanse of the wilderness. Moses was well aware that these copper-colored crags had cast a spell of fear on the Bedouins and shepherds of the area from the most ancient times, and men avoided the region. Moreover, the land thereabouts was waterless, the sound of streams was never heard there; and over all reigned a stillness which spoke of death and was not restful; for it was a stillness of petrifaction. The disposition of the crags was such that when the stillness was in any way disturbed, mighty echoes multiplied the sound a thousandfold. A stone falling down the slopes into the valley reverberated with the thunder of tremendous torrents and spread far and wide across the empty vastness. These echoing sounds in the dry, vibrant air had created, in the fantasy of the Bedouins, the legends of the spirits and fallen gods imprisoned in the fire mountains. These were gods whom their ancient followers had forgotten because they had not been able to come to the help of the faithful in a time of need. They were gods who had fled from the resentment of men, or from the enmity of the stronger gods, the rivals who had pursued them, taken them captive, and imprisoned them here. The lamentation of the defeated and forgotten gods it was, that filled the desert nights with ululations.

And not only wandering Bedouins and strange tribes, but Jethro himself—as Moses knew—believed that the higher Spirit, which Abraham had worshiped, had proved himself unable to save the Hebrews from Pharaoh's hand and had therefore found his place among the defeated gods on Sinai; so Jethro and his household believed, though they did not speak of it in the presence of Moses.

Moses had himself avoided, till now, the slopes of Sinai. The soil was poor in pasture; it consisted for the most part of copper ore and of the sandy detritus of rocks which fell from the peaks. And even if, in the winter season, some sort of herbage might be found in the clefts, the area was dangerous by reason of the falling rocks and the sudden declivities.

But now Moses cut across the green oasis of Ezion-geber and led his flock toward Sinai. He went first along the arm of the Red Sea and then in the direction of Mount Horeb, because his brother-in-law Hobab had told him that in the shadow of this mountain there was grass; there were even date palms and cacti, and there was water accumulated in the clefts which were concealed from the sun.

Moses set out as if there were a compulsion on him and he acted not of his own free will. He could not account to himself for his

105

behavior. There was of course no notion in his mind that there could be anything in the wild talk of the seers concerning the imprisonment of the God of Abraham among the other gods on the fire mountain. What compelled him was altogether of another nature, indeterminate, obscure, but utterly irresistible.

Before his last departure from Jethro's house, he had, in a fit of despair, actually proposed that he return to Egypt and deliver himself up to Pharaoh, in the hope that his surrender would lighten the burden of his brothers. Jethro and Zipporah had with difficulty dissuaded him from this resolve. They had, instead, encouraged his return to the desert, out of fear that the blind seer, Balaam, would report his presence in Midian to Pharaoh's officers. But his flight toward Sinai was something that Moses could not explain.

As he went deeper into the peninsula, his heart was restored to him, and in the shadow of Horeb he found peace. During the day he looked for the patches of green which the sunlight had not yet burned out. In the foothills he found a cactus growth which carried on a precarious struggle with the winds and sandstorms. The little plants were a pleasant and welcome food to his sheep, which nibbled them down to the roots. In one place he discovered as by a miracle a store of water in a cavern; not accumulated, for it was fresh and cool, but apparently welling up out of the rock. Moses brought his flock to the cavern and would have been willing to remain there a while. Horeb, in the midst of the mountains of Sinai, was flatter than the others, more suitable for grazing. It was of limestone, and in the clefts of the stones grew thistles, thorns, and other plants and roots affording modest but sufficient nourishment for the flock. There was also the tiny white lichen floweret, covering the rocks like a moss.

The other mountains were steep, pointed, and craggy, thrusting rocky fingers toward the heavens; but the surface of Horeb consisted of a range of plateaus; and when, at night, Moses sat down in his shepherd mantle and lifted his face and arms to heaven in prayer, the dome of the sky, set with stars, lay in an arch about him, unbroken by wild stony eruptions, so that the sobbing of his prayers spread out unarrested into the heights.

He saw, indeed, the fire which the sun's first and last beams lit on the copper peaks. He heard the voices, the reverberating echoes, which spread in circles of thunder from the peaks. But neither the flames nor the voices made a particular impression on him, since

106

he knew them for what they were. And he considered the frightened reports of those who believed in demonic prisoners on the
heights nothing more than the babbling of children terrified by
shadows on the wall. False gods did not exist for him.

Yet one morning, starting out of a doze into which he had fallen
while he sat by the sheep, he was aware of deeper stillness than
usual, as though the space about him had been separated out from
the rest of creation and gathered into a tabernacle. And as he
looked about him, it seemed to him that this, indeed, had happened.

Gray clouds had descended from the zenith and surrounded the
hills. Through the clouds were thrust the craggy fingers of the
highest peaks, and from below seethed up endless wreaths of mist.
The wreaths fluttered white, drifting from peak to peak; then they
began to close in a circle about the spot where he was seated by
his sheep. They hung closer and closer over him and over the sheep,
which were huddling together as if against a danger.

An unwonted and unfamiliar power and authority was taking
command of Moses. A profound tranquillity reigned about him,
and it was as if the creation were holding its breath in anticipation.

A mood of piety and awe welled up in Moses. He felt himself
nearer than ever before to his Creator. His heart was flooded with
compassion for all created things, and he was seized with a deep
need for prayer. He knelt by the side of his sheep, lifted his arms,
and prayed:

"God of grace and mercy, look down from Thy heights and see
what has happened to Thy creation. Thy children wander like sheep
without a shepherd. There is none to show them the way and to
bring them under Thy will. Have mercy on the children of man,
whom Thou has created, reveal Thyself to them as Thou didst once
in the days of Abraham. After Thee thirsts the whole creation, and
Thee all men seek, for Thou alone art the creator of all that lives."

When he arose from his prayer the clouds had drawn away from
the place and were afloat above the peaks. The sun was breaking
through the cloud rifts. Tranquil and grateful, the sheep were dry-
ing their damp fleeces in the emerging sun. Moses looked about
him, and it was as if earth were steeped once more in the freshness
of the first six days of creation. And he himself was steeped in
purity like a newborn child.

Then suddenly his eyes were drawn to something in the distance.

A flame rose clear from the earth, like an uplifted column. A thornbush was on fire.

There was nothing astonishing in the sight; it happened often enough that a dried and withered thornbush caught fire in the desert, caught fire, flared up, and died down, since there was nothing about it to feed the flame. But this time the fire endured a long time, and Moses stared and wondered, and said to himself: "The thornbush burns and is not consumed."

And Moses rose and said: "I must turn aside and see this great sight, why the bush is not consumed."

And as he drew near the burning bush he heard a voice calling him gently and softly by his name:

"Moses! Moses!"

Moses was not frightened at first. There was something familiar in the voice, as if it had been the voice of a father. He answered:

"Here I am."

The voice spoke to him out of the midst of the burning bush:

"Come no nearer. Take thy shoes from off thy feet, for the ground on which thou standest is holy ground."

Amazed by the voice, Moses obeyed the command.

The voice issued again from the fiery bush:

"I am the God of thy fathers, the God of Abraham, the God of Isaac, and the God of Jacob."

When Moses heard these words he lifted the hem of his mantle and covered his face.

The voice continued to speak to him:

"I have seen the affliction of my people in Egypt, and I have heard their voices uplifted against their taskmasters. I know their suffering. And I descend to save them from the hand of the Egyptians and to bring them into a good and broad land, a land flowing with milk and honey, in the place of the Canaanite, the Hittite, the Amorite, the Perizzite, the Hivite, and the Jebusite. For the cry of the children of Israel has come up to me. I have seen the oppression which is laid upon them by the Egyptians. Come, therefore, and I will send thee to Pharaoh, and thou shalt take my people, the children of Israel, out of Egypt."

All this time Moses had stood before the burning bush, his face hidden in the hem of his mantle. He saw no image; he heard only the voice speaking out of the flame. He had considered himself the unworthiest in Israel, surely not destined for redemption with the others, because he had not endured their slavery. And how was this? He who considered himself guilty of having made heavier Pharaoh's yoke—he was to be God's emissary, to bring the Bnai Israel out of Egypt? With face still covered he bowed to the earth before Him Whom he did not see, and in a tremulous voice, which groped for words, he stammered:

"Who am I that I should go to Pharaoh and that I should bring forth the children of Israel from Egypt?"

Warm and gentle, the voice still spoke to him as if it would allay the terror which had descended on him.

"I will be with thee, and this will be the sign that I have sent thee. When thou wilt bring my people out of Egypt, ye shall serve God upon this mountain."

But the words only increased his terror. "Ye shall serve God upon this mountain!" Was this the God of Israel who spoke, or was it—God forbid!—one of the spirits haunting the mountain? For perhaps there was some truth in the rumors of the demons dwelling here abouts. And, taking heart, Moses determined to prove the Spirit which was speaking to him, and he said:

"When I come to the children of Israel and I say: The God of your fathers has sent me to you, and they ask: What is His name? what shall I answer them?"

The voice replied:

"I am that I am. Thus shalt thou speak to the children of Israel: 'I am' has sent me to you. The Lord, the God of your fathers, the God of Abraham, the God of Isaac, the God of Jacob, has sent me to you. This is my name forever, and my memorial to the generations." And the voice now took on a tone of command. "Go, assemble the elders of Israel, and say to them: The Lord, the God of your fathers, the God of Abraham, Isaac, and Jacob, has appeared to me and has bidden me say that He has remembered you, and He has seen all that is done to you in Egypt. And He said further: I will take you out of Egypt and I will bring you into a land flowing with milk and honey. And they will hear thee, and thou wilt come, thou and the elders of Israel, to the king of Egypt, and you will speak to him thus: The Lord God of the Hebrews has met with us, and now let us go, we pray thee, a distance of three days in the wilderness that we may sacrifice to the Lord our God. And I know that the king of Egypt will not let you go, except by a mighty hand. And I will stretch out my hand, and I will smite

Egypt with all my wonders, and then he will let you go. And when you go, it will not be empty."

But now, when Moses had become convinced that the voice which spoke to him was the voice of the God of all being, the God of creation; now, when he realized that to him of all the Bnai Israel and the Bnai Levi God had vouchsafed Himself, entrusting to him the mission of the deliverance; now he foresaw with what distrust he would be greeted when he came with his mission before Korah and Aaron—they who had driven him from Egypt. And in an onrush of fear he cried:

"But they will not believe me, they will not listen to me, they will say: 'God has not sent thee.' "

"What is in thy hand?" asked the voice.

"A staff."

"Throw it to earth."

Moses cast the staff from him; it fell to earth and turned into a hideous snake. Moses fled in fear.

"Stretch out thy hand, and take it by the tail," commanded the voice.

Moses obeyed the command, took hold of the snake by the tail; instantly it became his familiar staff.

"This in order that they may believe thee that the Lord God of their fathers appeared to thee," said the voice. "Thrust thy hand into thy bosom."

Moses obeyed, thrust his hand into his bosom. When he withdrew it, it was leprous—white as snow with leprosy.

"Put thy hand back into thy bosom."

Moses obeyed, and when he drew his hand forth again it was like the rest of his body.

He heard the voice again: "If it will be so, that they will not believe thee with the first sign, they will believe thee with the second. And if it will be so that they will not believe even the second sign, then take of the water of the river and pour it on the dry land, and the water thou takest from the river will turn to blood on the dry land."

In the midst of the exaltation and joy which filled Moses, in the midst of the first signs of the fulfillment, and even with the divine assurance of his role in it, an invincible humility made him doubt his fitness for the mission: how should he, with his stammering tongue, his proneness to excitement, be the spokesman of Israel before Pharaoh? In a broken, supplicating voice he said:

"I pray thee, Lord, I am not a man of words, neither heretofore nor now since Thou hast spoken to Thy servant, for I am heavy of tongue and slow of speech."

But the voice of God was not raised in anger, nor did a burst of flame come from the bush to destroy him. The voice spoke tenderly, as if a mother were comforting and strengthening a little one. So God comforted and strengthened him:

"Who has made man's mouth? Who makes a man dumb, or deaf, or seeing, or blind, if not I, the Lord? Therefore go, and I will be with thy mouth, and I will teach thee what to say."

But Moses was as it were fixed in his timidity. He now lay with his face buried in the sand, before the burning thornbush. He was imagining his return to Egypt; he imagined Aaron, in the midst of the elders, perceiving him, and turning pale, and saying: "Why hast thou come again to bring misfortune upon us? Is it not enough for thee what Pharaoh did to us since thou didst kill the Egyptian? Why hast thou come, to stir us up again with lies, that God has shown himself to thee? Leave us, thou and thy dreams. Thou art nothing but a disaster to thy brothers." And Moses saw the terrified faces of the elders turned on him. How could he go down to Egypt after what he had done? No, no. He burrowed with his head into the sand, and stretched out his hands to the burning bush:

"I pray Thee, Lord, send whom Thou wilt."

But he had no sooner uttered these words than it seemed to him that he had been lifted up by a whirlwind, which threatened to cast him into an abyss. And he heard the voice thunder:

"Is there not Aaron, the Levite, thy brother? I know that he can speak well. And see, he comes out to meet thee, and when his eyes alight on thee his heart rejoices. And thou wilt speak to him and put the words into his mouth, and I will be with thy mouth and with his mouth, and I will teach you what to do. And he will speak for thee to the people. He shall be thy mouth, and thou shalt be to him in God's stead. And thou shalt take in thy hand this staff, with which thou shalt do the signs."

God had spoken, and who was to withstand Him? He had known all the thoughts of Moses and had answered all his fears. He had given him divine authority over Aaron and had made Aaron his mouthpiece. He had bidden him take up his staff for the signs and had sent him to redeem the children of Israel from Egypt.

Moses rose slowly from his place and made deep obeisance again to the Spirit of Israel, which had spoken to him. Then he turned and went about the fulfillment of his mission.

He gathered his flock together and led it back to Midian.

He returned the flock to Jethro and said to him:

"Let me go, I pray thee, to my brothers in Egypt, and see whether they still live."

Jethro made no effort to detain him. He did not interfere even when he saw that Moses was preparing to take his wife and children with him to Egypt, where they would be in danger of becoming slaves. He understood, without a word from Moses, that something had happened to him in the wilderness of Sinai; for there was a light on the face of Moses, and Jethro and the rest of the household were filled with awe.

He said to his son-in-law:

"Go in peace."

And Moses took his wife, Zipporah, and the two sons she had borne him, and went into the wilderness toward Egypt.

CHAPTER THIRTEEN

IN the cave were assembled the elders of Israel. The aged Uziel was propped against a stone and supported on each side by other ancients. About him were the leaders of the tribes, of whom some were elders, while others were young men with new-sprouting beards and heads of curly hair. There were also present the leading figures of the tribe of Levi, among them Korah and his sons; also Dathan and Abiram, who, besides being the chiefs of the Jewish overseers and guards, were the elders and leaders of the tribe of Reuben. On this occasion they did not wear on the breast the metal plaques of their official rank, they did not wear their colored robes, nor did they carry their copper-loaded rods; for the meeting of the elders of Israel was held in secret.

Before the assembly stood Aaron and Moses, and Aaron spoke for Moses.

Aaron told of the marvels which had happened with his brother: how God had appeared to him in the wilderness of Sinai, by Mount Horeb, and how He had commanded him to assemble the elders of Israel and tell them that the God of their fathers, of Abraham, Isaac, and Jacob, had spoken to him; he was to tell them, in God's own name, that He had remembered them and what was being done to them; and He would bring them forth out of Egypt into a land flowing with milk and honey, into the land Canaan; he was to say that God commanded Moses and the elders of Israel to go before Pharaoh and say: "Our God, the God of the Hebrews, has appeared to us. And now let us go into the desert a distance of three days, to sacrifice to our God."

And Aaron told them further, for himself, that he too had heard the voice of God, which had bidden him go into the desert to encounter his brother. And he had gone forth and he had met Moses and his wife by the mountain of the Lord, as they were coming toward Egypt, without fear or anxiety, to fulfill the mission. There Moses had told him of all that had happened and had shown him

113

the staff with which God had bidden him do wonders and signs; and Aaron had been commanded by God to believe all the things that his brother told him. Now they were standing before the elders of Israel with the tidings of the redemption according to the word of God.

For a long time after Aaron had ended a deep silence hung over the assembly. What they had heard was strange beyond belief. God had appeared—and not to them, the elders of Israel, but to him who, of all persons, had not been with them in their bondage, to him who did not know them: and God had appeared to the Israelites not in Egypt, but somewhere in the wilderness. How could this be? At last one of the elders spoke:

"How shall we indeed know that this was our God, the God of Abraham, Isaac, and Jacob, who showed Himself to our brother? Did He tell him His name? May it not have been a demon, an evil spirit of the wilderness, drawing us into an evil purpose of its own?"

Then Moses himself addressed the assembly:

"Indeed I asked Him for His name. I said to the Spirit which appeared to me: What is Thy name? And who shall I say sent me? And he answered: I am that I am. Say to the children of Israel, '*I am* hath sent me to you.' And tell them further: 'The God of your fathers, the God of Abraham, Isaac, and Jacob, hath sent me to you. That is my name forever, and that is my memorial to the generations.'"

When Moses had finished speaking, the blind Uziel fell forward on his knees, lifted his arms and cried: "I recognize Him! This is He that is. This is His name from generation to generation. He was with our fathers, Abraham, Isaac, and Jacob, and showed them the way. With Him they made the covenant for us and for our posterity until the end of days. He is with us here, in Egypt. He sees our affliction and our pain. And He is afflicted with us. He will free us from the yoke of Pharaoh, and He will bring us to the land of milk and honey, which He promised our fathers. And He will be with our children throughout the generations, in all ages, in all worlds, in all happenings, in all that they do. For He is Being. There is no being without Him, for in His name, Jehovah, is combined the past, the present, and the future."

After blind Uziel uttered these words a deep awe silenced the gathering of the elders of Israel.

Then Moses spoke again: "Three times I would have turned and avoided His command. Not because I had no faith that it was He —for in His voice I recognized the God of our fathers; and not because I was afraid to bring His utterance before Pharaoh. For I am ready at all times to come before Pharaoh and demand that he obey the command of God. Moreover, He warned me that Pharaoh would not let us go, that He would harden the heart of Pharaoh, so that he and all Egypt might see His justice and His mighty hand, when He will demand an accounting for every infliction that Pharaoh has laid upon us. I believe, and I know, that he will exact from Pharaoh and the Egyptians payment for every drop of blood they have shed; and he will make of Egypt an example and a horror, even as He did with Sodom and Gomorrah, so that all oppressors in the time to come may know that there is an eye that watches and a hand which exacts justice. Yet I would not go at first, and I sought to evade the commandment. And I exposed myself to the danger of His wrath, only because I did not feel fit to be the messenger of God to my people. Who am I? I am the least among you. I have not tasted on my flesh the taste of your suffering; I have not borne oppression and slavery with you. I have only caused your yoke to become heavier, while I myself fled into the wilderness. What am I that it should be my lot to be God's emissary to Israel? But God has taken me captive, as an eagle takes captive a lamb. God has bound me in fetters, and He has placed His mission upon my shoulders. He has put the staff of His anger in my hands, and he has sent me to you with the tidings in my mouth. I stand before you. Believe in our God, the God of Abraham, Isaac, and Jacob."

There was silence again, and then the voice of Korah: "Yet we would have a sign, that it is indeed the might of God that is with thee, to perform wonders in His name."

"Not I will perform wonders, but God, the God of Abraham, will do wonders," and he cast his staff at the feet of the elders.

A hideous snake sprang up from the floor of the cave, and it seemed that its head was pointed at the unbelievers. Moses took hold of the snake by the tail, and it became the staff in his hand.

"The wrath of God is the staff of Moses, to destroy His enemies," cried out voices among the elders.

"And to help Israel," cried out others.

And like one man the assembly of the elders and leaders knelt, with faces bowed to the floor of the cavern, hands uplifted.

"God of Abraham, Isaac, and Jacob, Thou that hast remembered us and hast seen our affliction, to Thee be praise, to Thee be praise."

One man alone, Korah, sat moveless in his place, his massive flesh untouched.

"Surely this is a sign of power in the hand of Moses," he said, coldly. "But do we not all know what the magicians of Pharaoh are able to perform with *their* magic? They put speech in the mouth of the dead, they conjure flames out of the air. And what weight will this miracle carry in their eyes? If Moses and Aaron ask the elders of Israel to go with them to Pharaoh, they must show other signs, mightier wonders with which to terrify Pharaoh, signs and wonders which the God Shaddai has assuredly entrusted to them."

Then Moses displayed before the assembly the second sign. But the same doubting smile hung on the lips of Korah.

"Is it with these signs that you would frighten Pharaoh and his magicians?"

"Are we concerned with signs?" asked Moses, angrily, and as always when anger overcame him he stammered and found words only with difficulty. "Are not *all* things possible with God? Are not the hosts of heaven mustered to carry out His commands?"

"God has not even opened his mouth and made his tongue swift," said Korah to the assembly. "How shall he speak to Pharaoh?"

"I myself spoke to God of my defects. And He comforted me, and appointed Aaron to be my mouth, to speak for me," said Moses, and the humility of this answer seemed to impress even Korah.

"And what wilt thou say to Pharaoh?" he asked.

"Whatever God commands us to say. God Himself will put the words in our mouths, and He will tell us what to do."

"If such be the case, then I counsel that Moses and Aaron go alone to Pharaoh and speak to him in the name of the God of the Hebrews. They will know what to say to him. We cannot expose all Israel to this frightful danger, for if it should happen that Pharaoh is thrown into a rage, there must be some to placate him."

The Hebrew overseers and guards, with Dathan and Abiram at their head, murmured their approval.

"We will go alone to stand before Pharaoh," said Aaron.

"And we will wait, and see what the end of the matter will be," answered Korah.

When Moses vanished from Pharaoh's court, the leading courtiers, headed by the priests, exerted themselves to wipe out all memory of the alien who had achieved princely status and who might have become a threat to the dynasty. They forbade all mention of his name. In the course of the years many of those who had known Moses died, among them Becknekos and Pharaoh himself. And though the new ruler Menephthah retained some memory of the young alien Prince who had been the adopted son of his sister Bathiya, he did not recognize him when he appeared with his brother Aaron as spokesman for the Hebrew slaves.

Menephthah was no Rameses the Second, and the Egypt of his days was no longer the Egypt of the days of Rameses. The power of Babylon had increased, and, spreading its wings over the other Asiatic lands, had encouraged them to revolt from Egypt. On the other side the Libyans, famous warriors from of old, entered into an alliance with the forefathers of the Etruscans of the island of Sicily and even dared to carry war into Egyptian territory. It was true that in the end the Egyptians threw them back, and Pharaoh had been able to boast upon his monuments that he laid waste Libya, also that he had arrested the march of the Hittites. But the rebellions in the Canaanite lands, particularly of the Philistines of Askelon and Gaza, kept up the fight against the Egyptians for many years. All these circumstances moved the slaves of Egypt, in the temples and courts, in the fields, workshops and weaving mills—the countless slaves who worked for the living and the dead—to launch their own rebellions and to demand, if not complete liberation—of this they did not even dare to dream—at least an improvement in their condition, better nourishment and shorter hours of labor. Sometimes Pharaoh had been forced to make concessions.

So it was that Menephthah consented to receive the spokesmen of the Hebrew tribes, believing that they would at most ask for more free time in which to work their own parcels of land.

It was not, of course, an official audience which was accorded to Moses and Aaron; such an honor was not for slaves. He received them in one of the many sculptors' studios where he was wont to pose. He was at this time posing for a gigantic royal figure in black granite, to be placed in the mausoleum which some day would receive his mummified body. It was a law of the Pharaohs that they did not appear before their subjects without the double crown and the golden ornaments, which made them blaze like the sun of which they were the personification; but this law, again, did not apply to slaves, who were not considered worthy of seeing the Pharaoh in all his splendor. He therefore received Aaron and Moses exactly as he posed for the master sculptors, that is, Adam-naked, and only holding in his hand the scepter of his power.

Menephthah was by now an old man, less because of the years than because of the many rebellions and invasions with which he had had to contend. His fleshy body fell into folds, rising and falling as he breathed. The skin of his face and neck hung down in sacs. But the body which the sculptor had produced in granite was that of a young man in the full tide of strength, massive, hard, athletic, and lionlike; the hands and feet were chiseled out in severe, straight lines, and the face was that of lad with a new-sprouting beard: the whole figure a monumental lie, like the chiseled hieroglyphs which told of his mighty victories.

Moses and Aaron appeared alone before Pharaoh, and Aaron was the spokesman.

He began by recalling that the tribes of Israel had never been prisoners of war. They had come to Egypt on the invitation of Pharaoh and Joseph. They therefore did not fall into the slave category; they were the free sons of a foreign people whose settlement in Goshen had been proposed by Pharaoh in recognition of the services rendered by one of them, who had saved Egypt from famine. In Goshen the Hebrews had been enslaved in complete contravention of the law. They had refused to adopt as their own the gods of the country. But they were not without a god, like other slaves, for they were bound to their own God Who had made a covenant with their fathers. But they had been remiss in their worship of Him and had failed to bring Him sacrifice. "Now the God of Israel, who has revealed Himself to us as 'I am that I am'—which is to say, Jehovah—has commanded us to appear before Pharaoh and to say: 'Send forth My people to sacrifice unto Me.'"

Pharaoh was stupefied. This had never happened before. Spokesmen of slaves had humbly petitioned for better food, more rest. What the Hebrews asked for was the right to worship God. It was an unheard-of thing. The very mention of the name of an alien God, another than Pharaoh, was both blasphemy and treason. The blood came into Pharaoh's face, flushing even the sacs of flesh hanging from his cheeks and throat. In the frightful confusion, the one fanbearer who attended him forgot to do his duty, but stood there openmouthed, waiting for Pharaoh to call for the guard to arrest the two impudent representatives of the slaves. But Pharaoh did not call for the guard; instead, he let the flush of fury die down and cried out in a shrill voice, which sounded not at all like his own:

"Who is Jehovah that I should listen to Him, that I should send forth Israel? I know of no Jehovah, and I will not send forth Israel."

But the two incredible emissaries were not content with this decision of Pharaoh's. They went on speaking:

"The God of the Hebrews met with us and commanded us to say to thee: 'Let us, I pray thee, go a journey of three days into the wilderness, there to sacrifice to our God, lest He fall on us with pestilence or the sword.' "

Still Pharaoh did not order their arrest. He said furiously:

"Why do you, Moses and Aaron, tear the people away from their work? Go back to your burdens. The people of the land are lazy enough as it is, and you would even make them rest from their work."

With these words he dismissed the emissaries, without harming a hair of their heads, to the astonishment of those who had been present. Only later, when Moses and Aaron were gone, Pharaoh seemed to come to, and he issued an order to the commander of the slave overseers: "Let no straw be given to the people for the making of the bricks, as was the custom hitherto. Let them find their own straw. But the tally of bricks which they must deliver shall be the same. They are lazy! That is why they cry, 'We would go and sacrifice to our God.' Lay heavier work on them so that they may be fully occupied and waste no time listening to lying words."

The straw, without which bricks could not have been produced, had always been collected in the grain fields and delivered to the laborers in the mud pits. Goshen had supplied a certain proportion of the straw. Pharaoh's new decree threw the system into disorder. The Hebrew overseers who were responsible to the Egyptian overseers for the tally of bricks had to deliver the same number as heretofore although no straw was supplied from the outside. They had to detach a detail of laborers from the mud treading and send them into the fields to collect straw. They also drew the Hebrew women into the work.

Whatever opportunity had been left to the women to prepare the meals for their husbands and bring them into the field—a great help and comfort to the cruelly driven laborers—was now withdrawn. Nor were they able to do any work on their own plots of land. They were out in the fields, collecting straw. The children, too, were harnessed to this work. On the roads and field paths of Goshen the wives and daughters of the Hebrew slaves were seen, half naked, half starved, wild looking, following the ox-drawn grain carts and picking up the straws that fell from them. The Hebrew slaves, with tangled beards and earlocks, with sun-scorched bodies, were seen tugging, like draft animals, at the wagons of straw. They were seen throughout Goshen and adjoining parts of Egypt, and everyone knew that Pharaoh had degraded them to the condition of draft animals for their insolent ambitiousness, for clinging with such obstinacy to their native God who, they believed or pretended to believe, still lived and had demanded sacrifice of them. They were mocked everywhere for the impudent folly of their dreams of liberation.

The Hebrew overseers saw the people bleeding under the new yoke. They saw the little girls returning from the fields with torn and bleeding feet, with bodies doubled up under their burdens, with marks on their flesh from the flails of the threshers. Women aborted in the fields, falling under their loads. But with it all, the straw gatherers could not supply their proportion of material. The bricks, with insufficient binding, fell apart in the baking. Within two days the tally of bricks had fallen by a half. The Hebrew overseers were held responsible.

They argued with the Egyptians: "We cannot squeeze more out of the Jewish laborers. Pharaoh asks for the impossible."

"Pharaoh will punish you."

"Let him do with us what he will. We cannot compel the people to perform that which is impossible. The people bleeds to death under our eyes," they answered with one voice.

The Hebrew overseers were taken, stripped naked, and whipped in the presence of the people. None of them was spared, not even Dathan and Abiram. The two principal Hebrew overseers were whipped like common slaves; and such was the spirit then among the Hebrews, that even they bore with resignation and love the shame and pain of the punishment and refused to harry the people further in their impossible task.

They were whipped daily for their contumacy. They sought audience with Pharaoh, believing that this new burden did not come from him, but was the vicious invention of the Egyptian overseers, Pharaoh being in ignorance of it. Audience was refused.

Some of them hung about the golden palace in Rameses and tried to bribe their way through, seeking out the courtiers with whom they had dealt in the past. Finally the highest Hebrew officials, Korah, Dathan, and Abiram, were admitted to Pharaoh. They fell on their faces before the throne, lifted up their hands, and broke into weeping and supplication:

"Great king, splendor of the sun, why dealest thou thus with thy servants? No straw is given to thy servants, but they tell us: Make bricks! And thy servants are beaten, and it is thine own people that is at fault."

"You are lazy, lazy!" cried Pharaoh, wrathfully. "That is why you say: We would sacrifice to our Jehovah. Go to your work! Straw shall not be given you, and you shall deliver the full number of bricks."

And they were driven from Pharaoh's presence.

Now they saw the full extent of their calamity. From Pharaoh himself had come the order that they were not to be given straw and that the number of bricks to be delivered was not to be diminished. And they knew who had brought the calamity upon them.

Coming out from Pharaoh's presence they encountered Moses and Aaron, who were waiting to find out what had happened at the audience. They turned on the brothers in a burst of bitterness:

"God look down upon you and judge you. You have made our name an abomination to Pharaoh, and to Pharaoh's servants, and have put a sword in their hands, to slay us. See what you have done to your unhappy people."

Aaron tried to make some kind of answer, but Moses was silent. His head drooped earthward, and he thought: "I am nothing but a misfortune to the people; I have been nothing but that since the first day I appeared among them. Why has God sent me to them?"

Heavy hearted, he turned from the others and went his own way. He, too, had seen the new calamity which, because of him, had been visited upon the people. God had done nothing to lighten their burden. It had been made heavier. What was this, then? Was God making trial of him? Was He strewing the road to triumph with stinging thorns and fiery stones? How was he to bear this trial? The shame he had brought on his brothers, the mockery, the trails of blood which the Hebrew women left on the roads of Egypt, the fainting of the little children under their burdens—how could he look on all this? Where should he get the patience and endurance demanded of him? He envied the rebellious Hebrew overseers who carried on their whipped flesh the responsibility of the Bnai Israel. He felt very differently now toward Korah and his assistants, toward the brothers Dathan and Abiram, even though they spread slanders about him among the people, saying that his reports of God's revelation to him were nothing but lies.

The behavior of Korah and his assistants had exalted them in his eyes. He wanted reconciliation with them; and he asked his brother Aaron to take him before them.

He made obeisance to them, to Korah, and even to Dathan and Abiram, and said: "Happy are you, and great is your merit, that you carry the suffering of the Bnai Israel. May my portion be among you. But I tell you that Jehovah, the God of Israel, foresaw all and foretold me all: He would harden the heart of Pharaoh in order that He might display His signs and wonders. For hundreds of years the Egyptians and their Pharaohs have sinned against Jehovah. For hundreds of years they have held the Bnai Israel in bondage, and God will demand an accounting for all their sins, as a sign to all the wicked of the world that there is a Judge. Wait and see what the Lord God Jehovah will do with Pharaoh and the Egyptians."

"Aye, but meanwhile all His arrows have lodged in the flesh of His own people. And thine is the hand which has shot them. Had the Lord God of Israel appeared unto thee, He would have put a sword in thy hand to slay Pharaoh, not thy people. No, thou hast been a stumbling block to us from the day of thy returning to us. Thy sword is lifted not against Pharaoh and his servants, but against our unhappy people, which bled by a hundred wounds even before thy coming. If thou indeed lovest thy people, as thou sayest, get thee gone from us. Or go to thy mother, who found thee in the Nile. They say that she alone is left of thy former friends and foes in Pharaoh's court. She is Pharaoh's sister. Go to her. Fall at her feet. Perhaps she will help thee undo the evil thou hast brought upon us and persuade Pharaoh to withdraw the decree concerning the straw."

"No," cried Moses. "Is it now, when the God of Israel has heard our cry, and has seen our affliction, and is coming to draw us out of Egypt with a mighty arm—is it now that I should do this thing, and belittle the name of God in the eyes of His people, so that they should think him weak, needful of the help of one of flesh and blood? Do you not see God's sign in my hand, the staff through which He works His wonders?"

"God will need other means than thy staff to move Pharaoh. It was a dream thou sawest, Moses. The God of Israel never appeared to thee."

It was not only the Bnai Levi, the leaders of Israel, who felt thus about him. What was far worse, the people, the plain people, shared the view. When he tried to approach a group of terrified laborers, they refused to listen. Voices called out: "Deceiver!" "Fire bringer!" "Author of our calamities." And even those who pitied him, and would not humiliate him, said of him: "He had a dream, he dreamed of a vision in the desert. The God of Israel never appeared to him."

Once again Moses was left in almost complete isolation. There were only two who believed in him now—Aaron and Miriam. Aaron's faith was complete and unshakable, for he too had heard the voice of God. He had been bidden to go into the desert, to meet his brother at Sinai. He had gone, and his brother had been at the designated place. Moreover, he had seen the light which God had kindled in his brother's eyes; and whenever that light shone on him, Aaron felt his heart turn to water with awe. He knew that God was with his brother in all his ways and that his brother had full authority over him. He knew that God would perform the wonders he had promised, through the words which Moses would put in his brother's mouth. And Miriam's faith in her brother had been firm from the first. As in the days before his flight from Egypt, she tended him and was his mother as well as his sister. But for these two, Moses was alone in Egypt. His parents were long dead. His wife Zipporah and his two sons he had sent back to his father-in-law Jethro halfway on the journey to Egypt, at the urgent pleading of Aaron.

Miriam attended to all his wants; moreover, she guarded him, and she sought to strengthen his faith in himself by means of her own.

"Has not the God of Israel given thee power over Pharaoh, to deal with him and his people according to their deserts? Why dost thou not show the strength of thine arm to Pharaoh? Hast thou not the staff of God in thy hand?" she asked.

"The strength of my arm?" said Moses, darkly. "What am I? A thing of flesh and blood, potter's clay, which God can break with His breath. I am but the messenger of the word, and I can do nothing, I cannot turn to the right or left, without His command. My heart shakes with terror at the thought of a single step taken of my own accord; for I am only a man, whose heart is stopped up and his eyes unseeing. I cannot see my fellow man. I am as a dumb animal when I must judge what is good and evil. He alone is judge of all the world and of all men. He hears all and sees all, and justice is with Him alone. For he alone knows His creatures. And Pharaoh and the Egyptians are His creatures, too, and He will deal justly with them."

"But thou canst pray to Him, and bring before him the affliction of Israel, and thine own affliction."

"That I can do."

Since the wondrous revelation on Mount Horeb Moses had felt a peculiar nearness to God. It was as though the divinity were poured into him in a ray, which penetrated his heart, illumined thence his whole being, and issued again from his eyes. Irradiated by this light, his flesh and spirit were cleansed of impurity, of egotism and lust; and he saw the world from one angle only, and weighed it with one measure only—the angle of justice, the measure of righteousness. Though his heart overflowed with love and pity for his own people, he could consider the condition of the adversary, of the oppressor. Pharaoh's dominion—his booty, his great empire—was not the creation of idols, of a Ra or Ammon, which were impotent to create; it was the creation of the God of Israel, who ruled the world with righteousness. If Pharaoh had risen to such power, there was a purpose in it; if Israel was persecuted and humiliated, there was purpose in that too. No one could change this but the God of Israel. He was the judge of the whole world, and His will alone was to be carried out.

Hence the caution and hesitancy, which Moses displayed, not to sin even against Pharaoh. He feared that therein he might be sinning against God. He would therefore do only what God willed him to do.

But again since that wondrous revelation, a door into the heavens had been opened to him. He could always come before his God and call to him, as a child calls to its father. He could bring his doubts and plaints before God and always receive an answer. God spoke to his heart. Moses heard the voice, which spoke with gentleness and love, as if a father were speaking to his son.

Now too he brought his heaviness of heart before God.

At night, in the fields, behind the tents of Israel, Moses stretched out his arms to heaven and called:

"Jehovah, Jehovah, where art thou? See our shame and affliction. God, wherefore dost Thou inflict suffering on this people? Wherefore hast Thou sent me to them? For since I came to Pharaoh, to speak in Thy name, his wickedness toward this people has doubled, and Thou hast not saved us from his hand."

And Moses heard God's voice in his heart, comforting him:

"I am Jehovah, and I appeared to Abraham, Isaac, and Jacob, as the Lord Shaddai, but by My name Jehovah I did not reveal myself to them. And I made a covenant with them. . . . And I have heard the groaning of the children of Israel, because of their bondage to the Egyptians. . . . Therefore I say to the children of Israel: I will take you out from the bondage of the Egyptians and I will deliver you from slavery; and I will redeem you with an outstretched arm and with mighty judgments. And I will take you unto Me for a people, and I will be to you a God. And you will know that I am your God, who has taken you out from under the burdens of the Egyptians. And I will bring you to the land which I have sworn to Abraham, to Isaac, and to Jacob, and I will give it to you for a heritage. I am the Lord."

And Moses came again to the Bnai Israel, and told them of God's reassurance to him; but they would not listen to him, out of impatience, and because of their cruel bondage.

Again and again the assurance of God came to Moses, but He never showed him how the promise could be fulfilled. God gave him no power. And Moses fell lower and lower in the regard of his brothers, and of Pharaoh. Yet Moses did not cease from believing the word of God. He endured all humiliations and insults, and waited. Until one day he heard the voice of God in his heart:

"See, I have this day made thee a God to Pharaoh, and Aaron, thy brother, shall be thy prophet. Thou wilt speak all that I shall command thee, and Aaron thy brother shall speak to Pharaoh that he shall give the children of Israel leave to go from the land. And I will harden the heart of Pharaoh, and I will multiply my signs and wonders in the land of Egypt."

And now Moses knew that the time of the redemption had come. For now God had given him divine authority over Pharaoh.

CHAPTER FOURTEEN

IT was God's will that Pharaoh should know of every plague before He visited Him with it. Not without warning was it to come on him, but on each separate occasion he was to learn from Moses and Aaron what punishment he would receive if he refused to let the Hebrews go. For however God hardened the heart of Pharaoh, it was still His desire that Pharaoh should overcome his evil inclination, should repent him of the wrongs he had done the Hebrews, and liberate them. And Moses was scrupulous in carrying out the instructions which God directed to the hearing of his heart.

First God commanded Moses and Aaron to appear before Pharaoh and show him that they had the power to compel him to free Israel. They informed Pharaoh that they wished to display before him a sign which God had entrusted to them as proof that they were the carriers of His command. Pharaoh was curious to learn what kind of sign the emissaries of the Hebrew God could display, and he granted them an audience to which were also invited many of his advisers, sages, magicians, and priests.

It must be said that the sign, which Aaron showed on the command of Moses, made no little impression on Pharaoh, but among the courtiers and others it aroused only derision. How right Korah had been! In the eyes of the courtiers and magicians it all looked like a childish game. Was it with this that they sought to terrify the might of Egypt—a staff turning into a snake? Who could not imitate that? The staves of the magicians also crawled about on the floor at their command and also showed the red, forked tongues flickering in the green mouths.

But then something happened. The snake which was the staff of Moses suddenly launched itself at the other snakes and swallowed them up. They disappeared. It was as if they had not been. Was not this to be interpreted as meaning that Moses was a greater magician than they? The incident did something to raise his reputation as a magician, yet not to any significant degree. The magicians and sages of Egypt were obviously not overimpressed; and in a little while Pharaoh dismissed Moses and Aaron good humoredly, with a contemptuous smile for their simplicity.

Pharaoh went out every morning along the Nile to bring forth the sun over the seven heavens.

He sat high on his golden throne, carried on the shoulders of his guards, in their stiff cylindrical helmets. The double crown of Egypt was on his head, adorned with golden chains and with jewels: a dazzle of light in the sun. Trumpeters, drummers, and players on the sistrum announced the progress of Pharaoh. Two of "the friends of Pharaoh," high officials, carried lofty fans, which they held over his head. Two lions, chained one to each side of his throne, accompanied him. Before the throne, walking backward, went his oldest son, the heir apparent, with the lock 01 his youth hanging from his forehead. He held a lotus flower to the nostrils of the Pharaoh. Behind the throne the highest official in the land walked with little mincing steps, carrying a bouquet of flowers and a small symbolic fan; the other fanbearers followed him. At the head of the procession walked the priests, with shaved heads and white faces, burning incense and strewing roses on the way. A choir of blind singers carrying harps, guided by the priests, sang hymns to its own accompaniment.

> "Turn thine ear to me, O thou rising sun,
> Thou that illuminest the two lands with beauty.
> Thou sunlight of all men,
> Thou drivest away the darkness from Egypt;
> Thy form is of thy father, Ra,
> Who lifts himself high in the heavens.
> Thy rays pierce into the remotest lands."

The masses, which came out from the city to see the son of the god Ra, flesh of his flesh, coming forth in his splendor, in his glory on the heavens, fell face forward to the earth; they stretched out their hands and prayed:

> "Thou Son of Ra, Ra is enthroned in thy heart."

128

Others chanted:

> "Give praise to his fathers,
> The Gods of upper and lower Egypt.
> Give praise!
> They bring him power and victory,
> Long life of millions of years."

The priests rattled their sistra and threw flowers on the way.

> "Come, god Ra, father and son together,
> And light with thy rays the land of thy children."

Then suddenly two men leaped out in front of the procession, two men whose black beards were sprinkled with gray. One of them, the taller of the two, carried a staff, which he lifted up in the air, arresting the procession; and in a loud voice he called out to Pharaoh:

"Jehovah, the God of the Hebrews, sent me to thee: Let My people go, that it may sacrifice to Me in the wilderness. Thou hast not hearkened to me till now. Therefore God says: Thus shalt thou know that I am Jehovah. See, I left up this staff, which is in My hand, and I smite the water of the river before the eyes of Pharaoh and the servants of Pharaoh. And all the water which is in the river will be turned to blood. And the fish which are in the river will die; and the river will be polluted, and the Egyptians will not be able to drink of the water of the river."

And without waiting for an answer from Pharaoh, without even casting a glance at Pharaoh's stupefied countenance, the man turned to his companion and said, in a loud voice:

"Aaron, Jehovah has commanded me: Take thy staff and stretch it out over the waters of Egypt, upon all the streams and lakes and swamps and water courses, and they will become blood: and there shall be blood in all the land of Egypt, both in the wooden vessels and the stone ones."

Aaron took the staff from the hand of Moses, and in the eyes of Pharaoh, and his courtiers and servants, he smote the waters of the Nile.

Paralyzed at first by the daring of the two men, Pharaoh and his courtiers and servants remained motionless a while. Then they looked at the Nile. No sooner had it been touched by the staff in Aaron's hand than the water broke into furious agitation. It was as if a panic had fallen on the waves which had been flowing tranquilly seaward. They rose skyward, flinging out fish. In an instant the color of the water had changed. It reddened, deepening from pink to crimson, becoming thicker and thicker, to a pitch-like consistency. The carcasses of the fish, multicolored, in strange forms, swollen, with split bellies, fell back on the water, and their viscera ran out, black, and transformed the water unrecognizably.

An unbearable stench began to rise from the river. Pharaoh's nearest attendants thrust bouquets of flowers under his nose, and the priests surrounded the throne, crying:

"Fear not, Pharaoh, this is magic. We can also do this thing."

"It is the summertime. Many fish become swollen and pollute the water at this season," said the wise men.

Pharaoh did not answer. With a gesture, he commanded to be carried home. He neither looked at nor addressed Moses and Aaron. Everyone was astonished that he did not order their arrest.

Later, in the palace, he sat on his throne, attended by his counselors, his sages, his highest officials, and the priests. He was distraught. The sages sought to calm him; they demanded with one voice that he order the arrest of the two rebels and have them executed.

"Son of Ra, flesh of his flesh, two mortals have blasphemed against thy supreme divinity. When the sun came out, two emissaries of the Hebrew slaves sought to cover it with darkness. The shame of it must be washed out in the blood of the blasphemers."

And "the chief friend of Pharaoh," his highest officer, the major-domo of the golden palace, the senior fanbearer, threw himself at Pharaoh's feet, pleading:

"Ruler in the house of Ra, if the Egyptians will learn that thou wert hindered in the sacred ritual of thy father, and thou hast permitted the blasphemers to go free, they will interpret it to mean that thou, the god Ra, in his own flesh, wert afraid of their God."

"The Egyptians know it already," answered the king. "They drink the blood of stinking fish in place of water."

"Shining sun, lord of eternity, eye of Ammon, it is not blood they drink, but colored water, the work of the two blaspheming magicians. We too can do this thing," argued the magicians, prostrate at Pharaoh's feet.

"Do it, then!"

The eldest of the magicians sprang to his feet and performed the wonder. With mystic incantations, in the midst of a cloud of incense, he poured water from one vessel into another, and the water became red as blood.

The king took up the vessel with the magically transformed water, held it to his face, breathed in through his nostrils, and said:

"There is no odor whatsoever. This cannot be blood; it is only colored water. But we will wait, and see how it all ends. No, I will not act in haste, lest afterward I repent."

The attendants left the presence of the king, profoundly disturbed. No one could understand, no one could begin to explain, why Pharaoh showed such forbearance toward the two Hebrew magicians.

But Pharaoh had his secret reasons.

When the two men appeared before him for the first time in the sculptor's studio, and had dared to mention the name of an alien God, he had almost issued the command to have them arrested. But he had suddenly caught a glance from the eyes of one of them—the man they called Moses—and a nameless fear had pierced him. It seemed to him for an instant that before him stood the god Horus in his own flesh. But he dismissed at once the wild notion that the god Horus would appear to him as the emissary and protector of a slave people and would speak in the name of an alien God rather than in the name of his father Osiris, or of Ra, or of Ammon. Yet the face of Moses had a strange familiarity for him; it seemed that he had seen him somewhere.

Long after Moses had withdrawn, Pharaoh continued to think of him, and the face gave him no rest, until he cried out to himself: "Is not this the Prince of alien blood whom my sister found in the swamps of the Nile, as Isis found Horus?" For the persistence of the Princess had established the legend, and many of the courtiers had seen the image of Horus in the black-haired little boy whom the daughter of Pharaoh had carried so tenderly in her arms. Yes, yes, he now remembered the Prince, who had attended with him the military academy, who had later won a name as a warrior in Pharaoh's army—the alien whom the priests had hated. He remembered also that this Prince had left Pharaoh's palace and had gone away to the slaves of Goshen. Yes, this Moses was the Prince, now returned with an embassy from a strange God.

That same day he had sought out his sister Bathiya in the temple of Osiris where she now lived as the high priestess and official wife

131

of the god, the incarnation of the goddess Isis. The Princess, who was older than he, being the oldest child of Pharaoh, should, according to the law, have married the reigning Prince and ruled together with him. But she had renounced the throne. When Moses left her she withdrew from court life and dedicated herself completely to the god Osiris, never leaving his temple. From much fasting she became shriveled like a mummy; her eyes were all but sightless from her continuous weeping for the death of her lord. She was given to visions and was ever prophesying that her son, Moses, would return to her in the likeness of a god and perform many wonders.

When her brother brought her the tidings that her son had returned, she threw herself before the god Osiris and thanked him:

"I knew that thou wouldst send me my son to comfort me before I go to thee."

But her brother said:

"He speaks not in the name of the gods of Egypt, nor have the gods of Egypt sent thy son. He comes in the name of an alien God, the God of the Hebrew slaves. In His name he speaks, and the punishment therefor is death."

When Bathiya heard these words she rose in an access of fury. Her half-blind eyes blazed with an inner light; she laid her shriveled hands on her breast and began to chant in the tones of the prophetess of Osiris:

"Thus says the great god Osiris, my husband and lord: Go to the son of Ra and say to him: Beware lest thou touch a hair on the head of my son Horus-Moses, for I am with him, and whosoever harms him, I will avenge myself on him, in this world and in the next."

The prophecy, which Bathiya uttered in the name of her god, did not make any particular impression on Pharaoh. Nor was he much impressed by his sister's belief in herself as the incarnation of Isis. For that matter he had not been deceived by her stories concerning Moses. But his forbearance toward Moses sprang from his regard for his sister, just as the forbearance of the older Pharaoh had been rooted in his regard for his daughter. And so he had passed over in silence the first act of blasphemy and rebellion.

On the second occasion, when Moses had dared to break in on the sacred ritual by the Nile and had insulted him in the presence of court and the people with his demands in the name of the alien

God, Pharaoh had again felt the impulse to punish the man as he deserved, and to have him executed on the spot. There would be an end to the blasphemer and an end to his sister's delusions. He had already lifted his hand, his lips were parted to give the order to the guards, and suddenly he was dumbstruck, and his hand became petrified with fear. He had again caught a glance from the eyes of Moses. This was a new Moses; not the Prince he had once known in his father's court, but such a one as his sister had spoken of: in the likeness of a god, a doer of many wonders.

Pharaoh felt dominion in those eyes; they could subdue his will, paralyze his muscles. He dared not return the man's gaze; he had to turn his own eyes away. His faith in his own divinity was strong enough to keep him from surrender; it was not strong enough to move him to the open test of battle with the Divinity which had armed the Hebrew slave. He avoided open battle for fear of the outcome. He saw clearly that before him stood not a man, but a god; a god even like himself, like Pharaoh.

Battle between them there was, but obscurely and undeclared on Pharaoh's side. He fought against the power which streamed from the eyes of Moses, and he called to his help all the gods of Egypt. The priests and high officials argued ceaselessly that the incident with the waters and fish of the Nile was a natural thing; it would soon pass away. To meet the cry for fresh water they dug new wells, and the water was fresh. Pharaoh felt his confidence return. And when seven days had passed and the waters of the Nile began to clear and freshen, he was certain that his gods had risen to do battle for him and had repulsed the God of the Hebrews. Still, he did not dare to lay a hand on Moses.

But no sooner were the waters of the Nile fresh again than Moses reappeared before Pharaoh. Uninvited and unannounced he appeared, as if neither guards nor soldiers had seen him, or as if they had not dared to address him. He stood before Pharaoh and warned him once more:

"Thus says Jehovah: Let my people go, to bring Me sacrifice. And if thou wilt not let them go, I will send a plague of frogs in all thy land. The river shall swarm with frogs, and they will come up into thy house, and into thy bedchamber, and into thy bed, and into the house of thy servants, and upon thy people, and into thy ovens, and into thy kneading troughs. And the frogs shall come up upon thee, and upon thy people, and upon all thy servants."

133

And what Moses had foretold came to pass without delay. Moses bade Aaron, in the name of God, smite the waters of the land of Egypt. In the waters, and among the heaps of rotting fish, which lay on the brink of the waters, frogs began to swarm: frogs of many kinds, forms, and colors. Now Egypt had been famous for frogs from of old. A folk saying ran: "Wherever the croaking of frogs is heard, there are Egypt's borders." But frogs like these had never been seen before. They multiplied like mosquitoes, and they grew to an unheard-of size. They rose out of the swampy waters and out of the heaps of stinking fish. It was as though earth itself were nothing but frog flesh, now casting itself out: big-mouthed frogs with many, widespread legs; thin, long frogs, with pouting pig mouths; frogs with stripes, like snakes, and mouths like snakes. Some had fat, smooth, whitish bellies, from which protruded many-branched claws, others had protruding teeth and bristling whiskers; there were frogs which looked like turtles, with hard carapaces, from which stuck out wrinkled leather necks, with the faces of bats, mice, and birds. As varied as the forms were the colors: a repulsive, fatty whiteness, a sickening yellow suggesting poisons, a dull reddishness of spotted snakes. And the frogs crept and leapt away from the waters, from the swampy holes, and appeared everywhere, in the most unexpected places. They slid somehow past closed doors into homes, they were found in water vessels, in cooking pots, in troughs of dough.

In the night, the Egyptians felt in their beds the crawling of sticky things. A frog rubbed its white belly against a man's flesh, sharp claws fastened on a woman's breast, a frog snout sucked at a sleeping child. There was no refuge from the frogs. There was no rest, and there was no working, because of the frogs; there was no eating. Day and night, awake and asleep, the Egyptians had frogs.

In vain did the sages and advisers of Pharaoh advise him that the frog pestilence was a natural thing; that it had risen from the fish carcasses, and it would die down as soon as the supply of rotting fish came to an end. And the priests and magicians proved to him in vain that they too could bring forth worms from polluted water.

The frogs were an unceasing torment. They came into Pharaoh's house; they fell out of his golden wine cruses; they were kneaded into his bread, as into the bread of the meanest slave; they were in his bed, clawing at his flesh, they crawled between him and his concubines. Life became to him hideous and hateful, as it did to his lowest donkey driver. And the cry of the Egyptians went up over the whole land of Egypt.

Pharaoh called to his help his dead parents. He prayed to himself as the god of the sun. Nothing availed.

He wrestled with his own thoughts. He could not admit that there could possibly exist a might and authority outside of the gods of Egypt, which could have dominion over the country. It was inconceivable that an alien Horus could hold the rod of punishment over a Pharaoh's head.

But from day to day the pressure became stronger. It became unbearable. The frogs paralyzed the life of the country and made existence insupportable. In the end Pharaoh yielded.

He asked to have Aaron and Moses brought before him.

"Beg Jehovah," he said, "to take the plague of frogs off my people, and I will release your people to do sacrifice to Jehovah."

And Moses answered him humbly:

"Thine be the honor of deciding: for what time shall I pray for thee and for thy people, that the frogs be destroyed from thee and from thy houses?"

"For tomorrow," said Pharaoh.

"According to thy word, so that thou mayest know that there is no God like unto our Lord Jehovah."

So Moses talked to Pharaoh's face, and Pharaoh was silent.

But no sooner had God answered the prayer of Moses and destroyed the frogs than the pride of Pharaoh reawoke in all its strength. The blood of his fathers spoke in him. He, the god Ra, flesh of his flesh, the sun of heaven, the life of the earth, should have to submit to another authority in his own land of Egypt! No! He would not recognize the God Jehovah, and he would not permit His people to sacrifice to Him. There were no other gods in Egypt than Ra and his son Pharaoh.

Now the greatest of the miracles which God wrought in Egypt was this: that in the beginning each miracle did not look like a miracle. It looked like a natural phenomenon such as recurred at some season of the year in Egypt. It was quite natural that in the height of the summer, when the waters of the Nile had sunk low, fish should become swollen from the heat and their carcasses should float to the bank, giving out a poisonous stink. And the putrefaction of the fish had multiplied the frogs, turtles, and bloodworms. Now, when God destroyed the frogs, and they lay in heaps on the river-banks, on the edges of the marshes and the water channels, it was natural that clouds of gnats should rise from them. The dense clouds floated outward and fell on men and animals in pitiless attack, sucking out their blood. They crawled into the tiniest cavities of the flesh and stabbed there as with pointed burning needles. Some were so small that they could barely be seen; others could not be seen at all. Men and animals were tormented day and night. On the skin, and in the inmost organs, the insects sucked continuously. Every man felt himself to be a living carcass. His flesh became hideous to him with his scratching; it was covered with swellings, sores, and boils. His spirit became hideous to him, too, because of the sickening filth which had interpenetrated him.

But superficially it seemed that the plague of insects had come naturally and must soon disappear, as soon as the heaps of putrefying frog carcasses had disappeared.

And it was precisely in the naturalness of the plagues that the Egyptian magicians saw the finger of God. These were not illusions, sorceries of appearance. They were the work of a powerful god, with might over nature, plaguing Pharaoh not with incantations which could be counteracted, but with natural plagues, which followed one on the other. The magicians finally recognized that they could not imitate these wonders with their own sorceries, and therefore they could do nothing countervailing. They said to Pharaoh:

"Pharaoh, a mighty god wages war on thee; this is the finger of God."

And precisely because they spoke thus, Pharaoh became more obstinate than his sages and magicians: for if this was not magic, but indeed the sign of a hostile god, then he must resist to the bitter end. Moses was not working with the power of the Egyptian gods and was not an incarnation of Horus. Moses was working through Jehovah, a god of Pharaoh's slaves. How could Pharaoh possibly yield?

He sent to inquire whether the Hebrews in Goshen also suffered from the plagues. The report came back that the natural plagues had manifested themselves there, though not in so sharp a form as elsewhere in the lands of the Nile. Hearing this, Pharaoh was inspired to believe that the ultimate victory would be his. The God

Jehovah could perhaps intensify the processes of nature, but he could not command them completely. When the natural plagues came, they came upon everyone, upon the Egyptians and upon the people of Jehovah alike. This was proof enough that they did not lie within the authority of Jehovah. For it was this that the representatives of the Hebrews pretended, when Pharaoh boasted of his kingship, which was the embodiment of the god of the sun, Ra.

"The sun shines not in Egypt alone," pointed out Moses. "And when it sets, it sets likewise in other lands than Egypt."

However that might be, the God Jehovah had not power over the sun, not having power over nature. And therefore He had not power over Egypt, and over the gods of Egypt.

On this occasion he did not even stoop to placating Moses with promises in order to arrest the plague.

He mocked, instead. "The Egyptians are accustomed to the biting of gnats. Let them scratch a little more."

And it was as though the God of Moses and Aaron knew his thoughts, for again He sent His emissaries to him, and again it was during the morning ritual by the Nile.

"If thou wilt not let My people go, I will send swarms of flies upon thee, and upon thy servants, and upon thy people, and into the houses; and the houses of the Egyptians shall be full of swarms of flies, and also the ground whereon they are. And I will set apart in that day the land of Goshen, in which My people dwell, that no swarms of flies shall be there; that thou mayest know that I am the Lord in the midst of the land."

It came to pass exactly as God had declared through Moses. The land of Egypt was suddenly covered with a plague of flies. They came out of nowhere, dense black clouds, innumerable hosts, spreading with unbelievable speed. In an instant the houses were full of them. They covered all the furniture, all the utensils; they covered the bodies of the human beings, and with a million mouths they sucked at the blood, consumed the food, and stripped the fields and gardens of green.

Pharaoh sent at once to discover what had happened in the land of Goshen. No. The land of Goshen, where his slaves lived among the mud pits, was free from the plague. It was as though God had drawn an invisible curtain through the air between Goshen and the rest of Egypt. Thus far and no farther! On the borders of Goshen the pestilence of flies hovered motionless.

Meanwhile the visitation of flies became more and more frightful. The source and origin of the flies was unknown, and it was therefore impossible to surmise when they would disappear—as had been the case with the other plagues. One could not fathom the natural causes of the plague. No one had ever seen flies like these before; no one had known that such varieties of parasites existed. They did not behave like flies. They could not be chased away. They were insolent in their aggressiveness, as if they knew who had sent them; and as if they knew why they had been sent, they demanded the blood of the Egyptians for nourishment and took it freely and fiercely. The bodies of the Egyptians were given up to the needle mouths of the flies; and in the eyes of the Egyptians the winged things of prey began to look like winged beasts of prey, lions and leopards and the like.

The unnaturalness of the insects, their astounding variety of form and color, their massive aggressiveness, and above all their absence from the land of Goshen and the settlements of the Hebrew slaves, cast a pall of fear over Pharaoh's servants and weakened the heart of Pharaoh.

CHAPTER FIFTEEN

IT was as if the God of Israel had decided to take vengeance on Pharaoh and this generation of Egyptians for all the crimes which the Egyptians had committed against Israel; and He blinded the eyes of Pharaoh and confused his understanding, so that he might not perceive that it was God Himself who had taken over in the battle for His people Israel.

Pharaoh still believed that it was no god that was waging battle against him; it was only Moses. His ambition was to lead the Hebrew slaves out of Egypt and to become their ruler in the desert. To this end he put to use everything he had ever learned from the magicians of Egypt. The God Jehovah was an invention of his, with which to frighten Pharaoh. Actually his staff, with which he did his miracles, was the familiar Egyptian serpent god, which he —Moses—had placed under a spell with incantations learned from his mother, so that the god was compelled to serve him. No, he would not concede, he would not even consider the possibility: that Moses worked with the magic of the Egyptian gods against the Egyptian gods; but he would consider another possibility now: that Moses had acquired new magic powers from contact with an alien God of the desert who was the Spirit of the slaves. This was the source of his miracles; and from this source came his power to master the serpent god. But soon the gods of Egypt would come to the rescue of Pharaoh. His father Ra, the great god of the sun, would send out powerful rays to do battle with the desert God, and would overwhelm him. He would slay the serpent god, which Moses held in his hand, and then Moses would be helpless.

All that Pharaoh played for now was time, so that his gods might have the opportunity to come to his aid.

From the first instant when Moses appeared before him, and asked leave for the Hebrew slaves to go a three-day journey into the desert to sacrifice to their God, Pharaoh understood that the pretext veiled a larger purpose. Moses intended to lead the slaves out of Egypt so that he might become their king. Nor did Moses deceive himself as to the effect which the pretext produced on Pharaoh. But Pharaoh was determined to make no concession to the Hebrews; for this would have been a signal to all the other slaves in Egypt, and the slave system would have collapsed. There was the possibility of a general uprising throughout Egypt, which Pharaoh was determined to avoid at any cost.

For the moment, perceiving himself at a dangerous disadvantage, his only recourse was to play for time; and he began the pretense of bargaining with Moses over the conditions of the request.

He proposed: "Let them sacrifice to their God, but not in the desert. I will give you three days, make your festival, and sacrifice to your God—here in the land."

Moses entered into the play. He answered: "Knowest thou not what the Egyptians will do to us when they see us offering sacrifice to an alien God? We will go a three-day journey into the wilderness, and there sacrifice to our God, as He has commanded us."

Pharaoh answered cunningly: "I will let you go into the wilderness to sacrifice to your Jehovah, but you shall not go far away. Pray for me."

"See, I go forth from thee, and I will pray to Jehovah to remove the multitude of flies by tomorrow, and it shall be removed from Pharaoh, and his servants, and his people. But let not Pharaoh mock us again and refuse to let the people go to the wilderness to sacrifice to Jehovah."

"I, Pharaoh, will not keep my word? How canst thou speak thus, Moses?"

But that was what happened.

It was as though both of them, Moses and Pharaoh, knew that Pharaoh would not honor his word. Yet Moses went forth from Pharaoh and prayed that the multitude of flies might be withdrawn. And God hearkened to the prayer of Moses, and the flies vanished as suddenly as they had appeared.

Again the heart of Pharaoh hardened, as God had foretold.

Then God sent Moses to Pharaoh to warn him that He would send a murrain on the cattle, horses, and asses in the land, but that He would spare whatever animals Pharaoh had left in the possession of the Hebrew slaves. And to make it clearer to Pharaoh that the plague was for the Egyptians alone, He would send it at a declared moment, and suddenly. So it came to pass. Immediately after the withdrawal of Moses from Pharaoh's presence, the plague appeared everywhere among the livestock of the Egyptians.

Pharaoh sent at once to make inquiry of conditions in Goshen. And at once the answer came back that there was no sign of the pestilence among the livestock of the Hebrews.

Still the heart of Pharaoh did not soften.

The struggle became bitterer, more obstinate. It was no longer, in Pharaoh's eyes, a struggle between him and Moses, but one between gods, the God of Israel on the one hand, the gods of Egypt on the other. The more convinced Pharaoh became that Moses worked, not through magic formulas, but by the power of a genuine Spirit, a mighty Force, which had command over nature, the more his obstinacy hardened. He was no longer fighting for his hold on the slaves; he was fighting for his gods and for his own divinity. And in his eyes the struggle was so unequal that there could be only one ultimate issue.

On the one side stood an organized religion, with Pharaoh as the mightiest of the gods; a religion with a strong-wrought discipline, sanctified by the tradition, customs, and sacred ritual of hundreds of years; a massive sacerdotal hierarchy, with countless temples whose gigantic statues and dazzling ceremonials oppressed and dazed the spirit; a horde of gods and goddesses who divided among themselves the dominion over every activity and possession of man —his wisdom, his well-being, his nourishment, his productions; gods of fertility, gods of health, gods of his life, and gods of the life after death. And over all this stood the god Ra, the sun in heaven, incarnate in Pharaoh: Pharaoh, the ruler of the two lands of Egypt, whose kingship extended over every known part of Africa, down to Ethiopia, and over Hither-Asia to the boundary of ordered settlements. His hosts, equipped with the mightiest weapons, with wild horses and with chariots, had brought to their knees the nations of the world. And Egypt was filled with slaves of all races, black and white, working its fields and gardens, tending its cattle, building its cities and pyramids and temples, manning its ships.

And on the other side, who was it that dared to challenge Pharaoh and Egypt? A little, unworthy slave folk, possessed of nothing but a tradition of the forefathers, believing in one living God, nourishing a feeble hope of redemption. And in their name spoke one who himself had once been an Egyptian, who had acquired his knowledge and skill among the Egyptians. He spoke in the name of a desert God who until now had been unknown among gods and men. This renegade Egyptian had not yet been able to liberate his people from bondage to Pharaoh. Now he was making use of a serpent god whom he had transformed into a staff, to frighten Pharaoh with ridiculous and trivial plagues which made the skin of the Egyptians itch. Oh, the Egyptians would put up with all that. Pharaoh's hour would come soon. Soon the power of Ammon, Osiris, the sun god, Horus, the goddess Isis, and of all the other gods of Egypt, would manifest itself, would fill Pharaoh's loins with might, for the destruction of the rebel.

So Pharaoh did not yield, he did not listen to the command of the God of the Hebrews, he did not let the people go. It did not matter to him that the God of his slaves had made a mockery of him and had covered the heads and bodies of his priests with sores and boils so that they were a frightful sight in their priestly robes. Pharaoh held out.

Then the God of Israel gave a darker turn to the struggle. He prepared a grimmer plague. Moreover, Moses now went over the head of Pharaoh to the Egyptian people, to warn them of the new affliction which was in store for them. He bade them gather the remaining cattle and horses and asses from the fields and lock them in their stables, for a mighty hail was about to fall on Egypt, and it would destroy whatever was left in the open fields.

Only when the windows of heaven were opened and there descended, amid thunder and lightning and flickering fires, such a hail as had never been known in Egypt before; when everything in the fields was destroyed, vineyards, vegetable beds, standing grain; when trees were uprooted, and those who had not heeded the warning, and went out, were slain, they and their cattle; only then did Pharaoh take fright again, and he sent for Moses and Aaron and pleaded:

"I have sinned this time. Jehovah is righteous, and I and my people are wicked. Pray to Jehovah, and let there be enough of these mighty thunderings and hail; and I will let you go and you shall stay here no longer."

"It is well," said Moses. "As soon as I am gone out of the city I will spread my arms to Jehovah; the thunderings will cease, and there will be no more hail, so that thou mayest know that the earth is the Lord's."

Moses went forth. The thunderings ceased, and there was no more hail. And again Pharaoh lied.

Again Moses came before Pharaoh and warned him that God would send a plague of locusts, which would consume every green leaf and sprout that had been left by the hail. And this time Pharaoh's own servants, his counselors and officers, were filled with fear. They filled the audience chamber, and they pleaded: "Let the men go, that they may serve the Lord their God." And only then did Pharaoh send again for Moses and Aaron.

"Go," he said, "serve your God Jehovah. But who are they that shall go?"

"We will go with our young and with our old, with our sons and with our daughters, with our flocks and with our herds; for we must hold a feast unto the Lord."

Then anger once again overmastered Pharaoh. For now Moses had brought his purpose into the open—the leading forth of the Hebrews from Egypt, forever.

"So may your God be with you, as I will let you go with your little ones," raged Pharaoh. "Evil is written on your faces. Go, you, the men, and serve your Jehovah. For that is what you want." And Moses and Aaron were driven out from Pharaoh's presence.

"We will wait till the locust come," said Moses to Aaron. "He will speak more softly then."

So it was. The locust came in black clouds, which covered the sun and darkened the whole land of Egypt; they settled on the fields and consumed their produce with millions of mouths. Then Pharaoh sent again for Moses and Aaron, and again he was all repentance and supplication:

"I have sinned against your Jehovah and against you. Forgive me my sin only this once, and pray to your Jehovah that he take away from me only this pestilence."

Moses prayed to God, and God answered his prayer, as always. And Pharaoh lied again.

Now a covering closed down on Egypt like a massive vault of copper, which concealed the light of the sun, the moon, and the stars. No fragment of the heavens was seen, and within the stifling enclosure rose winds laden with dust and sand. At first the Egyptians thought that it was the *hamsin* wind, which was due in that season of the year; and the beginning of it was indeed like a *hamsin*. Wherever the Egyptians turned, they breathed sand and dust; but the sand and dust were damp and thick, as though all space were filled with flying mud. The mud clung to the eyes, so that no man could see his fellow. The Egyptians breathed and swallowed dust and sand. The particles lodged grittily between the teeth and crept into the joints, so that man and animal staggered about. Hemmed in under the asphyxiating vault, they felt as though they were trapped in webs of darkness, which lay as heavy by day as by night. Again Pharaoh sent to inquire whether this horrible *hamsin* cloud oppressed the air and covered the sky in Goshen. No, the air in Goshen was bright and clear. And this time Pharaoh was ready to let the women and children go to the festival of Jehovah; but he demanded that the cattle be left behind as guarantee of their return to Egypt.

The answer of Moses was:

"Thou must give us sacrifice and burnt offerings to sacrifice unto our God, Jehovah. Our cattle shall also go with us; not a hoof shall be left behind. For we must take them all to serve the Lord our God; and we know not with what we shall serve the Lord our God until we come thither."

This was the extremest blasphemy and insult that Moses could fling in Pharaoh's face: not only was he to let his slaves go, to sacrifice to an alien god, but he, Pharaoh, the god Ra in his own flesh, was to provide them with cattle for the sacrifices to the alien God of a horde of slaves.

"Begone!" he shouted. "Take heed to see my face no more, for in the day thou seest my face thou shalt die."

"Thou hast spoken well," answered Moses. "I will see thy face again no more." And he went out from Pharaoh's presence.

Of the plagues which God had sent hitherto upon the Egyptians the last one, the plague of darkness, made the deepest and most terrifying impression. They had, indeed, begun to see the finger of the alien Hebrew God in those earlier plagues which had made a clear division between Goshen and Egypt; the fear of Him came on the Egyptians, and they began to respect the Hebrew slaves. Many of the Egyptians had heeded the warning issued by Moses before the falling of the hail, had remained under shelter, and had saved themselves and their cattle. But the last plague, that of darkness, had had a peculiar effect on the Egyptians, for it struck direct at their chief god and at the authority and prestige of Pharaoh. Now it seemed that the insolent God of the Hebrews had conquered the Egyptian gods in their own territory, on their own ground. Whatever else might be thought, whatever other gods there were, the sun was the peculiar property of the Egyptians. Ammon-Ra was their greatest god, and Pharaoh was his son, flesh of his flesh. Pharaoh was the sun, giving light and life to all creatures. His rays warmed the earth and made it fruitful. He reigned over the whole world in his splendor. When he showed himself in the heavens with the first beams of morning, he brought joy to all the inhabitants of the earth. When he set, darkness and death covered the earth. And here the god Ra had been conquered by an unknown power! For three days he had been covered with darkness; for three days the God of the Hebrews had enslaved him and had kept him in bondage in the kingdom of Osiris, the god of night and death. And precisely in Goshen, precisely among the Hebrew slaves, Ammon-Ra had spread his radiance, exactly as though the Hebrew God had compelled him to illumine the land of the Hebrews and to leave his own land in darkness. Was not this a proof that the God of the Hebrews had stepped over the frontiers of the desert and was now in Egypt, and that this was His hand extended over the Egyptians?

Now since Moses had brought back the marvelous revelation of Jehovah, Aaron had not ceased to meditate on his priestly mission, and on a ritual for Jehovah. He had always dreamed of such a ritual, which, with its grandeur, its festiveness, and its severe, exact prescriptions, with its mysteries and, above all, with its sacrifices and rich offerings, should rival the ritual of the Egyptian temples. It was his opinion that the masses of the Hebrew slaves, who had neither an explicit faith nor an established ceremonial, who had, in fact, nothing more than a dim tradition and a recollection of their forefathers, could not be molded into a people and adapted to the necessary discipline without a ritual which should dominate their minds by means of a mystical symbolism supported by a mighty caste of priests and temple slaves. But a ritual of this kind, on which Aaron had brooded all his life, and for which he had prepared both himself and his sons, implied a people capable of supporting a priesthood in fitting opulence. The Hebrew slaves whom Moses was about to liberate were poor and naked. Where were they to find the gold, silver, and purple for the priesthood Aaron had in mind?

After the plague of darkness, when the Egyptians were filled with fear and began to toady to the Hebrew slaves, Aaron and his sons spread abroad the information that God wanted them to borrow from their Egyptian neighbors all manner of gold and silver vessels, rich woven stuffs, purple silks, rich raiment, to be used when they went on the festival of the sacrifice. Further, it was hinted that it was the will of Jehovah that the Egyptians should be spoiled.

The hint was taken, and the Hebrew slaves made use of the panic which seized the Egyptians.

With the plague of darkness the Egyptian overseers had reluctantly abandoned their discipline over the slaves. They had not the courage to continue in their old ways even though the command came from Pharaoh, through the higher officials, to make still heavier the yoke of the Hebrews. They were frankly afraid of these men, who were now under the protection of the fearsome desert God; and they began to compete with each other in their groveling protestations of friendliness and good will.

"Thou seest, dost thou not, that I am altogether different from the other overseers, who were never content with Pharaoh's decrees, but forever went beyond them and squeezed the life out of you Hebrews. My sympathies were always with you. When you fell behind in your work, I looked the other way. Tell me now, was it not so?" asked an Egyptian of one Hebrew overseer.

And now the status of the Hebrews was altogether changed in the eyes of the Egyptians. As long as the slaves had been without a protector and no voice had been lifted in their behalf, they had been like the dust of the earth, to be trodden underfoot. They had been of less account than the beasts of the field. It simply did not occur to the Egyptians that a Hebrew was human, that the Hebrew mothers were human mothers, who agonized when their children were torn away from them. And all of a sudden the Hebrews became "equals." They were invited with hospitable gestures to the homes of the Egyptians; and the Egyptians spoke respectfully of the great festival, which the Hebrews were about to celebrate in the wilderness, and of the great quantities of cattle and fowl which they would bring as sacrifices on the altar of their God; they spoke of the wonderful ceremonial by which all this would, of course, be attended, the dances of the priests, the choruses of the singers, the spectacles, the feasts, the many-colored robes, the magnificent ornaments.

"But where do you expect us to get all these things? Until now

146

we have worked for you, even though we were never really slaves. Pharaoh left us nothing but the skin on our bones—and even that has on it the marks of his cruelty."

Now for the first time the Hebrews, coming to and, as it were, catching their breath, were able to perceive the wealth of Egypt and the luxury which surrounded the upper classes : their gardens and orchards, their cisterns and artificial pools, filled with fowl; their houses with ceilings of cedar, painted and decorated; their armchairs and beds, set with ivory; their coverlets of purple and brocade; their vessels, their basins and cruses and vases, their plates and beakers of pure gold. And their wives, bedecked with countless ornaments, nose rings and earrings, bracelets and finger rings, glittering stones, great robes of cloth of gold; and slave girls to minister to them, to anoint them, fan them, hold perfumes and flowers under their nostrils.

A natural jealousy was awakened in the hearts of the Hebrews. Moreover, who had accumulated these treasures for the Egyptians, if not they, the slaves? Had they not stood from morning till night in the fields, their backs breaking under the burning sun, while the Egyptians had reclined on their ivory couches? Had they not been yoked like draft animals to the threshing machines and carts of the Egyptians? Had not Hebrew wives spun and woven the linens which covered the luxuriously tended bodies of the Egyptian women? Who had created all this opulence, the Egyptians or the Hebrews?

They knew well enough that Moses had been sent to them by the God of Israel to lead them out from Egypt never to return. The elders of Israel had declared it, the overseers had repeated it. And they were in fact making preparations for the great, long night of their liberation, as Moses admonished them. Precisely for this reason they felt that they could not leave Egypt empty handed after so many years of enslavement; for this reason they wanted to take into the unknown which lay before them the wealth which was theirs by right.

But they were not strong enough to take it by main force. Pharaoh had not yet yielded; and the great event which Moses foretold had not yet come to pass. Egyptian order and discipline still existed; the military still surrounded the great residence city of Pharaoh; the Egyptian overseers still make their rounds, carrying the copper-loaded rods. Force, then, was out of the question. But there were ways of exploiting the mounting uneasiness of the Egyptians.

"My God will be ashamed of me," said Dan ben Joseph, of the tribe of Dan, to his aristocratic owner, Sernapus, whom he served as dyer of linen and woolen stuffs. "I come before Him with nothing but my loincloth. And my wife is as naked as I. Thou wilt sin against my God if thou sendest me thus to serve Him in the wilderness. He will ask me: Who is thy lord? And I will answer: The highborn Sernapus. And He will ask again: Has he paid thee for thy labor? And I will answer: Thou seest, my God, I served him as a slave, and save for black cakes and sour beer I received nothing from him. He will then ask: Did he send thee forth in these rags to serve me? Did he not even give thee a decent robe to cover thy nakedness? And did he send thy wife away without a nose ring, without a bracelet, without a neckband? And thou knowest, my lord, my God is an angry God; He will send upon thee calamity after calamity. What he will do I know not. Perhaps thy flocks will no longer multiply; perhaps thy fowl will sicken and die; and perhaps He will take vengeance on thee and thy children. Anything may be expected of Him. See, I am a good friend to thee, and I have come to warn thee."

"And what wouldst thou have me do?"

"Thou hast such richly colored robes. Lend me of them for the days of my visit to my God. And thou mayest lend me, too, a pair of earrings, a neckband, and of course thy wife's silk mantle to cover my wife's nakedness. And I will mention thy name favorably to my God, and He will bless thee."

And when Dan ben Joseph was given the desired objects by his lord Sernapus, was given them with many a sigh and groan, and many a warning that he was to return them in good condition, with nothing missing; and when the scribe had entered all the objects scrupulously on a sheet of papyrus, the slave, or the former slave, still stood there with outstretched hand.

"And what shall I do for a little anointing oil? My body still sweats from my labors. Thou wouldst not have my God offended by an evil odor ascending from our bodies to His nostrils."

And when Dan ben Joseph had received the pyx of solidified perfume, which the Egyptians carried on their heads, so that it might melt and drip over their bodies, he turned again to his lord:

"Hast thou not thought of a sheep, a calf, a young steer, a pair

148

of ducks and geese? Thou wouldst not have me appear empty-handed before my God, and have Him send scorpions into thy house. Thou rememberest the frogs, dost thou not?"

And that which Dan ben Joseph did with his lord Sernapus, other Dans and Josephs and Uziels did with their lords.

But before long they were not content with the first gifts. When they saw the terror of the Egyptians increasing, the Hebrew slaves became more and more agitated; the resentments which they had repressed in their hearts during the generations of slavery flamed up in them. Together with the slaves of other peoples, Negroes of Africa and Asiatics from the Canaanite lands, they came in bands into Rameses, forced their way into the wealthy houses and palaces, and "borrowed" their contents. They tore silken hangings from the walls and coverings from the doors; they collected gold and silver utensils, cruses, basins, plates, and beakers. They adorned their heads with lotus flowers, which they took away from the lotus girls; they drenched their sweaty bodies with perfumes and salves; they snatched from the bodies of the Egyptian women their neck-bands, bracelets, rings, girdles, for their own wives, to take with them for the festival of the Lord. And already here and there a slave was seen parading with a lotus flower stuck behind his ear, a golden ring between his teeth, a richly sewn silk robe thrown over his naked body. Some carried away on their backs large stools set with ivory, or delicately carved couches ornamented with gold; others drove away sheep and oxen to sacrifice in the wilderness.

Korah and his associates came before Moses with the alarming news that the people had got out of hand; they were attacking the Egyptian homes and plundering right and left.

Moses was silent; then, after meditation, he said: "Return to me in a little while, and I will instruct you."

In the scales of justice which were locked in his heart he weighed the deeds of the Hebrews. He exerted himself to see the case of the Egyptians even as he saw the case of his brothers. He was responsible for the Hebrews and for their deeds. It was of course against God's wish that the people which He had chosen to be an example to all peoples should commit injustice on the very threshold of redemption. The plundering must cease; but the borrowing of objects from the Egyptians was justified. For hundreds of years these slaves had labored for Egypt. The Egyptians had used them; they had exploited them as if their labor, their sweat, and their lives were of no account. And Moses heard in his heart the voice of his God, the voice of justice.

Later, when Korah and his associates returned, he said to them: "No, Korah, the Bnai Israel are not robbers; they are only fulfilling the commandment of God. For thus God declared to me: Speak now in the ears of the people, and let them ask every man of his neighbor, and every woman of her neighbor, jewels of silver and jewels of gold; and let them spoil the Egyptians for the oppression which was laid upon them, and for the bitter labors which they did for them."

CHAPTER SIXTEEN

IN the private room which served as his retreat, Pharaoh lay stretched on his couch, and before him stood "the friend of Pharaoh," the powerful Mephesta, governor of Rameses, in his official robes, with the outspread golden eagle on his breast and in his hand the little fan which was the insignia of the "friendship." By the side of Mephesta stood the high priest of Ammon-Ra, his shaven head covered by a wig, the curls of which hung down, like those of a mummy, to the shoulders.

Close to the couch, on a little stool, sat Pharaoh's oldest son, the heir apparent.

Pharaoh had aged greatly. Not all the skill of his Assyrian cosmeticians could quite disguise the deep folds which the misery of the plagues had worked into his pulpy face.

The heir apparent, who was already a man in the thirties, looked, with his smooth, rounded face, like a boy of eighteen. His head was all shaved, except in the middle, where the hair grew to full length, and was gathered and twisted into a single braid, which hung down over his cheek.

Pharaoh's hand rested tenderly on his son's head, and the son held a lotus flower close to his father's nostrils. This was an expression of reverence and love. The heir apparent was already regarded as Ra's son, a portion of the divinity. He accompanied his father on every ceremonial occasion, a stiff, rigid, official figure. Here, in his father's private room, he showed himself in a tender and intimate relationship.

Despite the robes of the governor and high priest, the reception was not an official one. It was more in the nature of a secret conference on the condition of the country. The governor and the high priest were delivering to Pharaoh a report on the effect which the plague of darkness had produced on the Egyptians.

Something in the nature of a revolution had occurred. The slaves of all the races were rising against their masters; bands of them roamed about plundering; and they too shouted that they were "borrowing" clothes and ornaments to take to the great festival of their god.

"We counsel thee, great king, to yield to the demands of Moses. Let them go, the Hebrew slaves—let them go, the sooner the better, to their festival in the wilderness, before it is too late. For the control of all the slaves is slipping from our hands. Our overseers are terrified and exact no work. Even the garrison in Rameses is intimidated—not to speak of the population at large. They have begun to believe that the gods are fighting against us, not with us. Everywhere they now speak of Moses as the incarnation of Horus and say that Horus works these wonders for him. Against this superstition we have no force," concluded the governor.

Pharaoh was white with anger. He took away his hand from his son's head; with the other hand he thrust away the lotus flower.

"And these are the words of 'the friends of Pharaoh,' the high priest and the governor of Rameses! This is the counsel they bring to Pharaoh—that I surrender to my bloodiest foe, the God of the Hebrews. No! It is not by surrender that we will rid ourselves of the wild disorder which the alien traitor has brought into our kingdom. Today it is Moses who persuades the Egyptians that he is Horus; tomorrow some other Canaanite or Syrian or Libyan slave will perform magic and persuade the Egyptians that he is the incarnation of Osiris, or of a god of the wilderness, of the hills, the fields, the seas. No! There are no other gods than the gods of Egypt; and Ammon-Ra is god of all the gods, and I am his son, flesh of his flesh, blood of his blood. And my son, my heir, is flesh of my flesh, blood of my blood. And we are the gods of the Egyptians, not of slaves. No! It is not by concession that we will subdue the slaves, but by sword and spear, by rod and lash. Bring into Rameses the Negro garrison stationed in the desert. Names of gods are unknown to them. Let them make an iron ring of war chariots about Goshen. Send my Negro garrison into Goshen, I say. Let them crush with their hammers the skulls of all the men, women, and children in Goshen, and let them set fire to their huts and tents. And if any are left, to flee from the burning city, let the chariots ride them down; and let no trace be left of the Hebrew slaves. Let them be a sign and a warning to all other slaves. This is the only way to crush the revolt which Moses has set off. Let Moses and Aaron be taken, and let them be beaten to death with the staves of

Hebrew slave overseers. Let the whole tribe of Levi be sent in chains to the copper mines of Sinai, as I warned Moses I would do if he ever appeared before me again."

Pharaoh had not ended speaking, and the foam of his rage was still on his lips, when the noise of a great confusion was heard spreading through the palace. The door of Pharaoh's room was flung open by terrified guards who had dropped their spears; they flung themselves to the floor and babbled:

"Moses, with his staff in his hand, has come into the palace!"

Pharaoh started from his couch as if a serpent had stung him and in mingled fury and terror screamed:

"How dared you let him enter? Have I not bidden you to drive him from the threshold?"

"His staff spits fire, son of Ra. Serpents with a hundred heads issue from his staff, and their mouths spit flames. We were afraid!"

In that same instant Moses, his staff uplifted, crossed the threshold, advanced into the room, and, towering over Pharaoh, whose face was bloodless, spoke:

"Know that this time I have not been sent to thee by God. This time I come of my own accord to warn thee. Until now God has smitten thee only in thy possessions. He has destroyed thy harvests, He has slain thy cattle. And thou hast not obeyed His command. But now, this last time, He will smite at the lives of men. Therefore I have ignored thy threat, that thou wouldst slay me if I appeared before thee again; and I have withdrawn my own word; for it is a matter of human lives. Hear me then, thus speaks God: 'About midnight I will go out among the Egyptians. And there will die in Egypt every first-born son, from the son of Pharaoh, who is to sit upon his throne, to the first-born son of the servant woman at her millstones. And there will be a great lamentation in Egypt, such as has never been before and will not be again. But against the children of Israel not a dog shall whet its tongue, whether against a man or against a beast. So may you know that I have made a division between the Egyptians and the Israelites.' So speaks the Lord. And all these, thy servants," said Moses, pointing to the terrified officials and guards, "shall bow down to Jehovah, and they shall implore His people, and they shall say to me: 'Now get thee gone, thou and all thy people which is with thee.' And after that we shall go."

There was silence for a long time, before Pharaoh mastered himself. At first he thought of lifting his hand and issuing the order for the arrest of Moses. The command did not leave his lips. Not only was he quite certain that the guards would not stir, for fear of the staff which Moses held; but he felt a great weakness in himself. Something happened to his will, something paralyzing, whenever Moses appeared before him. He became powerless, as though Moses were his lord and God. So, being weak, Pharaoh used the instrument of the weak, and spoke, not of power and might, but of justice and pity:

"And this is the God for whom thou hast exchanged the gods of Egypt? Where is the justice whereof thou ceasest not to speak, if He is prepared to slay the sons for the sins of the fathers? And where is His pity?"

"And this is Pharaoh that speaks? Pharaoh who slew the sons of the Hebrew women? Is it thou, by whose orders sucklings were torn away from the mother's breast, and slaughtered that thou mightest bathe in their blood? Thou, by whose orders the bones of young and old were trodden into the mud, to make firmer the bricks of thy treasure houses? Speakest thou of justice and pity?"

"But wherein are the Egyptians guilty? Wherefore should they be punished? Why will thy God slay all the first-born?"

"All Egypt is infected and corrupted with sin; one putrefying sore on the face of the earth is the land of Egypt. Year after year and generation after generation the Egyptians have looked on while the overseers laid the lash and rod on the old and weak, who could not longer work; they looked on while the bodies of those that fell at their labors were kneaded into the mud; they looked on and were silent. Every one of you held in his hand the life of every Israelite. You yoked them to your plows, to your wagons, till the breath went out of their bodies and they were no more. In your eyes only you were human; you alone were the children of your gods, who created the world only for you. And all others were your beasts of burden. Every one of you was a Pharaoh to his slaves. The soil of Egypt is soaked with the blood of your victims, with the sweat of the laborers, and the blood of the mothers. A day of reckoning comes, a day of vengeance of the God of Israel against the Egyptians."

"Speakest thou thus, Moses, thou, whom my sister the Princess drew out of the water, to make thee her son? A mother she was to thee. She is likewise the eldest among her father's children. Shall she too die? Are these thy thanks to her?"

"I have prayed to my God, and my God has taken her to be His daughter. 'And her name is Bathiya, my daughter,' said the God of Israel. 'And her portion shall be with Israel, and not with the Egyptians. Not a hair of her head shall be harmed, and she shall live in the memory of My people, the one ray of love and compassion in the black and cruel land of Egypt. She shall be counted among the matriarchs of Israel.'"

And Moses went forth from Pharaoh in anger. And, going forth, he heard in his heart the voice of God: "Pharaoh will not listen to thee, that My wonders may be multiplied in the land of Egypt." And thus God did. Pharaoh did not yield even to the last warning delivered by Moses; he did not let the children of Israel go; and he continued with his plans for their complete destruction.

That night Moses had a vision concerning the last preparations for the great night of the liberation.

The next morning he called an assembly of the elders of Israel.

It was no longer the body formerly known by that name. Some time before, when Pharaoh's hand was still strong on the people, Moses had broadened the base of the elders, so that it should not consist solely of members of the tribe of Levi and the official representatives of the slaves. He had given representation to all the tribes. First each tribe had elected its own elders, then these had chosen from among themselves their representatives among the elders of Israel.

Moses, the man of humility, who considered himself the least in Israel, was devoid of any feeling of revenge and guarded himself with the most scrupulous care from any action which would transform him into the dictator of the tribes. He soon put out of his mind what Korah, or Dathan and Abiram, had done in their opposition to him. Certain of their loyalty to the Hebrews, as they had demonstrated it in their latter-day courageous defense of the slaves, he considered them the right men to instill into the masses of the Israelites the discipline of the God of Israel. He not only confirmed them in their old positions but extended the range of their authority. He included them in the new body of the elders of Israel and consulted them on the practical arrangements for the great exodus, which they all held to be at hand. He had also added to the number of the elders Hur, the husband of his sister Miriam, and a young man, almost a lad, who had found favor in his eyes, Joshua, the son of Nun, of the tribe of Benjamin.

And so, among the elders of Israel, there were fresh faces; there were young men, filled with energy and the will to freedom, ready for every sacrifice, and moved by a deep faith in the God of Israel and in His emissary, Moses.

To the assembly of the elders Moses delivered God's command, as it had been given to him and Aaron:

"On the night of the fourteenth day of the month, God will pass among the Egyptians to slay them. Therefore the Bnai Israel shall make signs upon their houses, wherever they find themselves. Every family that is a household shall slaughter a lamb, and they shall dip a bundle of hyssop in the blood of the sacrifice, and they shall sprinkle it on the lintel and on the two side posts, and none of you shall go out of the door of his house until the morning. For God will pass over to smite the Egyptians, and He will pass over your doors and not suffer the destroyer to come into your house to slay you. Therefore the festival of the liberation shall be called the festival of Passover. And this day shall be kept as a memorial; throughout your generations you shall keep it a feast by an ordinance forever. And when you come to the land which God will give you, you shall keep this service. And when your children will ask you: What is the meaning of your service? you shall answer: It is the sacrifice of the Lord's passover, because he passed over the houses of the children of Israel when He smote the Egyptians."

This was the first commandment which Moses brought to the Hebrews in the name of God—the commandment of the festival commemorating the passage from slavery to freedom. It was a festival not for them alone, but for their children and their children's children, for all the generations to be, a memorial of the liberation. And the people bowed and worshiped the invisible God, whose commandment they heard for the first time through the mouth of Moses.

The discipline of the slave system had crumbled to pieces, and the former Hebrew overseers of slaves were now able to carry out without hindrance the instructions of the elders. The Hebrews came from all their places of work in Rameses and Pithom to their native villages in Goshen. Thus the scattered members of families were brought together; brother met brother again, and parents and children were reunited. No one was afraid any more to bring out the little ones into the open, for no Egyptian dared now approach the dwellings of the Bnai Israel.

Everyone knew that this was the night of the liberation; this night God would lead them out of Egypt forever. They therefore assembled all their possessions; there were bundles to be carried on their backs and bundles to be loaded on asses. There were the objects which they had "borrowed" from the Egyptians, now displayed openly. There were sheep, goats, and cattle, cages of fowl, cruses of honey and oil, baskets of fruit, sacks of flour.

All that fourteenth day of the month there was a rushing about and a humming as of a beehive among the tents of the Hebrews. The Egyptians looked on at the preparations, from a distance, and no man dared to hinder.

Pharaoh did not have time enough to bring in the Negro garrison from the desert, and the Egyptian garrison quartered in Rameses was infected with the general panic; it feared the staff of Moses more than the threats of Pharaoh; and Pharaoh was afraid to put his authority to the final test.

The Egyptian slave overseers had long since abandoned their posts and gone into hiding. And the Israelites went about their preparations in complete freedom, carrying out all the commands which Moses had delivered in the name of God. During the day every family of a household killed its sheep and with a bundle of hyssop sprinkled the entrance of its tent or hut. A fire was built outside the entrance, and the sheep was roasted whole. When evening came the Israelites shut themselves in their dwellings and ate hastily, because the liberation might come at any moment.

They kneaded the flour with water and packed it in sheets, not having the time to bake bread. With loins girded, with their bundles on sticks, they stood, ready to do what Moses bade them, and they waited for what would happen.

For a time nothing happened. The night was like any other spring night. They did not see the stars shining with extraordinary radiance, as though the heavens were especially adorned for the festival of the liberation. They were afraid to go out of their dwellings, or even to look out. They only heard the croaking of the frogs, the murmur of the insects, the hum of the weaving of creation, the breathing of growth, the whisper of the palm leaves when the wind stirred them. Then suddenly there came complete silence, as though all creation had suspended motion and stood waiting for something with bated breath. The stillness threw a terror into the hearts of the people. Faces paled. The children gathered about the mothers, the men stood in a group, each man with his staff in his hand, and waited tensely.

Suddenly they heard above their heads the whistling of winds, as if a mighty bird were in passage; they felt the vibrations which the gigantic wings set up in the air. The echoes of that immense agitation resounded in space for a long time after the invisible body had passed, then died down. There was silence again, and it was as if the night were petrified. And then they heard, or rather, they apprehended through all their senses, a tumult such as they had never imagined possible. It was as though a myriad herd of deer were leaping over the tents, and the wind of their passage was like a frightful storm. In pure terror the men and women sank to the ground, thinking that not only their habitations but the entire vault of heaven would be carried away. Then again followed the terrible stillness.

In that infinite ocean of silence a sound was born, and at first they could not distinguish its nature, whether it issued from a human or an animal throat. It came from a great distance, drew nearer and nearer, and when it was quite close to them they discerned that it was the cry of a human being. And at first it was the cry of a single voice, but soon it was joined by a second, and by a third, until it swelled out from a hundred directions. Like harts in a panic, like terrified birds, the voices flew hither and thither; or like the tongues of flame in a forest fire, which the changing wind carries to all points in turn. So the land of Goshen was encircled by a conflagration of voices.

The shrieking lasted through all the night. And all night long, from the fourteenth to the fifteenth day of the month of Abid (Nisan), all that night, the family of Nachshon ben Aminadab, of the tribe of Judah (in whose tent the soul of the writer of this record then was, for he is of that family) was gathered in full assembly. Their staves in their hands, their sandals on their feet, their loins girded, they waited, men and women, young and old, for the outcome. They did not know the meaning of the dread shrieking in the night or of the distant sound of myriads of footsteps which accompanied it for a long time. There were moments when they feared that the Egyptians were gathering for a terrible act of vengeance on the children of Israel. They had been forbidden to leave their habitations; they did not dare to look out; so all night long they remained on the alert, alternating between hope and fear.

When the first ray of the sun flashed over the horizon, a hand smote on the entrance of their houses, and a voice cried:

"Come out! The God of Israel has liberated you."

They had not the time to fall on each other's necks in joy for the fulfillment of the promise; for scarcely had they issued from their tents and huts when a horde of Egyptians, among whom the family of Nachshon ben Aminadab recognized their own former overseer and the scribe who had made the tally of their bricks, burst in among the tents. The faces were those of men who had wept all night; their hair was disordered, there were bloody marks on their bodies, self-inflicted in grief. With hands outstretched, not in rage, not with insults, as had been their wont, but humbly, beseechingly, with lamentation in their eyes, they cried:

"Go, remember your God, and go at once!"

They helped load on the shoulders of the Bnai Judah of ben Nachshon's family their bundles of household goods and of gold and silver utensils; they did not permit the women to take out the dough and dry the flat cakes in the sun, but wrapped them again in costly cloths, and piled them on the oxen. And they continued to cry:

"Go, go at once, for if you stay a little longer we shall all die!"

"There is not a house in Egypt which has not its dead," wailed the women.

"Menephthah's own son, his heir, the child of the sun, was found dead in his bed."

"Go! Go!"

The members of ben Nachshon's family scarcely had the time to collect their belongings, to look round for their sheep and cattle, to make certain of their children. Driven by the lamentations and prayers of the Egyptians, they left their hut.

When they came out into the open, they saw an outpouring of men, women, and children, from all the habitations of the Israelites, from all the corners and alleys of the encampment. The men were loaded with their possessions, and such was the number of golden cruses and beakers, plates, and basins, which flashed in the sun, such was the number of ebony chairs and couches, brocaded curtains and robes, that it seemed as though all the wealth of Egypt was being carried away.

For a time there was no entering or leaving Goshen. The alleys were jammed with laden men and women, with flocks of sheep, herds of cattle and asses; clouds of dust rose from the feet of the travelers and their animals. Out of the thickness of the clouds rose a song, an upwelling of joyous shouts.

As the mass moved slowly forward it swelled in numbers. Pilgrims poured into it from every side; and not only from Goshen, but from the adjacent district of Rameses. Many of them were naked, and all of them carried their household goods, with fowls in their hands. Who these last newcomers were, to whom they belonged, no one knew. Among them were men and women with Asiatic faces, there were Negro slaves in colored robes thrown over their nakedness. They drove cattle before them.

The numbers of the latest arrivals grew larger and larger. It was as if all the slaves of Egypt were leaving the land, joining themselves to the Israelites. And no one knew whither the mass was moving. But all knew that Moses and Aaron were at the head of the host, and all followed them.

CHAPTER SEVENTEEN

WHEN the Israelites had drawn out of Goshen and were on the edge of the wilderness, Moses and Aaron proclaimed again, in the name of God, that the night of the liberation was to be kept as a memorial night by all the generations of Israel; and they repeated the manner of the observance of the festival, with the prescriptions for the slaying of the lamb, and the permission and prohibition as to who might eat of the sacrifice and who might not. And the festival was to be a rehearsal, every year in the years and generations to come, of the act of liberation.

Now it soon became apparent that to the hundreds of thousands of Hebrews who went up out of Egypt (the Egyptian chroniclers, writing under totalitarian pressure, avoided mentioning the exodus as a defeat of Pharaoh) many non-Hebrew slaves had joined themselves. They took advantage of the general panic and confusion to mingle with the Hebrews. Ethiopians, Canaanites, and other Asiatic peoples were among them. And the question arose immediately how they were to be regarded. Were they to be reckoned to the Hebrew people, or were they to be considered camp followers who had no share in the redemption and could not be included among the families of Israel in the celebration of the great festival? The question was placed before Moses, who issued a command in the name of God:

"He that went with us is of us. There shall be one law for the citizen and for the stranger who is in your midst."

Moses was clear in his own mind as to his plans and purposes. During the last warnings which he had issued to Pharaoh he had already revealed that he was not concerned with merely taking the Hebrews for a three-day journey into the wilderness: it was his intention to lead the Israelites out of bondage into the land which had been promised to their forefather Abraham. They would cross the desert and conquer the land. But the ultimate objective was a far higher one. The former slaves were not merely to be a people which conquered a land for itself: they were to be a holy people, a chosen people, a people which by its moral life should be an example to all the peoples of the world, the people of a law which in its justice should express the will of the one living God.

For the fulfillment of this higher purpose he had to bring this people to Sinai, where God had revealed Himself to him and had entrusted him with his mission. There they would receive and accept the laws and commandments of God. There they would be born again, born into the law of God and their new freedom. As the night of Passover had brought the liberation of their bodies, so Mount Sinai was to bring the liberation of the spirit.

If he was to re-educate the people from bondage to freedom, he could not lead it by the shortest route to Canaan, along the seacoast by way of the land of the Philistines. The Israelites had only just emerged from slavery; at the first clash with the Philistines they would turn tail and flee back to Egypt. They must first pass through the swamps of the Sea of Reeds, as he himself had done; they must enter the desert of Sin—only there would they be entirely freed from the Egyptian yoke—and pass into the peninsula and the mountains of Sinai, between the two arms, Suez and Akabah, of the Red Sea.

From his own experiences Moses knew how dangerous would be the passage through the Sea of Reeds, where the growths of hyssop and bamboo concealed innumerable treacherous depths of swamp into which men and cattle sank, never to be found again. He led the people lengthwise along the swamp to the oasis city of Succoth, not far from the earlier treasure city of Pithom, which the Hebrews had built for Pharaoh. He knew quite well that he was still within the shadow of the might of Pharaoh, whose armies could overtake him without difficulty. Only by a miracle of God could he lead this people with its herds in safety through the Sea of Reeds. How the miracle would come to pass he did not know; but he had faith that when the moment arrived, God would show him the way.

The Hebrews, or Israelites, as Moses called them, meanwhile had enough to eat. They baked in the hot sun the cakes of dough which their wives carried in wrappings. They had large supplies of oil, honey, and vegetables; there were also the cattle and fowl which they had brought out of Egypt. Well fed, still intoxicated with the triumph of Jehovah over the Egyptians, they did not perceive the threat which hung over them.

The immense mass of foot travelers, which, together with the cattle, followed Moses and the other guides, raised such a cloud of dust that by day they were concealed as by a curtain of smoke; and in the bright spring nights of the time of the liberation, the light of moon and stars playing on the dust cloud tinged it with red, so that it seemed that pillars of fire advanced before the people on its path.

Moses moved rapidly, urging the people on by night as well as by day, even though he did not know what point in the Sea of Reeds God had designated for their crossing.

The marchers were in high spirits, moving forward tirelessly. The cries of triumph, which kept breaking from the women, the laughing and crying of the children, the lowing of the cattle, the bleating of the sheep made the air quiver. There was as yet no order in the march, and the tribes were mingled with one another.

The third day after they had left Succoth, when they were at the entrance of the desert, where the foothills marked the approach to the sea, Moses received God's command to turn the march in the direction of Egypt, and to pause at the edge of the swampy passage of the Sea of Reeds, between a place called Migdal and the Sea of Reeds itself. They would again be not far removed from Succoth, and opposite Pithom, where the Sea of Reeds ended in the broad Bitter Lakes.

These lakes divided the territory of Egypt from the desert of Shur. The waters, though not altogether free from mud, were considerably clearer than those of the Sea of Reeds. Here it was impossible to advance by laying down rafts of bamboo and reeds. There was only one way of crossing, and that was in boats, as the Egyptian armies did.

The entire area, though it lay on the rim of the wilderness, was studded with garrisons. A caravan road passed near-by through the desert of Shur, linking Egypt with Canaan and Arabia. Here, too, the path lay—through the wilderness of Sin—to the port on the Red Sea, Ezion-geber.

Thus the march was an open challenge to the Egyptians. It was impossible not to mark the progress of the "runaway slaves," not to see their encampments along the foothills or the fires they kindled at night, not to hear the jubilant cries which floated from their midst.

The men slaughtered the fowl and roasted them on open fires; here and there several families assembled and roasted a sheep in a sand bed. The women put on the silk, embroidered garments, which they took out of their bundles, and adorned themselves in finery. With golden rings in their ears, with tiaras and chaplets on their heads, they paraded before the men.

One man in the host put on a pleated skirt, which he had pulled off an Egyptian god in the days of the darkness, donned a heavily curled wig with a mighty helm, which flashed in the sun, and, with rings on his fingers and a bamboo rod in his hand, played the role of "the friend of Pharaoh," of the governor of Rameses, or of the Egyptian high priest. Another had his portion of roast sheep served on a gold plate, while he reclined on an ivory-studded couch, which he dragged with him on his shoulders.

Besides the utensils and robes which they had "borrowed," many of the Hebrews had brought with them out of Egypt weapons of war, bows and arrows, spears, swords, copper-tipped lances, and copper armor. And they clothed themselves like soldiers and officers.

There were also in the camp of the Hebrews many trumpets, cymbals, and rams' horns. The blowing of the trumpets and rams' horns, the clashing of the cymbals, mingled with the throaty singing of the women, the shouting of the men, the laughter of the children, the crackling of the camp fires: and the tumult went up into the moonlit night, a jubilation of freedom, in the heart of Pharaoh's country, in the shadow of the pyramids and by the borders of the Red Sea.

Moses knew well that the liberation was not yet complete, that great trials still awaited him. God had told him that Pharaoh would set out in pursuit and God would let the Egyptian know that He was the Lord. But concerning the manner in which He would save the Israelites, and how He would lead them through the sea, God had told him nothing. Moses only believed that even as God had helped them till now and had revealed the might of His arm to the Egyptians, so He would help them when the next trial came; and he rested in his faith.

But it was not so with the other leaders of the Israelites, with Korah and his circle, with Dathan and Abiram. They went about in the midst of the pealing jubilation of the Israelites heavyhearted and with gloomy looks. After the wonders and miracles which God had performed through Moses, they had of course become believers in the liberation. They had also believed that after Pharaoh had liberated the Bnai Israel, Moses, with the help of God, would perform one more miracle and carry the people over the Sea of Reeds straight into the wilderness, before the three days of the intended festival had expired. But now three days had passed, and Moses had not carried the Israelites into the desert; and Korah, Dathan, and Abiram, together with their circle, trembled before the danger which now confronted them.

Korah called together his intimate followers for a conference. They consisted of leaders of the tribe of Levi and former slave overseers to whom Moses had left important functions in the congregation pending the time when he could reorganize the exodus. The former overseers were under the leadership of Dathan and Abiram, who also brought to the secret conference a few others of like mind with themselves. Here Korah put forward his own plan:

"Moses is wandering blindly in the wilderness. If he could not take us across the narrow swamp passage by Succoth, where the Sea of Reeds is at its narrowest and passage is easy, he will certainly not be able to take this immense multitude, with its possessions, its herds, and its flocks, across the wide stretches of the Bitter Lakes. Where will he get the ships for such an undertaking? Even if Pharaoh himself were to furnish him with ships, there are not enough of them in Egypt to transport this people across the water. The three days of the festival in the wilderness have passed, and Pharaoh must have realized by now that Moses has no intention of bringing the slaves back to Egypt. We may expect any moment to see Pharaoh's chariots in pursuit of us. We must be prepared for that. We must put the whole blame on Moses. We never thought of leaving Egypt. We only wanted to serve God in the wilderness, and it was our intention to return. Moses deceived us. He led us into the wilderness only that he might be able to become ruler over us. The danger is great. If God has not helped Moses till now, and has withdrawn from him, nothing is left to us but to return to Egypt. For Pharaoh will drive us all into the sea, if we do not betimes save as many of the people as we can."

Korah's followers were in accord with him. They knew the Egyptians, and they did not believe that Pharaoh was defeated yet; he was preparing an attack on the Israelites.

And it turned out as Korah had foretold. Despite all the wonders which Moses had wrought, despite all the calamities which had been visited on the Egyptians, Pharaoh clung to the belief that the power of Moses was temporary and limited, entrusted to him by a god with a temporary and limited rule—not a god of eternal rule; a god, in fact, resembling the Aton whom Amenhotep the Fourth had for a time installed in Egypt. Like Aton, this god could also overcome the gods of Egypt, but for a short time only. Indeed, it was possible that the Jehovah of the Hebrews was none other than Aton, who had returned under another name, this time to make war not on the gods of Egypt, but on the Egyptians themselves, whom he had exchanged in favor of a slave people. If this was so, there was nothing to fear. Just as the gods of Egypt, soon after Amenhotep's death, had conquered his god and driven him from Egypt, so they would conquer him again in his new form.

The heavy blow he had suffered with the death of his beloved son had for an instant so shattered Menephthah that he had let the Hebrews go. When he recovered, he repented of his weakness; he repented of the momentary fear which had overcome him that his gods had by now been decisively defeated by an alien god, that the entire kingdom of Egypt, built on the power of Ra, was in danger of dissolution.

He sent out spies to discover the intentions of the Hebrews. Would they indeed return after their three-day festival, as they had originally said they would? Or would Moses lead them across the narrow passage into the desert? And if Moses planned to lead them through the ring of waters which surrounded Egypt, how would he do it? There was but one way: his God would have to send down His heavenly hosts in the form of mighty eagles, with wings strong enough to lift and carry the immense multitude across the swamps. Other means were out of the question; there were not even ships enough for the task.

But when the miracle held off, when hosts of eagles failed to descend from the heavens, and Moses led the fugitive slaves back and forth along the stretch of the Sea of Reeds between the narrow passage and the Bitter Lakes, without finding a ford, Pharaoh saw the triumph of Ra over Aton, as in the days of Tutankhamen.

Swiftly Pharaoh called a council of "the friends of Pharaoh," the fanbearers, the high priest, the governor of Rameses, the commander of the chariot brigades, and held forth to them:

"Jehovah, the God of Moses, is none other than the god Aton, the foe of the Egyptian gods, whom Amenhotep the Fourth—may his name be obliterated till the end of time—sought to impose on Egypt. Jehovah-Aton tolerates no gods beside Him. It is true that He was able for a time to overcome the gods of Egypt and to smite the Egyptians with plagues; He was able to desolate their temples, slay the priests, and destroy the images of the gods; but He showed himself to be powerless when Ra arose in the incarnation of Pharaoh Tutankhamen and swept Him out of Egypt, desolated *His* city and temples, destroyed *His* images, and forbade the mention of His name. Jehovah, like Aton, is a god of devastation, not a god of blessings who can help His followers. This is now evident to all who have eyes. He cast terror upon us with His plague visitations so that we hastened to liberate the Hebrew slaves. But He is impotent to save them from our hand. They wander back and forth in confusion. The desert is sealed to them. Jehovah cannot lead them to the other side of the Sea of Reeds. The gods of Egypt have delivered them up to us. Assemble the chariots," said Pharaoh, turning to the commander of the chariot brigades, "and set out in swiftest pursuit. Thou wilt find them, terrified, desolate, and confused, on the shore of the Sea of Reeds. Drive them into the swamps, and let the name of Aton-Jehovah be wiped out forever."

"Son of Ra in his own flesh!" cried the high priest. "Thou wilt henceforth be likened to Tutankhamen, the avenger of the gods of Egypt!"

"Thou avenger of the gods of Egypt!" exclaimed the governor of Rameses. "Thy victories over thy foes, the Hebrews, will be inscribed to thy eternal glory on the walls of thy pyramids!"

And the commander of the chariot brigades cried: "Thou, Pharaoh, art our power and our glory, and victory is thine! When thou wilt ride forth in thy golden chariot at the head of thy hosts, Ra the god in his own body will set out in his sun splendor, to slay with the rays, which are his spears, his enemies among the gods. Thy charioteers long for thee. They call to thee. Sun of Egypt, lead us!"

"Thou speakest well. I, even I, Ra the god in his own flesh, will lead you into battle against my enemy, Aton-Jehovah. Let my chariot be harnessed."

Clad in the double helmet crown, Pharaoh Menephthah stood upright, for all his years, in the chariot which was to lead the

Egyptian hosts against the Hebrew slaves. Four white horses in golden harness tugged at the reins, their hoofs drumming impatiently on the ground. The golden shield which his armor-bearer carried before him blazed like white fire in the sun. With his right arm stretching the bow which he held uplifted in his left, he received the benedictions of his people and the salute of his warriors for the deeds he was about to perform against the god Aton, who had become the god of the Hebrews. Blind temple slaves knelt before him and sang to the accompaniment of harps:

"Thou art like Ra in all that thou dost.
All things happen according to thy heart's desires.
We have seen many of thy wonders
Since thou wert crowned king of the two lands.
When thou commandest, the waters cover the mountains,
The sea hears thee forthwith;
In thy loins is Ra,
Thy creator dwells in thee."

Scribes with styluses and rolls of papyrus knelt in rows and recorded for the generations to be the manner of Pharaoh's departure to do battle with the god of the Bnai Israel.

But of course the departure of Pharaoh at the head of the hosts was only a ceremonial pretense. He was too old and too weak to lead the troops in battle; moreover, it was not the custom for a Pharaoh to take part in an action on the field. No sooner had the chariots reached the desert beyond the city when Pharaoh returned to the palace. His place was taken by one of "the friends of Pharaoh," to whom were henceforth addressed all the panegyrics and prayers intended for the king; and the victories of the substitute were to be ascribed by all the chroniclers to Pharaoh himself.

As far as the eye could see stretched the rows of chariots. The bowmen who drove them burned with eagerness to avenge the name of Egypt; the horses, filled with the fury of battle, flew over the level sands of the desert. At the head rode the surrogate Pharaoh. Clouds of dust rose from the hoofs and wheels, curling like crimson smoke to the heavens and eclipsing the light of the sun. And the host sped irresistibly toward Baal-zephon, where they knew the Hebrew slaves were looking helplessly for a crossing.

On the second day, toward evening, the Israelites descried the clouds of dust rising like fire smoke in the desert. The clouds drew ever nearer, and the Israelites knew that these were Pharaoh's chariots in pursuit. In an instant the encampment was in an uproar. They became like a huge flock of sheep which has suddenly caught the scent of a wolf. They abandoned the possessions to which they had clung so fiercely and began to run. Mothers ran, holding their little ones by the hand, or in their arms. Whither they were running they did not know; and in the confusion of their flight they only drew closer together, so that the center of the encampment became a dense, boiling mass; and men and women pushed against each other and remained locked in one place. A wild cry went up from the encampment, and hands were uplifted:

"God of Israel, help us! God of Israel!"

Moses was in the midst of the camp. He was calm and confident. He knew that the Egyptians would come in pursuit, as God had told him; and he also knew that God would show the Egyptians that He was the Lord. Great indeed was the danger to the Israelites, trapped between the Egyptians and the sea; but though God had not disclosed to him the manner of the rescue, he awaited it with certainty. Had not God shown wonders enough in Egypt?

And the confidence which Moses felt became all the stronger when he heard Bnai Israel, the slaves whom he had led out of Egypt, calling upon Jehovah. At any moment now, before the Egyptians reached the encampment, help would come.

But as he stood thus, and before he had opened his lips to pacify and reassure the masses, he found himself encircled by the Bnai Levi. Their hands were stretched out toward him, their eyes blazed vengeance.

"Did we not know what the end of this would be!" screamed Dathan, his voice carrying through half the camp. "Were there not graves enough in Egypt that thou broughtest us here, to perish in the wilderness?"

But Korah's calm, powerful voice carried even further:

"This is what we always said to him in Egypt. 'Let us serve the Egyptians!' Is it not better to serve the Egyptians than to perish in the desert?"

The words "perish in the wilderness" fell like poison into the ears of the people. The panic intensified, and now a wailing arose, the wailing of beaten slave hordes:

"What hast thou done to us? Why didst thou bring us out of Egypt?"

The danger which Moses now feared was not the approach of the Egyptians, but something more deadly—the work of Korah, Dathan, and Abiram. It was they who threatened to undo all his work. He could see the Bnai Israel turning in an instant, streaming toward the Egyptians, imploring them to take them back as slaves. And now Moses did something he had not dared to do hitherto. He took upon himself the responsibility of Jehovah, even before he had received a command, before he knew how God intended to deal with the Bnai Israel or the Egyptians.

With two powerful arms he flung aside Korah and his aids and thrust his way into the center of the wailing camp. Towering head and shoulders above the mass, he called out in a voice which rang with confidence and power:

"Fear not! You will yet see the help which Jehovah will bring you this day. Even as you see the Egyptians this day, so you shall never see them again. The Lord will do battle for you today. Be silent and wait!"

It was Moses who spoke! Moses, who knew the will of God! He spoke in the name of God! And though the Egyptian hosts drew nearer, and the thunder of hoofs and chariot wheels was clearly audible, the Israelites became calm.

Jehovah would do battle for them. Moses had spoken in his name.

Only when calm had been restored did Moses withdraw from the camp. He went to the edge of the sea, threw himself on his knees before the swelling waters, and lifted his mighty voice:

"Lord God! Lord God! Look upon our need. I have spoken in Thy name. In Thy name I reassured them. Lord God, tell me what to do."

And this time he heard a voice, not in his heart, as hitherto, but sounding in his ear: the voice of God, which he knew so well:

"Why criest thou unto Me? Tell the Bnai Israel to go forward!"

Then, after an interval, the voice spoke again:

"And thou, lift up the staff which is in thy hand upon the waters, and divide them, and the Bnai Israel shall enter into the dryness in the midst of the sea. And I will harden the hearts of the Egyptians, and they will follow after the Bnai Israel. And I will be glorified through Pharaoh and through all his hosts, his chariots, and his horsemen. And the Egyptians will know that I am the Lord."

Like a flash the unrevealed intent, which lay in the words of

Jehovah, was made clear to the eager perception of Moses. First God had commanded him to bid the Bnai Israel advance; then afterward He had told him to lift up his staff upon the waters. It was God's will that the Israelites should advance into the sea before it had been split. It was God's desire that thereby the Israelites should show their faith in Him. It was His desire that the Israelites should thereby contribute their portion to the redemption and liberation, demonstrating that they were now the sons of freedom, ready to plunge into the sea for Him. And Moses kept the thing in his heart.

Meanwhile the clouds of dust had drawn still nearer, the galloping of hoofs, the thunder of wheels, came still more clearly. In another instant the clouds would open and disclose the Egyptians. But the clouds did not open. On the contrary, they became thicker and heavier; they accumulated in smoking folds, and remained hanging, a pall of ever-increasing darkness, between the Israelites and the Egyptians. It was as if an angel of the Lord had erected a terrifying wall of smoke between the encampment and the army.

Pharaoh could no longer see the encampment. He issued the command to dismount for the night.

But no darkness fell on the encampment of the Israelites. There the stars shone with a radiance which filled heaven and earth with brightness.

Now Moses did as God had commanded and lifted up his staff upon the sea.

Suddenly a mighty east wind began to blow and to drive the waters together. Like a pack of wild dogs let loose on a flock of sheep, the winds snapped and hissed and howled at the scurrying waves; and as the waters fled, terrified and foaming, before the onslaught, they gradually divided and began to rear themselves in two towering walls to right and left. It seemed as though, under the fierce pressure of the rushing air, the water had become thick and viscous; and between the two walls there was a flatness. But the flatness was not yet that of dry land; it was a flatness of water still deep enough to engulf human beings.

So the waters remained almost throughout the night. The children of Israel gazed with awe on the gigantic spectacle, and they were aware beyond all shadow of a doubt that something miraculous was taking place. But as yet it did not spell their rescue. Moses, whose custom it was to lead the host like a pillar of fire, did not advance as yet into the water. He was waiting for something.

Moses was indeed waiting for something. He was waiting for another miracle; he was waiting for their life to be divided as the waters were divided; he was waiting for the great division between slavery and freedom. He did not advance before the children of Israel because he wanted them to obey blindly the will of God and enter the waters before these had been wholly divided. He issued the command which God had instructed him to issue. He bade them march forward into the deep swamp between the walls of water, and he stationed himself on the edge to mark how the children of Israel obeyed the command of God.

Here and there one moved forward; but no sooner had he sunk in as far as the knee than he turned and fled back. And Moses waited obstinately, and his thoughts were sharp and hard: "Are they worthy of the miracle? If they do not go in, they are slaves, and they will not be redeemed." And the people too was thinking, thinking wildly and wondering. Something marvelous was happening before their eyes, and yet their rescue was not at hand. Men pushed their neighbors forward, and themselves remained where they were. The people began to be afraid. The night was passing, and in the morning Pharaoh would discover them. And Moses stood there like a pillar of marble, his mighty head uplifted to heaven, his face steeped in moonlight. His lips moved, and prayer welled up in his heart:

"O God, work thy miracle with Israel!"

And then it happened. A man sprang forward from the host, pulling his wife and child with him. He came to the water's edge and cried out:

"Sons of Israel! Show now that you are sons of freedom, and that you are worthy of the redemption. Come! Let us go forward into the sea to meet the God of Israel!"

He advanced. The water rose to his knees. He still advanced. A wave rolled toward him, washed over his thighs; still he advanced, leading wife and child by the hands.

Then a second followed; then ten more; then hundreds. . . . No, they were no longer blind cattle, driven forward by terror. They were freemen, advancing of their own accord and will. Their bundles on their shoulders, their little ones in their arms, they plunged forward into the water. And now the whole sea front was in motion: flocks and herds and human beings. A sound of singing went up, and jubilant cries: "God of Israel!" The first man was up to his breast in the water. He did not pause. He had snatched the little one on to his shoulders, and he still advanced. His wife followed, a bundle on her back. They advanced and the host followed.

The water came up to their throats, up to their lips. And then it happened.

The sea trembled from end to end, as though a mountain had burst in its midst. The two walls of water moved away from each other, and between them a flat, hard path lay, dry and firm. The water retained its own nature, even though it was piled in walls; the children of Israel could see the fish swimming in it. And the earth under their feet had the nature of earth, with the worms and grasses which grow on the earth. For the remainder of the night they marched along the dry pathway, with their children, their possessions, and their cattle. Moses stood at the water's edge, his staff in his hand; at his side stood the youth Joshua, his chosen servant. And only when the last of the host had entered did Moses and Joshua leave the soil of Egypt and follow after.

The morning star had risen, and now began to pale. The dust cloud which had settled like a pall over the Egyptians dissolved, and Pharaoh beheld the children of Israel not as he had expected, wallowing in the waves, but marching on a dry path in the heart of the sea, with a wall of water on either side.

To the surrogate Pharaoh who led the Egyptians only one interpretation of the event was possible. This was Ra, intervening for his hosts, and creating a dry path in the midst of the swampy sea, so that they might ride down the enemy. Indeed, was not Ra now emerging in the heavens, to give them the signal?

"After me! See! Ra has dried the deeps for us! He commanded the waters and they made a path for us, that we may overtake his enemies."

Cries broke from the ranks:

"Ra! Thou hast commanded the sea to divide! Ra in his own flesh!"

"Ra goes before us in his heavenly chariot!"

"After me!"

And Pharaoh, at the head of the host, galloped into the waters; and the hosts of chariots followed.

This time Moses had believed that when the Egyptians beheld the miracle of the divided sea, they would be terrified, just as Pharaoh had been terrified momentarily by the slaying of the first-born and had let the children of Israel go. But now, bringing up the rear of the advancing Israelites, he turned and saw the Egyptians, blind with hatred and lust of revenge, rushing forward into the heart of the sea. The horses, refreshed by a night's rest, shot fire and foam from their nostrils. The faces of the horsemen and charioteers were like torches. Already the bowmen had stretched their weapons and were pointing the arrows at the backs of the Israelites.

And Moses, whose heart was filled with God, heard the voice once more:

"Stretch out thy hand upon the sea, that the waters may come back on the Egyptians, upon their chariots and their horsemen."

And Moses stretched out his hand upon the sea.

But the walls did not collapse on the Egyptians, as Moses expected. They began to melt. It was like the thawing of a winter sea. Gusts of water fell here and there, flooding the pathway which had been dry a moment before. A thick mud spread under the wheels of the chariots, which began to sink. The horses reared and pulled, lifting their hoofs with difficulty out of the slime. The Egyptians were now in the heart of the sea, sunk in mud, trapped between walls of water, which would soon swallow them up.

"No, Pharaoh, this is not the god Aton against whom thou leadest us to do battle! Thou hast deceived us! This is Jehovah, the God of Israel, who fights against us here, as he fought against us in Egypt!"

"It is Jehovah, not Aton! Back! Let us flee!"

These were the last words heard from the Egyptians before the walls collapsed and overwhelmed them.

When Moses issued, the last of the Israelites, on the farther shore, he flung himself on his knees and sang a song of praise to Jehovah:

> "The Lord is a man of war,
> The Lord is His name!
> Pharaoh's chariots and his host has He cast into
> the sea,

174

And his chosen captains
Are sunk in the Sea of Reeds."

Later tradition added that when Moses sang his song of triumph and praise to the Lord, it was taken up not only by the host which had witnessed the miracle, but by the unborn children in the bodies of their mothers. But when the heavenly hosts, too, began to sing the song of triumph, God turned to them, saying:

"My people, the creation of My hands, are drowning in the waters, and you sing songs of praise to Me?"

The angels stopped singing, and in that same instant Moses broke off his song and did not end it.

PART II

CHAPTER ONE

NOW at last they were free, sons of freedom on the farther shore of the Sea of Reeds, on the rim of the wilderness of Shur.

The timbrels and cymbals still clashed in the hands of the women; still the wild figures rotated in joyous dance about Miriam. Some women blew out their cheeks, then expelled the air with an explosive sound; others shrilled in high nasal tones, or with a gurgling cry, and called out in chorus with Miriam:

> "I will sing unto the Lord,
> For He is highly exalted;
> The horse and his rider
> Has He flung into the sea."

Meanwhile the men had more pressing affairs. The swelling waters of the Sea of Reeds were casting up on the shore the bodies of the Egyptian warriors, clad in copper armor, the officers adorned with golden chains set with precious stones. More precious than the gold and silver were the quivers full of arrows, suspended by straps from the shoulders of the corpses, and the short swords on their thighs. The older men made for the gold and silver, but the younger ones fastened on the weapons, the bows, the swords, the shields. Every piece of iron, every copper clasp, every leather strap or piece of harness was gathered up; these things would be useful in the desert. They went into the swampy water up to their necks and pulled out what they could. One group of young men harnessed themselves to a half-buried chariot and hauled it ashore. The copper-covered wheels and the golden ornaments testified to the high battle record of the dead warrior.

There seemed to be no bounds to the wealth which the Egyptians had carried into battle: it was as if they had taken with them all the golden and bronze images of their gods, all the teraphim and figurines of their temples, to help them defeat the god Aton who had returned in the form of Jehovah; numberless were the purple wrappings and silken scarves which the Israelites took from the waves. In vain did Moses command them to abandon the Egyptian treasures and to set out once more; he could not pull them away from the shore. In the frenzy of acquisition they forgot the purpose of the redemption, forgot the miracle of the liberation.

Finally the sign itself appeared, God's sign, the illumined cloud which had preceded them ever since they had left Goshen. This sign there was no ignoring; when it moved forward the children of Israel moved with it; when it became stationary they paused.

The gold-lined cloud, which in the setting sun took on the color of incandescent amber, moved forward now: not on the straight line across the desert toward Kadesh-barnea and the land Canaan, the goal of the journey, but downward toward the Suez arm of the Red Sea and toward the wilderness of Sin. Moses knew what this meant. It meant that the children of Israel were to proceed into the peninsula of Sinai, whither God had told him to bring them that they might serve Him on the mountain.

In the bags which they carried on their backs they still had the flat cakes of unleavened dough, which they had baked hastily in the sun, and the jars of oil and honey they had taken along in the first pride of their liberation from slavery. Laden with these, and with the weapons of the Egyptian warriors, they followed Moses into the wilderness.

On the third day they came to the gulf of the Red Sea, where the bitter waters of Marah emptied, and there Moses paused for rest.

In the night he went out into the encampment to see the Bnai Israel as they rested.

Closest to him of all his aides, nearer to him even than his brother Aaron, was the youthful Joshua, whom he kept always at his side. In him Moses had found a heart filled with faith in Jehovah, a will to freedom, and boundless loyalty. He took Joshua with him now when he went out in the night through the encampment of Israel.

In the bright starlight he saw them lying on their baggage—men, women, children, spread out along the shores of the broad Lakes of Bitter Waters. Farther than the eye could reach stretched the dark figures scattered on the white sand. They lay side by side, young and old, their fowl, their flocks, their goats enclosed in the family circle. And such was the multitude of man and beast that Moses could not take them all in.

He marveled at the number of children and young people. Pharaoh had not succeeded in uprooting the seed of Abraham. What mother had succored them and brought them up in secret? Surely it had been none other than the God of Israel, who had shielded them from the Egyptian destroyer and had guarded and nourished them. And now God would be again their nourisher, their shepherd.

Moses stood still for a while, sunk in deep and troubling thought.

"How great now is the number of strangers who have come with the Bnai Israel?" he suddenly asked Joshua.

"At first there went out with us from Egypt a great mixed multitude of alien slaves," answered Joshua. "At the Sea of Reeds, when they perceived the Egyptians in pursuit, many of them ran by roundabout paths back to Egypt. Part of them remained with us and with us passed through the Sea of Reeds."

"Those that believed in the God of Israel, and put their trust in him, are part of ourselves," said Moses. "There shall be no distance between them and the Israelites, and there shall be one law for the Israelite and the stranger."

"This Aaron has already proclaimed in thy name," said Joshua.

"Not in my name, but in the name of the Lord God," answered Moses, sternly.

After a pause he asked:

"The bread which the Bnai Israel brought with them—how many days will it last?"

"Some of them consumed all their provision by the time they reached the Sea of Reeds. But some still have supplies of vegetables, eggs, fowl, honey. As yet there is little hunger in the camp. But there is thirst, and the children suffer. The mothers have tried to quench the thirst of the little ones with the waters of the lakes, but the water is bitter, it cannot be drunk. If they try to sweeten it with honey, the water spoils the honey, and itself remains bitter. There is already some murmuring among the people. We have tried to quieten them with the assurance that God will soon slake their thirst, but the murmuring against thee grows stronger."

Moses meditated, and said to himself: "Why against me? Am I God?" And to Joshua he said, aloud:

"Concerning the unleavened bread, which the Bnai Israel took with them out of Egypt: it shall be a law and a commandment that

the Bnai Israel shall eat unleavened bread together with the Passover lamb, when they will celebrate the redemption on the fourteenth day of the month in which they went out of Egypt: it shall
be an eternal memorial of the wonders which God wrought for
them."

"Thy brother Aaron and the priests are working out the details
of this commandment, a fixed order and ritual for the observance
of the Passover sacrifice."

"Aaron and the priests are reworking God's commandment?"
said Moses, in astonishment.

"Yes; they are ordaining who may eat of the Passover sacrifice
and who may not; and how it shall be eaten; the flesh shall not be
taken outside, and no bone of the sacrifice shall be broken; further,
how the Bnai Israel shall eat the unleavened bread when they will
come into their own land, and how many days they shall eat it."

For a while Moses uttered no word. Then he lifted his massive
head to the heavens, and his mighty face was illumined by the starlight. He spoke to Joshua:

"There shall be a new order touching the laws of God; and it
shall not be established by the priests, but by God. And it shall not
be recorded by the priests, but by the chosen of the elders of Israel,
even as it issues from the mouth of God. A law and commandment
must be established, as soon as God will have sent water to the
congregation which He has liberated. For the shepherd does not
abandon his flock, and he leads it not into the wilderness without
knowing there will be water for the sheep; and from this day forth
Jehovah is the shepherd of His flock. And the Lord will show us
the bread which we shall eat and the water which we shall drink,
when the time comes for it." And having spoken thus, Moses left
Joshua and went into his tent.

He did not sleep that night. He waited for the word of God, to
show him how he was to nourish this mighty multitude, which he
had led out of Egypt. It was clear to him that the feeding of such
a multitude could be accomplished only by a miracle of God, and
He alone could perform it. God had not told him in Egypt to instruct the children of Israel concerning provision for the journey
in the desert. Even the Passover sacrifice He had commanded them
to consume in the night of the exodus, and to leave nothing for the
morning, but to burn whatever remained over. There was not to be
any preparation of provision whatsoever; the cakes of dough were

to be left unleavened and dried hastily in the sun. Jehovah—He who had drawn Israel out of Egypt—Jehovah Himself would provide them plentifully with food and drink in the desert. From that day forth He was their father, who would take thought for them.

It would surely have been easier for Moses if God had always shown him beforehand what he was to do. But it was God's will that the children of Israel have the utmost faith in Him, that they follow Him blindly, as the flock follows the shepherd. And even as it had been at the dividing of the Sea of Reeds, when God had desired that the Bnai Israel enter the waters before He divided them, even so He was doing in the matter of the bread and water of the congregation of wanderers, until their need became great and they called to him as children call to their father. For it was God's desire to have the children of Israel know that He Himself and He alone was their nourisher, on Him alone they were dependent in all things, since they had agreed to obey His word, to renounce the bread of slavery from the hand of Pharaoh, and to go after Him in the desert, in a land that was not sown.

Now Moses had once conducted an Egyptian army through the desert, and he knew well what it meant to provision a multitude during a long journey through desert land. He knew of the laborious preparations which went on for months before the expedition set out, of the caravans of camels and asses, laden with water and with many varieties of food. Yet on this occasion he had proceeded blindly into the desert, leading this army of freed slaves, with their wives and children, with their flocks and herds—making not the slightest provision for the journey. He well knew that the Bnai Israel, like other nomads, must henceforth be nourished by the desert. And this could come only through a miracle of God. Never before had the desert been called upon to provide for such a multitude.

But all the things that had happened to him since God revealed Himself to him—had they not all been miracles? The plagues which God had sent upon Pharaoh, the separation of the Bnai Israel from the plagues, the slaying of the first-born of Egypt—and then, finally, the splitting of the sea. God had taken this people to Himself for a destined purpose. He had not redeemed it as it were in a moment of caprice, but toward a certain end. He was leading it into the wilderness toward the mountain of Sinai. This people belonged to God alone. He was its nourisher, and when the moment was ripe He would show Moses what was to be done.

But was this known to the children of Israel and their leaders? Bitter had been the bread of Egypt, moistened with tears of anguish: but they could count on it with certainty, even as they could count on the lash which overhung them. Uncertain was the bread of freemen, and the believer had only his faith. And it was God's will that they eat the uncertain bread of freemen and believers. Would they understand this?

So Moses meditated in his heart all night long, until a far-off confusion, like a sound of distant thunder, coming to his ears from the camp, startled him out of his thoughts. At the entrance of his tent stood his brother Aaron, pale of countenance and frightened— and behind him others of the leaders of Israel.

"What has happened?" asked Moses.

"Go forth and see," answered Aaron.

Moses stepped out of his tent.

The encampment was empty. The Bnai Israel had left everything where it was and with a single impulse had made for the shore of the great lake. Moses saw them, from the distance, drawing water from the lake, drawing it in utensils, or in their cupped hands, drinking it and offering it to their children. And on the instant Moses had a vision of a flock which he had led into the desert; he saw the sheep, parched with long thirst, arriving at a water hole, he saw them thrusting their nuzzles wildly into the water, heard them swallowing, gurgling with fierce joy. But the thirsty Bnai Israel on the shore of the lake were not drinking with the quivering abandonment of the flock in his vision; they drank with distorted faces, obstinately, reluctantly. The children spewed back the water into the hands of their mothers, and split the air with their protests and laments. Even the sheep twisted their heads away from the water and bleated pitifully. The men held in their rage, and when they beheld Moses, they left the wives and children and ran toward him. In a moment Moses stood in the midst of a forest of outstretched hands and uplifted beards. Angry eyes flashed at him and a single reproach burst from a thousand throats:

"What shall we drink?"

In the heart of Moses a great cry ascended to God. He lifted his arms and said: "Shepherd! Shepherd! Thy flock is thirsty!"

He knew that God would come to his aid; and He would do it, as always, through His already created instruments, through that which had been created to give water to the Bnai Israel. He saw the Bnai Israel drinking water, not from wells which they had discovered, but from the bitter lake, and he said to them:

"The water of this sea has been created for another purpose—and not for the slaking of thirst. Why do you not seek out the wells?"

"We have found wells, but the water is bitter. We cannot swallow it."

"Take me to the wells."

They led him to the wells which they had found. Moses tasted the water. It was bitter, heavy, undrinkable. And then he remembered something which he had often seen in the wilderness of Midian; he had seen his father-in-law Jethro "healing" the waters of bitter wells with the leaves of laurel trees. The rich, sharp taste of the laurel leaves killed the saltiness of the well water, which issued near the sea or from the midst of salt fields. The Midianite priests it was who called it "healing" the waters, purifying them of their repellent taste.

Where was he to obtain laurel leaves in the wilderness of Shur? The wilderness was naked and empty of growth; moreover, the laurel flourished only in the moist shadows of oases.

He looked about—and there were laurels growing before him. God Himself had planted them. They were small and scraggy, to be sure; withered and eaten by the wind, but laurel leaves for all that. It seemed to him that they were beckoning and speaking to him, telling him that God had planted them here for the healing of the waters.

Swiftly he ran over, plucked a few laurel twigs and threw them into the well. A moment later he saw the white essence exude from the soaked leaf and mingle with the water; and the water became clear and transparent.

"Take and drink. Jehovah has healed the water for you."

And they drank; and the water was sweet and slaked their thirst.

Later in the day, when the congregation had drunk its fill, there came before Moses and Aaron the representatives of the people.

These were still the former overseers of the slave time in Egypt, with Korah and Dathan and Abiram at their head, together with a few of the elders and spokesmen of the tribes. For the representation of the tribes had not yet been reordered. Moses was waiting until the assembling of the people before Sinai, where he would receive the laws and commandments from the mouth of God. The leaders of the representation were still the Bnai Levi; and the first among the leaders were still Korah and his right-hand men.

It was only now, they told Moses, that they had bethought themselves and perceived that they had left Egypt all too hastily. They had not had the time to prepare food and water and other supplies in sufficient measure for so great a multitude proceeding into a wilderness. Had Moses and Aaron, the leaders and guides in this journey, seen to it that the congregation should have a sufficient supply of food and water? If not, how did Moses and Aaron propose to make good the deficiency? The preparations, which they themselves had made—they argued—had only been sufficient for the originally proposed three-day festival of sacrifice. But now Jehovah had led Israel through the sea, and Moses had turned away from the road which ran straight to the promised land; he was taking the people, instead, into the Sinai desert, where there was neither food nor water. They, the representatives of the people, therefore wanted to know how he would feed them, and where was the provision which a Pharaoh took with him when he led an expedition into the wilderness? And how long did he count on staying in the wilderness before they would reach the lands to which, as Moses reported, God had bidden him lead the children of Israel? The exodus from Egypt had been so hasty that they had not had the time to prepare and to provide for all the needs of the Bnai Israel.

Moses was standing before his tent, confronting the group of Korah, Dathan, and Abiram and their followers. His great eyes were turned on them and it was as if the lightning of God flickered in them; it was as if God's word broke from his tongue:

"*You* prepare? *You* provide? Who are you, then, that you should prepare and provide for the needs of Israel? Who has provided for the needs of Israel till now? They are provided for by the One, the only One, the God of Israel, Jehovah, the God of Abraham, Isaac, and Jacob. Think you that He is a Pharaoh, who must carry provision for his hosts on the backs of camels, with caravans of donkeys? The heavens are His, and the earth is His. He can command the clouds to send down rain and make the desert blossom like the garden of Eden. Wherever He is, which is everywhere, He has His servants, His creatures, the creation of His hands. He can command the crags to open their hearts and send forth springs of living waters. He can make bread rain down from heaven. He is our nourisher and our provider."

"Assuredly, assuredly, God redeemed us from the yoke of Pharaoh. But those He led out of Egypt are not angels; they are men. Those whom thou conductest into the wilderness are not heavenly creatures; they are children of the earth, who cannot live without their daily bread. When they are hungry, they cry out, and when they see their children thirsting, they weep. In Egypt, though their labors might be never so bitter, they were assured of their daily bread, betimes, and of good water when they thirsted. Now, when thou leadest them into an unknown wilderness, where the earth is stone and sand, where the heavens are blazing copper and its inhabitants the snake and the scorpion, we have the right to ask what promise has God made thee concerning provision for us. We have the right to know that our children will not perish of hunger and thirst before our eyes in this monstrous land which is without food and without water," said Korah in the name of his circle.

"God has given me no promise save the promise of the Law; saying: 'If thou wilt listen to the word of the Lord, thy God, and wilt obey Me, and do what is righteous in My eyes; if thou wilt hearken to My commandments and preserve My laws, then the plagues which I have sent upon the Egyptians shall not come near thee.' For know that the Lord God Jehovah took you out of Egypt not for your sakes, but for a higher destiny: that you might become His chosen people, which shall establish His law and His righteousness in the world He has created. And it is because of this destiny that I lead you now to Mount Sinai, so that you may hear His will from His mouth. You shall be His holy people, and God shall be your father; and like children shall you entrust yourselves to your father in heaven, and to Him alone shall you bring your needs and wants; and you shall obey Him blindly and have faith in Him. If you do not so, wherein are you better than the Egyptians from whom He has redeemed you? And as He has punished the Egyptians, so will He punish you. For as God can heal the waters, even so can He cause them to sicken, as He did in Egypt. Grave these words in your hearts and write them upon your foreheads. And now, return to your ranks, and prepare the people to go forward. I see the pillar of fire which leads us, and it moves in the direction of Elim."

Crushed by his words, the leaders went back to their stations and carried out the order. It was another Moses who had addressed them; the voice of Jehovah spoke through his mouth.

But Korah, attended by Dathan and Abiram, remained before Moses. Massive, broad boned, Korah stood firm and stared at Moses. He could not withdraw his gaze from the fiery eyes—yet he raised his voice in admonition, and said:

"Moses, Moses, may all that thou sayest come to pass. But if, God forbid, it be otherwise, the blood of His people shall be upon thy head. For thou hast led them, men and women and children, sheep and cattle, into the wilderness, without food and without drink."

For a time it seemed as though Moses was wholly justified by the event, and that he had known what he was about when he gave his promise in the name of Jehovah. It seemed for a time that God was making the desert blossom like a garden of Eden for the children of Israel and making the earth break forth in streams of living water. There where the winds lifted waves of sand, palm trees grew, heavily laden with dates; and where the earth was covered with massive rocks, springs and wells abounded. For at Elim, by the broad salt gulf of the Red Sea, a half-day march from Marah, they found an oasis and green meadows overshadowed by clusters of palms—an oasis of twelve springs of fresh water, as though God had provided a separate spring for each tribe.

There the Bnai Israel sojourned a while and rested from the fiery desert sands.

CHAPTER TWO

IT came to pass as Korah had foretold. From the oasis of Elim the children of Israel went forth into the wilderness of Sin; and here the desolate stretches which opened before them were altogether different from any desert they had seen till then. In the wilderness of Shur their herds and flocks had still found cactus shrubs and thorns to nibble at; here and there the coarse growths had protruded from the sand. But the wilderness of Sin was locked under a covering of stone, a reddish seal on the mouth of the earth. Crags of granite in the form of horrible monsters towered about them, reaching with their frightful heads into the blue-blazing sky. Terrace rose beyond terrace, making the way ever harder for the women and children. The herds and flocks faltered, tormented by hunger and thirst. They thrust their nuzzles between the stones, seeking a blade of grass or a drop of moisture. The sheep lay down, refusing to go farther, and the men had to drag them wearily along.

At intervals the stony walls parted to reveal a little valley once hollowed out by springing water. Man and beast flung themselves in that direction hoping to find the spring bursting from the hills; but where they found a cascade it was of sandy stones, falling with a dry clatter into the hot troughs. The desert, big with sandstone, gave birth to granite.

Toward the evening of their third day in the wilderness, they came to a stony valley descending from a plateau in the midst of the heights. They found nothing but some measure of relief from the arrowy rays of the sun, which had stung them all day long. Broken by the journey, they threw themselves down amidst their packs and their cattle.

A month had now passed since Moses had taken them out of Egypt. For a month they had been in the wilderness, and in that time they had consumed the last scrap of the provisions they had brought with them. The fowl, the unleavened cakes, the jars of oil and honey and wine, the baskets of vegetables were gone; some had even taken to slaughtering their flocks. Most of them, however, set their teeth, and kept their hands off the sheep and goats, the sole source of nourishment for the children. With the inherited instinct of shepherds they clung to their flocks as the foundation of their livelihood in time to come; with obstinate foresight they endured their hunger and shut their eyes to the sufferings of their children, always hoping that the next day, or the day after that, God would lead them into rich meadow lands, as Moses kept repeating that He would. But they were so exhausted by the journey through the first deserts, and now by the hideous experience of the wilderness of Sin, that they began to despair that they would ever reach the land of milk and honey.

In the night Moses heard the murmuring of the children of Israel. It was no longer the cry of protest which had gone up at Marah, when they had asked: "What shall we drink?" At Marah it had been a demand by men who believed that Moses could help them: he had only to turn to Jehovah and Jehovah would direct him to fresh water. The cry at Marah had resounded with faith in Jehovah; they had come like children to a father, asking: "What shall we drink?" Here, in the wilderness of Sin, among the hideous mountains, in a land which wore a stony covering, Moses heard a weeping of despair ascending from the shadowed groups of men and women huddling to their children and their flocks. It was a sinister lamenting which told of abandoned hope, of fathomless despair. These were not the freemen of the earlier days; these were slaves hankering for the slave bread of Egypt.

Then Moses sent for his brother Aaron and said: "Let us go out to them."

"They are in great agitation. Some have gathered into groups, and they call us by evil names."

"Shall we hide ourselves from them? Come."

They went out into the congregation. And now Moses saw that they were no longer resting. Men stood in groups, disputing hotly, flinging their arms about. Here and there a furious shout was heard, not like words falling from human lips, but like stones hurled at the heads of Aaron and Moses. The shouting and the protest were bearable; not so was the quiet weeping of the women who, huddled by the baggage, were trying to comfort the little ones. The heart of Moses became heavy within him.

Before long it became known to the congregation that Moses and Aaron were in its midst; and soon the two brothers were surrounded; they stood in the center of a circular wall compact of human bodies: black faces in the black night, red-flaming eyes which threatened, a forest of angry fists. No Korah, or Dathan, or Abiram this, but the people itself.

"What did you want of us? Would that we had died by the hand of the Lord in Egypt, when we sat by the fleshpots, when we ate bread to the full, before you dragged us into the wilderness to kill us with hunger."

Bitter words these were; and the worst was this, that they were right. The heart of Moses was stabbed by pain for the hunger of the people rather than because they murmured against him.

"Not we brought you out of Egypt, but the Lord. And the Lord knows that you are hungry and thirsty, and He will help you. We are even as you: if you starve, we starve with you, if you fail from thirst, we too fail from thirst. Not against us do you murmur, but against God."

"But who will give us to eat? Must we wait until we see our children dead at our feet? And how will He feed us? Look at this great people stretched out here in the wilderness. Will He make the desert bear bread for us?"

"Has the hand of Jehovah grown too short to feed you? He who split the sea for you can split the heavens and rain bread on you. But when He will do so, I know not, for He has not told me. And how He will do it, I know not, either. All I know is that He who took you out of Egypt will not let you perish of hunger in the wilderness."

"Thou knowest not when He will do it, and how, yet thou hast led us into a stony desert? Why dost thou not turn to Him? Why askest thou not how long He will let us hunger?"

"Who am I that I should tell Jehovah that His people hungers? Does he not know it Himself? Does He not look down from the heavens, and does He not see your pain, as He saw your pain and heard your cries when you were in Egypt? Not to me do you belong, but to Jehovah, and not I will give you to eat, but Jehovah Himself. Only He will answer you," said Moses, and turned from the people.

Hardly had Moses entered his tent than he heard Jehovah's voice in his heart. And the voice told him that Jehovah would give the people food and when He would do it. Jehovah had withheld food from the people to prove it, to test it, whether it would go in the way of His law or not.

And so Moses and Aaron were able to bring the good tidings to the Bnai Israel.

In the morning they stood again in the midst of the enraged congregation. Hungry eyes were fixed on them, but now the hearts which confronted the murmurers were filled with hope and faith. Marvelous were the words which the Bnai Israel heard, words which no one had ever heard before, concerning things which no one had ever dreamed of.

On the wings of eagles had He carried them across the sea, and from heaven He would send down bread.

The soil of the desert of Sin was sealed with a seal of stone, but the heavens would be changed into a field; the heavens would split, as Moses had told them, and God would send down a rain of bread.

"At even you shall know that the Lord brought you out of the land of Egypt; in the morning you shall see the glory of the Lord. God has heard your cry and has hearkened to your murmuring. And see, He comes hastening to help you."

Aaron pointed into the wilderness; and the congregation turned.

A flaming cloud had distilled downward out of the zenith and was hanging motionless over the desert. It was not a cloud of smoke and sand such as they were accustomed to seeing in the desert, but a dazzle of amber brightness, shading off into all the colors of the rainbow: and the shape of it was like a finger of the hand of God, pointing as if in affirmation of the words of Moses and Aaron.

"Toward dusk you shall eat flesh, and in the morning you shall be filled with bread; and you shall know that I am the Lord your God."

And now the whole congregation was seated on the reddish stony terraces of the wilderness of Sin; heads of families sat with their wives and children, and their faces were upturned to the heavens whence bread was to rain down upon them. Their eyes no longer burned with hunger and fever; the fire in them was the holy fire of faith in Jehovah.

And Moses waited with them for the bread of Jehovah. He had known from the first instant that God had taken these slaves away from Pharaoh so that they might become His servants. Henceforth God, not Pharaoh, commanded them; and as a master must care for the nourishment of his servants, so Jehovah would care for the nourishment of Israel. This sending of bread from heaven would be the sign and symbol of God's Lordship over Israel; and the children of Israel would know to whom they belonged and whom they had to serve.

For this reason Moses waited with impatience for the fulfillment of the miracle, knowing beforehand that now, as heretofore, God would work His will through the medium of already created things. Together they sat, Moses and the congregation, on the baking rocks of the wilderness of Sin, and watched the heavens throughout the whole day.

Slowly, lingeringly, the sun slid away behind the enormous hills, kindling a coppery-red brightness on the stony summits. The entire circle of the horizon caught fire. It was as though the ring of mountains was turning into molten metal in the furnace of the heavens. Meanwhile in the valley below, on the lower slopes of the craggy walls, bluish veils of shadow fell and wrapped themselves over the level stretches; the far-scattered groups of the congregation sank into the surrounding dimness and became one with the dun mass.

Then there was heard a twittering of birds. The birds themselves were not seen; only shadows of wings fluttered against the gleaming upper walls.

The congregation rose like one man, and ten thousand necks were craned upward. The twittering became louder, the shadows on the upper walls denser and heavier. Then suddenly they perceived the first rank of an immense flock of birds. These were not the haggard gulls which infest the shores of the Red Sea. No starvelings, these, but the fat, familiar quail, the homely quail of the Goshen swamps, with the feather crown on its head, with thick, appetizing folds of meat under its brown plumage. How did they get here, these denizens of the reeds of Goshen, which the Egyptians hunted so eagerly? They came flying across the mountains and deserts, rank after rank, until the multitude of their plump, brown-feathered bodies hid the upper air. And in an instant they descended and fell at the feet of the hungry congregation.

They needed neither arrows, nor spears, nor hunting sacks. The birds came down to the doors of their tents, begging to be captured, to be taken barehanded, to be dealt with according to God's command.

A jubilant cry went up from the midst of the congregation. There was running to and fro, a stretching out of hands, a snatching of birds, gay laughter, and delighted shouting:

"This is the flesh which Jehovah has sent us!"

"The flesh toward dusk!"

And in a little while there was a rapid plucking of feathers, so that a brown drift went up over the encampment, accompanied by joyous laughter. Where did they suddenly find twigs and wood in the dry wilderness? Here and there a little fire danced in the darkness of the night. Families were gathered cheerfully about the fires, mouths watered at the sight of the roasting birds, at the smell of the fat dripping into the flames.

Sleep came late that night to the encampment. They stuffed themselves with the tasty flesh till they were exhausted; their eyes closed of themselves; but they tried to stay awake for the rain of bread which Jehovah had promised them for the morning.

"Flesh without bread is nothing. It's the bread, after all, that satisfies, it's the bread that fills the stomach. And don't think God is going to send you a potful of meat into your tent every night. Good enough if we get it once a week, or even once a month. The chief thing is the bread. I'd love to see what it looks like, I'd like to know the taste of it."

"And I want to know where it will come from. Will it really come down from the heavens? If it does, it will surely have a heavenly taste."

"And don't you think that you're going to fill your sack with it, as you've filled that cage with birds."

"Let it only come—I'll know then what I shall do. I believe in the old saying: What I have in my hand is mine."

So they sat and babbled and waited for the bread. But in the end sleep overcame them and they could not keep their eyes open.

In the morning they woke in the midst of chillness. They shivered from the thick, rich dew which had settled on their bodies and on the flat stone terraces.

Soon the first pallor touched the skies, and the summits began to kindle again. It was as if the mountains were returning to the sun what they had swallowed and absorbed in the night. Bands of brightness were unfurled in the sky, and the light fell like a flood of fire over the terraces. With thousands of tongues it licked up the moisture which had settled on the stony levels; and when the mantle of dew had been licked up there was seen, covering all the rocky levels, a thin, white hoar. This hoar consisted of innumerable myriads of tiny, crystalline flowerets linked into each other like sugar crystals. The sunbeams broke against the flowerets, which dashed back the light, so that the whole valley was one brilliant dazzle. Men, women, and children gathered the hoar deposit in handfuls, and examined it wonderingly. They hesitated to put it to their lips, for the crystals looked like petrified flowerets. They carried the handfuls to each other, astonished, disappointed.

"*Man hu?* What is it?" whispering voices asked.

"*Man hu?*" other voices asked, loudly.

"*Man hu?*" It became a cry. They ran back and forth, showing each other their hands, sticky with the floweret crystals. "*Man hu?*"

Moses, meanwhile, stood in the entrance of his tent and beheld with radiant eyes how Jehovah was providing the daily bread of the Bnai Israel. He, of course, knew what it was. How many times had he not gathered, among the clefts of the rocks, or from the milky cactus leaves, the floweret crystals, a mixture of insect deposit and the thick essence of the dews? Dried in the sun, then rubbed, they yielded a sticky mealiness which could sustain man's life in the desert. How often had he not lived on them when he had tended Jethro's sheep? They were, as a rule, found only sparsely; the desert wanderer had to search diligently before he found them stuck to a rock or to a branch. The miracle of Jehovah consisted in this: that the winds and the dew had gathered the crystals from every corner of the wilderness in such quantities that they sufficed to feed a multitude. Secure in his faith that God would keep His promise and feed His people, Moses now experienced an intense delight in the manner of the fulfillment: Jehovah did it so simply; He supplied the wants of Israel through His created things, without changing the order of His nature.

"How wondrous are the ways of Jehovah!" said Moses, in his heart. And to the Bnai Israel, who held out handfuls of the mealy stuff to him, and inquired with one voice, "*Man hu?*" he said: "This is the bread which God has given you to eat."

He took a pinch of the brittle crystals, and when he rubbed it between his fingers it became a moist meal. He carried it to his mouth. The people watched him and imitated his action.

"A honey cake I have in my mouth, so sweet is the taste on my palate," cried one man, happily.

"It is kneaded in oil! Pharaoh has never tasted the like!" cried another.

"How should it come on Pharaoh's table? Are his bakers so cunning, do they know all the mysteries of the art? Jehovah has baked this bread for us."

"And I say that it tastes like the roasted white meat of a fat duck," came from a third, as he stuffed the manna into his watering mouth.

"Not a bit of it! Like a plump fish fried in oil and honey!"

"And look how much there is of it heaped on the ground! Enough to feed us for a month."

"Jehovah has steeped His congregation in bread! There it is! All you want! We'll collect sacks and sacks of it." And a man threw himself on the ground, as if to collect the manna with hands, eyes, and mouth.

But Moses warned them immediately:

"This is God's command: Let every man gather according to his need; an omer a head, for the number of souls in each family and tent—and no more. For this is the bread of Jehovah, which He has given you to eat."

As if carried on the rays of the morning sun, the news and explanation of the salvation sped from end to end of the great encampment: that white crystalline material, which the dews had left behind, and of which they knew not the name, was the bread which Jehovah had sent down from heaven. It was bread kneaded in honey and oil, Jehovah's bread. And the people ate their fill of it, smacked their lips, gathered more and more of the material, filled sacks with it, utensils, wrappings.

The overseers ran through the camp warning the gatherers—but in vain.

"An omer a head! As many souls as you are, so many omers, not more. It is Jehovah's bread, not yours. No more than an omer a head."

There were some that heeded, some that measured off an omer for each member of the family. But others went on snatching and gathering. They had already filled the cruses and baskets and sacks, which they had brought out of the tents, and still they went on gathering. But when they brought the filled sacks and baskets and cruses into the tent, and measured off the manna, there was still only an omer of it for each person! It was as Moses had said: "An omer a head shall you gather: God knows the nature of His creatures, and knows their needs. So much has He ordained for the day—not more."

But there were some who still would not rely on miracles. Miracles are not repeated, they said. And they knew only too well the meaning of hunger. Had they not just been going about with tongues hanging out? Did not the cry of their children still ring in their ears? An omer was a generous portion. No need to use it all up in one day. Half an omer a head would do. It was bread! Bread! What one didn't eat one could exchange, get a duck for it, a silver ornament. Others ate more than an omer: what would they not give for a piece of bread on the morrow?

The overseers warned them again:

"Leave nothing for the morrow. Jehovah is your provider from this day forth, and He knows you need bread daily. He will send you your measure of meal every day. Trust in Him. As He has provided you with your portion today, He will provide you to-morrow."

"But I'm the kind of man who likes to make sure. How many days were we without bread? The same thing can come to pass tomorrow. The birds have not returned, have they? The clever ones in the congregation filled their cages while they could. When I have something in my hand, I know it's mine."

"Tomorrow they'll be coming to me for a measure of meal. Jehovah will not be so good to us every day."

And the clever ones, those that took thought for the morrow, kept part of their manna. But when they came the next morning to inspect their treasure, a rank odor burst from the vessels; and in them were, instead of meal, crawling worms.

But outside, in the open valley, the earth was white again with the manna new-fallen from heaven. This time it did not linger in the sun's rays. The children of Israel had time enough to gather an omer a head in their cruses, and then the bread of Jehovah melted and vanished. Now they understood that God had His own way of providing them with their daily bread: and He would compel them to trust in Him, have faith in Him, from day to day.

When Moses learned that some of the people had ignored his

command to leave none of the manna for the next day, he became angry and said to those who were about him: "Why do you not obey the will of Jehovah your God? How long will you not believe in Him and not trust in His mercy?"

On the sixth day the children of Israel discovered that they had gathered twice as much manna as on the previous days—it came out at two omers a head. They could not understand it, and they were afraid to keep the additional omer, remembering what had happened before.

The elders of Israel came before Moses and told him what had happened, and the face of Moses became illumined with a great joy. He fell on his knees, lifted up his hands and cried:

"I thank Thee and praise Thee, God of Abraham, Isaac, and Jacob, that Thou hast fixed laws and ordinances of Thy nature. With the bread which Thou givest the Bnai Israel thou guidest them in Thy law, so that they may be worthy of becoming Thy people."

And to the elders of Israel he said:

"The bread which God sends you shall nourish not only your flesh, but your souls too. Through God's bread you will be nourished into a holy people. Mark well what God does for you. This is what God is now saying: A day of rest, a Sabbath of God, shall tomorrow be; cook and bake and prepare today, and whatever is left over, leave for tomorrow."

Filled with awe, the Bnai Israel obeyed the command. They left the extra portion of manna in their vessels, as they had been bidden; and behold, the next morning, when they opened the vessels there was no evil smell, no crawling of worms, but fresh manna.

And Moses rose and went out early and sent the elders through the camp with this message:

"Eat today of the manna which is left, for today is the Sabbath of God, and today you will find nothing in the field. Six days shall you gather, but the seventh day is God's Sabbath, and on that day you will not find anything."

And still there were the clever ones among the Bnai Israel who would not believe Moses. They thought to themselves: "But suppose we do find something? After all, how can this thing be? Every morning the dew falls, with the white flowerets: tomorrow morning it will assuredly fall, too; if not everywhere in the open, then at least in the clefts, where we find the fattest and best of them." And in fact they stole out on the Sabbath morning, and crawled on all fours looking into the narrow clefts between stones for fresh manna. But not a sign of it, not a single crystal, was there. And like disappointed thieves they stole back from the fields into their tents.

Moses heard the stormy voice of God in his heart:

"How long will you not obey my commandments?"

Moses felt shame overcome him; he threw himself to the earth:

"Be patient with them. Slaves Thou tookest out of Egypt, free-men wilt Thou bring to Sinai."

And in order that the desecration of the Sabbath might not be repeated, Moses commanded the Bnai Israel:

"See, God has given you the Sabbath. Therefore He gives you, on the sixth day, bread for two days. Let every man remain home. No one shall go out of his place on the seventh day."

And it became a law with the Bnai Israel, for all time to come, to rest on the seventh day of the week. Through the bread—which the Bnai Israel began to call manna—God revealed the Sabbath to them.

And Moses commanded Aaron, in the name of Jehovah, to take a jar and put an omer of manna into it and to place it before the Lord as a memorial throughout the generations. And this was the bread which the Bnai Israel ate in the wilderness until they came into their land.

Yet not so simple was this matter of feeding the mighty host which went out of Egypt. It is clear that Jehovah passed the Bnai Israel as it were through a fiery furnace. By hunger and privation he drove out of their hearts the slavishness of Egypt, turning them into a people fit to receive His commandments at Sinai. So the journey from the Sea of Reeds to Mount Sinai was not a long process of preparation and separation. Every advance through the wilderness was achieved by successive stages of privation, terror, and pain. It was as though Jehovah were whipping into the mind and flesh of the Bnai Israel the knowledge that, since the day they left Egypt, they were His servants, utterly dependent on Him. To Him they must turn for every mouthful of bread, from His hand drink every drop of water which kept them alive. And Moses knew all this and with a mighty hand brought them under the discipline of Jehovah, as a trainer brings a wild ass of the wilderness under the discipline of the yoke.

Moses had been in these parts more than once, in the days when he kept Jethro's sheep. He therefore knew that deeper in the wilderness of Sinai, beyond Rephidim, and at the foot of the limestone hills of Horeb, lay the richly watered vale of Paran, or Nahal-paran, as the desert folk called it. Nahal-paran had always been a bone of contention among the wandering tribes. Springs of fresh water, nourished by the snows on the summits of the copper mountains, poured down through natural stone gutters into the valley, and fructified God's garden, an oasis of green pastures, acacia trees, and date palms; and whoever possessed the place roused the envy and enmity of the others.

The Amalekites, descendants of one of Esau's grandsons, whose name they bore, were spread throughout the wilderness. They made frequent attacks on the shepherd tribes in the season when they led their flocks to the valley for pasture; sometimes they would be content with a number of sheep, sometimes they captured all the flocks and conquered the valley, where they themselves then pastured the sheep. They were no strangers to Moses, these Amalekites. His first clash with them had been on the very day of his arrival in Midian, when he had driven off a band of them from the well where Jethro's daughters were watering their sheep.

He knew, further, that the Amalekites had their scouts about the fat vale of Paran, waiting to signal the approach of shepherds and their flocks. Now whether it was because he sought to avoid a premature clash between the robber bands and the Israelites while the latter were weary from the journey in the desert, or whether it was because God had so commanded him, Moses did not, on the way to Horeb, make Paran a resting place; he chose, instead, to pause at Rephidim, which was a dry and desolate place.

No sooner had the Bnai Israel entered the stony area than they began to look for water. In Elim they had found a plentiful supply; they had filled the skins, jars, and cruses and had loaded them on their donkeys. Sparing as they had been in their use of it, their water had now given out, and here in Rephidim they were on a stony, waterless platform. They searched the cracks in the rocks, the little valleys and gulches, the occasional caves, where water would be apt to accumulate. There was not a drop. Thirst began to torment the host again. The first to suffer were the children and the flocks and herds; and the crying of the children, mingled with the bleating of the sheep, increased until the sound of it became unbearable.

They had no complaint now concerning food, for this they received every morning from the hand of God; but their thirst moved them to a new outburst of bitterness. And their complaint was not directed against Jehovah. Had they believed that God was with Moses, as He had been in Elim and elsewhere, they would have waited patiently. But they felt that they were waiting without hope, and this was impossible. In vain did the leaders come running to Moses: "The people perish from thirst!" Moses had received no command from God; he was waiting for direction. And so a rumor ran through the host: "Jehovah has abandoned Moses! Jehovah is no longer with him!" Whether it was started by the Bnai Korah, or whether it was born of itself from the bitterness of the people, that cry broke the discipline which had been created with so much labor. The wonders and mercies of the past were forgotten. Still, they considered that it was not the fault of Jehovah, Who had given them food and drink as long as He had been among them. But now, for some sin which Moses had committed, He had withdrawn himself. Moses alone was responsible for their present condition.

"Were Jehovah with us, we should not lack water. Did he not sweeten the waters of Marah for us? Jehovah is not here, He has abandoned Moses!"

"If this is so, then we are done for! We are imprisoned in the walls of the desert mountains. What shall we do?"

And Moses, standing near his tent, was suddenly surrounded; not by the leaders of the people, but by the people itself, by a wild mob of the thirsty and frightened. And again fists were stretched out against him, again teeth were bared at him.

"Give us water to drink!"

"Why do you quarrel with me? This is in Jehovah's hand. He knows your need, and He will help. Why do you try Jehovah?"

"Is Jehovah here among us, or is He not? Answer!"

And one sprang out from the crowd, reaching with his hands toward Moses:

"Why didst thou bring us out of Egypt? To slay us, me and my children and my cattle, with thirst?"

And now the mob was ready to lay hands on Moses, to strike him down. And this might have happened had it not been for the presence of Joshua and the small devoted band which he led. These were young men who had been brought up in the cave of the elders of Israel, where they had been concealed from Pharaoh's overseers. All of them had been chosen by Joshua for the spirit of freedom which burned in them. And all of them were armed with short swords, which they had taken from the Egyptians. With their powerful arms they thrust a way into the howling mob, made a guard about Moses, and brought him back to his tent.

There Moses poured out his heart to God in a great cry of sorrow and need:

"Tell me what to do with this people. In a moment they would have stoned me."

The answer came. He heard the word of God in his heart, and he knew what he had to do.

He called together the elders, took his staff of God, and went out with them. He led them to the wall of rock, and he began to search among the crags. At one point he stopped, and his massive stare settled on the stone before him. His breath became heavy, his nostrils fluttered, his eyes expanded, became brighter, fierier, laden with sanctity. Thus he stood a long time, and suddenly he perceived something in the rock: it was the ray, the ray, the ray!

"Jehovah!"

He lifted up the staff and rod of God and smote the stone with it.

"Jehovah! Jehovah! Jehovah!" was heard in a tremendous shout.

Like grain cut down by the sickle the people had fallen to the earth. In their terror and astonishment they even forgot to drink of the living water which burst from the stone.

A pool formed and widened at their feet, ran from channel to channel, filled the hollows and cracks. But they still dared not approach the water with their lips. Their thirst had been swallowed up by their awe.

"The staff of Moses!"

"The rod which smote the Egyptians!"

"The staff which is the help of Israel!"

"Jehovah is here amongst us!"

"This place shall henceforth be called Massah and Meribah, because here you tried the Lord and quarreled with Him," said Moses, and went back into his tent.

"Jehovah is with us, Jehovah is among us, everywhere, and forever," shouted the people.

CHAPTER THREE

BARELY had the children of Israel taken their first step toward freedom—even before their hunger had been sated with God's bread and their thirst slaked by the waters bursting miraculously from the rock—than there arose against them the first enemy to ignore the signs and marvels which God had wrought for them.

And strangely enough this people, which sought to block the approach to Sinai, was a close kin of the Bnai Israel, and from it one might have expected brotherly help and understanding. But it was a brother's hand which lifted the sword against them.

Before Jehovah fulfilled the promise which He gave the patriarchs concerning Israel, He fulfilled the promise concerning Ishmael and Lot and Esau. He did this through a natural course, without an Egyptian bondage and a splitting of the sea. The children of Ishmael, of Lot, and of Esau developed along the usual lines. When they had accumulated large flocks and herds in the wilderness, they set out in search of pasture; and so they passed through the phase of nomadic peoples before they acquired permanent habitations. They settled on the rim of the wilderness, in a part of the Negeb beyond Ezion-geber, and in the land of Sodom as far as the Jordan. The sanctity of their borders was confirmed in the promise of Jehovah to Abraham and Isaac. Moses knew this well, and it was never in his mind to expel the children of Esau, that is, Edom, or the children of Lot, that is, Moab, and to seize their territories.

The promise of Jehovah concerning Israel referred to the land from Jericho outward to the great sea, the land which had been settled by alien tribes, no descendants of Abraham, Isaac, or Jacob, but idolaters who had come into the country across the Carmel ranges from Tyre and Sidon, bringing with them their foul, polluting rituals of Ashdod and Moloch and their sodomitic practices and vices.

204

One of the tribes descended from a grandson of Esau was Amalek. This tribe did not pass through the cycle from wandering shepherds to settled tillers of the soil; it remained fast in the primitive nomadic stage, a robber folk preying on other nomads, passing from land to land, taking root nowhere. Now it would be found in the Negeb, now it forded the water by Ezion-geber to attack Midian, now it would climb the desert mountains and sojourn for a period near Sinai.

Moses had no intention of taking from the Amalekites even the land which they had acquired temporarily. God had not mentioned the people and their land when He spoke from the burning bush. The Amalekites, direct descendants of Abraham and Isaac, were duty bound to honor the covenant of the family tradition, the covenant which their forefather Abraham had made with Jehovah; they were duty bound to look with awe on the unknown and mighty God, Jehovah, for whom Abraham had been prepared to sacrifice his only son. Likewise, they should have obeyed certain laws and precepts, such as honoring of parents, refraining from intercourse with the nearest blood relations, not eating the flesh torn from living animals, and similar commandments and prohibitions which were faithfully observed by the other descendants of the far-off patriarch Abraham. Instead, however, they mocked Jehovah and rejected the sign of the Abrahamitic covenant, which the other descendants of Abraham held sacred; to them circumcision was a badge of shame.

They blasphemed the name of God when they mentioned Him. Their idolatry was made up of a collection of indecent rituals. They paid homage to cats and reptiles, and they abandoned themselves to the most dissolute sodomitic sexual practices. They polluted the purity of family life, they practiced incest, they slew their fathers when the latter reached old age, taking over their concubines. In the course of time this degenerate life told on them, and the people sank to a subhuman level. Half human, half animal, they lived exclusively on booty, a disgrace to the species, objects of terror and contempt to their neighbors.

Not envy of the blessings of the first-born, which Jacob had taken away from Esau, drove them from their caves in the Negeb to attack Israel; they were no longer jealous for the lost status of their forefather. Pure lust of murder and robbery led them forth. They had heard of the gold and silver, the purple and ivory, the

205

vessels of bronze, which the Israelites had brought from Egypt; they had heard of the flocks and herds, of the costly weapons, of the jeweled crowns and neckbands. And, wild for booty, the Amalekites poured out of the caverns and retreats of the swampy Negeb.

First they sought to persuade the neighboring tribes, the Edomites, the Canaanites, and the Moabites, to join them in the attack before the Israelites reached their borders. But the tribes refused.

"See you not that Jehovah leads them with a mighty arm through the wilderness? Have you not heard of the wonders He has wrought for them? Jehovah Himself is with them in their camp."

"Who is Jehovah, and wherein is His power? Our gods are stronger. Let us gather our gods, and they will do battle with Jehovah."

"If the gods of Egypt could not prevail against Him, how shall our gods? He divided the sea for them, He lays a path of bread and water for them through the dryness of the desert. Go, if you must, and it shall be with you as with the Egyptians when they pursued Israel."

And the Amalekites went.

First they hung on the flanks of the Israelites, like jackals hanging on the flanks of a flock; or rather, like foxes, which conceal themselves by day and attack at night, when the shepherd dozes. In the earlier weeks, when the Israelites were still on the shore of the Red Sea, the Amalekites had already made contact with them, but they had not dared to attack openly. They had played the friend in need, they had spoken much of the blood relationship; their spies had brought in asses laden with food, roast ears of wheat, sugarcanes, honey-coated leaves, dried cakes of cheese, old bread, cruses of water, and sour beer.

"Are we not your brothers? Is not Abraham the forefather of us all? Are we not the children of one family and covenant? What is a silver neckband between thee and me? For one silver ornament in thy sack I will give thee five cakes of dried cheese," crooned an Amalekite with the face of a goat and the eyes of a calf, his mouth a-drip with greed.

"We have heard that the God of our father Abraham has been good to you. We have heard that He delivered all Pharaoh's gold to you. *Ai,* what rejoicing there was among us when the glad tidings came to our ears, and we hastened to greet you with bread and water. Come out with me, O sons of Abraham, to the tents we

206

have put up in the wilderness for you. We have honey cakes and fresh well water. For one Egyptian robe you and your children may drink your fill. And we have brought cruses of water with us."

But if an Israelite ventured from the camp, carrying with him his pack, if he followed the diseased-looking Amalekite, he found waiting for him in the desert not a tent and refreshment, but a wild band of beasts in half-human shape. They fell upon the Israelite and bound him, they cut off his sex, in blasphemy against Jehovah, and they threw it skyward, crying out in mockery:

"Here, Jehovah! Thou art a lover of the circumcised!"

Later, when Moses had led the Israelites away from the Suez arm into the heart of the stony wilderness of Sin, the Amalekite spies hastened home with the news: "Israel is locked in the hills!"

Then they came on asses, on camels, and on foot, like an invasion of locusts; they came from the Negeb across the wilderness of Geber, and they swarmed into the hills of the wilderness of Sin. They avoided a clash in the open field. They crawled after sunset into the heights and took up their positions in the clefts. They were armed with bows and wooden spears; swords were few among them. But they did not need weapons. There were stones enough on the heights. By day they looked down into the valley, grinding their teeth with hatred and greed; when night fell the stones began to fly.

Moses was prepared for them. He had been aware, from the beginning, of the evil intentions of the cringing visitors. He had given instructions that they were not to be admitted to the camp. And now, when he learned that they were gathering on the heights, when he heard of the nightly attacks, he knew that it meant war with the Amalekites.

This time he did not turn to Jehovah for help and did not ask Jehovah to do battle for Israel. Israel himself must do battle. This would be the touchstone. Would the Israelites acquit themselves like freemen and stand up to the enemy without waiting to be rescued? Moses turned to Jehovah only when he had no alternative, only when the Israelites could not help themselves; he was sparing in his appeals and made use of them only in the last extremity.

Here was an opportunity to bring the Bnai Israel further along the path of freedom. They would have to defend themselves: certainly with the help of Jehovah, but on their own initiative.

He did not make use, either, of Korah, or Dathan, or Abiram, to whom the Israelites had been accustomed to listen from the days of Egypt on. Overseers of slaves could not be the leaders of freemen. He must put an end to the spirit of slavery; the Israelites must acquire the inner spirit of freedom. They must defend themselves against an insolent enemy not because they were whipped to it by their overseers, but of their own free will, from love of freedom. He therefore called upon Joshua, his nearest aid. Young though he was, unskilled in the handling of slave masses, Joshua was still the fitting leader in this pass, because he was of the young generation, because side by side with the tradition of the elders he had imbibed the spirit of freedom: in him the vision of the fathers was wedded to the daring of the freeman. He was the one to instill in the Bnai Israel the new discipline, the new order, which Moses had in mind for them.

Joshua, then, would lead the Israelites in the battle against the Amalekites; and in order that the Israelites might know that God was with them, they would have before them the rod of Jehovah in the hand of Moses. His arms would be lifted unchangingly to the heavens, and whenever they looked up they would see him in uninterrupted communion with Jehovah throughout the battle with Amalek. In the faith that God was among them they would acquire ardor of battle and heroic daring. Well did Moses know that in battle moral power transcends physical strength; from the sight of him on the height the Bnai Israel would draw moral power. Aaron would stand at his right hand, and Hur, the husband of Miriam, at his left. No Korah, no other slave overseer of the old time, would the Israelites see before them.

He turned to Joshua and gave him the command:

"Go, choose the men of Israel, and lead them to battle against Amalek."

Joshua started in amazement:

"What? I, among all the Bnai Israel? I am so young."

"Thou art old in the spirit of our fathers. Go, then, choose the men. Mark the word: Choose. Choose them well, one by one, young and free spirits who believe in Jehovah, who have faith in His promises, who live with their faith and are children of Abraham. I will take my stand on the summit of the hill, where all will see me. The staff of God will be in my hand. Go. Time is short, and the enemy is in the hills."

Joshua went into the camp and carried out the command of

Moses. Some of the young men he already had; they were the guard about the tent of Moses. After the incident at the waters of Meribah their number had been increased. These young men Joshua sent through the encampment, and later that day he could report to Moses:

"I have chosen only the young and courageous. They are filled with the spirit of Jehovah. The stock of swords among the people is greater than we expected. Surely the Lord prepared them for us when He commanded the Sea of Reeds to spew forth Pharaoh's warriors at our feet. But we have few bows and arrows, and there is no time to make them. The Amalekites are armed with bows and throwing spears. How shall we reach them? They will keep us at a distance with their arrows and with stones."

"As Jehovah destroyed the chariots of Pharaoh in the depths of the sea, so will He destroy the arrows of Amalek on the hilltops. But this time the will must come from us. We must prove to Jehovah that we are worthy of redemption, because we are willing to do battle for the freedom which He gives us, and to die for it."

Then Moses gave Joshua his final instructions concerning the strategy to be used against the enemy:

"This shalt thou do. Divide the host into two parts. Take those that can draw the bow and lead them to the foot of the hills where the Amalekites are assembled. Let the second part of the host, in which thou shalt place the expert swordsmen, be sent stealthily round the hills, to the other side. Let the swordsmen crawl stealthily up the hillside. Now when the Amalekites begin to throw their javelins and stones, and shoot their arrows, they will think that these are all our warriors, armed with the bow, and without swords. Then they will be heartened, and they will come down the hillsides to smite us with the sword. Then let those who have been sent round the hill rush forth, and attack them in the rear, and put them to the sword. And I will stand with the rod of Jehovah in my hand on the hilltop which is over against the place of battle. And when the warriors of Israel will perceive me, with rod lifted to heaven, the spirit of battle will grow strong in them. Then Amalek will be caught between the two hosts, and we shall destroy him."

Trained in Pharaoh's military academy, and with experience in wars against wild and unskilled African tribes, Moses realized that the only hope of victory against the Amalekites lay in forcing them into hand-to-hand combat, in which the sword—which the Israelites had in numbers—would be decisive.

At sunrise the next morning the Amalekites beheld a handful of warriors, with bows and arrows, ascending from the valley toward the hilltops. A cry of derision went up from them:

"See the warriors which Israel sends out against us. Not a swordsman among them—all bowmen. And their numbers! We will bury them under our stones!"

A hail of stones began to fly down on the advancing Israelite warriors.

The bows of the Israelites were useless. The arrows found only the stony walls of the hill; but as against this the Amalekites, dodging behind the rocks, could see the Israelites clearly, and take aim. Once or twice the Israelites retreated and took shelter. Then it was perceived that the Amalekites were already debating whether they had not wiped out the few Hebrew bowmen and could descend on the mass of unarmed, unprotected women and children cowering in the center of the valley. But when they made the attempt, the handful of Hebrew warriors reappeared, and the Amalekites concealed themselves behind the rocks. Where had these Hebrew warriors found this heroic spirit, to stand, one to a hundred, against a better armed foe? Whence did these slaves of yesterday draw their heroic will?

Then the Amalekites looked up.

They saw the mighty figure on the hilltop opposite. Tall, white bearded, he stood like a statue cut in the crags, dwarfing the two men who stood with him, one on each side. And whenever the figure lifted its arms to heaven, the Hebrew warriors came into the open, and drove the enemy back.

All day long the battle went back and forth. It became clear that the flanking movement was not an easy one, and the climbing of the swordsmen was proceeding slowly. Joshua, whose difficult task it was to hold back the Amalekite hordes from the camp of the Israelites, could not tell where and when the other half of the host would reach the position from which it could launch its attack. But he was certain that the stratagem planned by Moses would be successful, for he was convinced that it came from God.

Joshua had so disposed his men that the hail of rocks from above could not be concentrated. Nevertheless, many fell, and in the end he was left with a small group of heroes, of whom not a few were heavily wounded. Even these fought on, the blood streaming from them. And whenever weakness overcame them, and they retreated, Joshua pointed to the figure on the opposite hill.

There Moses stood like a dazzling column. His beard flamed silver in the sunlight, and his white robe was like a blazing shield about him. His naked arms, emerging from the robe toward the heavens, and holding aloft his staff, were symbols of valor.

"See! Moses stands on the hilltop and talks with Jehovah. Jehovah directs the battle!"

"The rod of Moses will break the neck of Amalek, as it broke the neck of the Egyptians!"

"Follow me, in the name of Jehovah!" shouted Joshua.

Again and again, recharged with new spirit, the dwindling group of fighters leaped out from behind the crags and threw the Amalekites back.

The attackers finally realized that it was not the heroism of the defenders, however sustained and obstinate, which stood between them and their booty: it was that towering figure lifting its arms to heaven. From him, whenever they glanced at him, the Israelites drew the strength to hold back the Amalekites, he, in turn, drew that strength from heaven. In desperation the Amalekites turned on him, direct: their best bowmen pulled back their strings and sent their arrows across the valley; their strongest men hurled stones at him. In vain. Like an angel of the Lord the figure reared into heaven, unreachable, inviolable. It was as though the sun had poured a carapace over him, and the light which was reflected from it threw the missiles off.

Then finally the stratagem which Moses had devised began to take effect. The Amalekites became impatient with the resistance of the handful of Hebrew fighters; they began to abandon their positions on the summit. It was toward nightfall that they determined to throw themselves into a hand-to-hand struggle. By that time the Hebrew swordsmen who had flanked the hill were waiting to launch the attack from the rear. The instant the Amalekites left their shelter, left the heaps of gathered stones which were their chief ammunition, the concealed swordsmen rushed on them with a tremendous shout: "Follow me, in the name of Jehovah!" The swords began to flash right and left, and the Amalekites fell before them. Dead bodies rolled down the slopes. Those that did not fall before the sword fled in panic.

With the setting of the sun Joshua led down into the encampment the camels and asses of the Amalekites, laden with provisions, and the trophies of victory, the weapons and instruments of war. He laid them at the feet of Moses.

Exhausted by the posture which he had maintained all day, but with a face which radiated joy, Moses drew Joshua aside:

"The word of Jehovah came to me, saying that this shall be written into a book as a memorial, and I shall rehearse it in thine ear: the Lord will utterly blot out the remembrance of Amalek from under the heavens."

The next morning, betimes, Moses sent for Joshua and Aaron and Hur, Miriam's husband, and bade them assemble the elders and the congregation. And Moses took stones and erected an altar to Jehovah in the wilderness.

"Thy name shall be *Adonai-Nissi*, the Lord is my banner," said Moses, and placing his hand on the altar, he added: "I swear, with my hand on the throne of God, that God will have war with Amalek from generation to generation."

Then he turned to the elders and the congregation of Israel:

"Know that in truth it was not against you that Amalek came out to do battle, when you were weary with wandering; it was against Jehovah. For Amalek is the eternal enemy of Jehovah, the eternal enemy of all that Jehovah teaches, of all that Jehovah is, of all that believe in Him. As Jehovah is pity and justice and order, so Amalek is cruelty and injustice and chaos. Amalek hates whatever Jehovah loves, and he will war upon you till the last generation, because you are the fulfillment of God's ordinance. For this you shall know: you will be despised and mocked for the sake of Jehovah. You will be oppressed with all manner of oppression, and you will be led to the slaughter and tormented in a thousand ways for the sake of God's commandments and laws. Till the last day this war shall continue. And in every generation a new Amalek will arise to renew the war against Jehovah. And the Amalekites will forever deny His being, spit upon His laws, and destroy the order He has created. And you shall be the warriors of God, the defenders of His glory, the guardians of His laws, the supporters of the order He has created. Jehovah is from this day forth your banner. It is not enough that you shall love with all your hearts the good and the just; you must hate with all your senses evil and injustice, till the day comes when these are wiped from the face of the earth, and Jehovah will be the only ruler on earth, as He is in the heavens. In that day the whole world will acknowledge the obstinate role you have played in the long war, will acknowledge your faithfulness to Jehovah and your love of Him, and will turn to Him. For it is not the will of God that the sinner shall perish, but only that sin shall be destroyed. Therefore do battle with evil until you have wiped out the memory of Amalek from under the sky."

The people answered Moses:

"The hand upon the throne of God, war with Amalek from generation to generation. The Lord is our banner, and His is all the earth."

CHAPTER FOUR

AT last the time came when Moses could make a pause and, as it were, draw breath. He had not known a tranquil moment since the hour of the exodus. Danger had succeeded danger: external dangers, from the Egyptians; internal dangers of revolt; hunger, and thirst; and finally the insolent attack of a vicious and cowardly enemy which had expected a quick and easy victory over the exhausted Israelites. Moses had not had the leisure to keep a record, or even to note down in chronological order the wonders and miracles which God had wrought with the Bnai Israel. There were also other things which needed to be committed to the record: the laws and customs which the Bnai Israel had inherited, together with the tradition of the forefathers—laws and customs which they had guarded even while they were still in Egypt; and since then new laws had been added from their experience in the wilderness.

All these things had to be set down in order, fixed in writing, cleansed of the versions and additions and special interpretations of the priests and the Bnai Levi, who were concerned with the maintenance and enhancement of their special status. It was high time to reduce all the traditions and spiritual heritages, the hymns and the benedictions of the forefathers, to a single style, to create as it were a book of the generations which should be sanctified for all time to come and no longer be subject to alteration.

And now, God having commanded him to record in a book the story of Amalek's attack on Israel and to place upon Amalek the stamp of the eternal enemy of Jehovah, Moses obeyed, and proceeded to the larger task.

There were various ways in which nations perpetuated the deeds of their kings, their wars and victories, and the laws and commandments of their gods. The Egyptians, for the most part, chiseled their inscriptions in rock or committed them to papyri. The Babylonians incised their laws and commandments and contracts and treaties in cuneiform on clay tablets, which they then baked in ovens or in the sun. Moses decided to put his record on lambskins, using as ink a dark fluid excreted by certain fish; such a record, durable and light, could be carried about by the Bnai Israel until they came into the land which God had promised them.

The book was to tell of the first things, of the six days of the creation, and of the works of God in the beginning; then it would rehearse all the generations and traditions of the fathers, their acts, customs, virtues, and laws, their prayers, and the benedictions which they transmitted to the Bnai Israel. It would also be the chronicle of the Israelites themselves, telling of the exodus from Egypt and the journey through the wilderness, and of the wonders which God had wrought for them. But above all the book was to be the book of the laws of Israel, containing all the laws and commandments which God had given and would give to the Bnai Israel, the book of the teaching, according to which they were to judge their acts, according to which they were to conduct themselves, and live. Therefore the book was to be called the Sefer-Torah, the book of teaching and law.

At once the tanners set to work; before the tent of Moses they scraped, with Egyptian swords, the sheepskins, cleaned them and smoothed them and made them fit to receive the sacred script. And a council of the elders of Israel, those who in time past had studied and rehearsed the traditions of the fathers in a secret cave in Egypt, now repeated the words for the scribes. Word by word they dictated the tradition, in the exact language in which they had received it from preceding generations. Each incident, as it came from many mouths, was scrutinized and made to conform; the style and manner of the telling had to accord with the incident. Every word had to fit, had to reflect the consensus of the elders. For it was not the incident alone which was important; equally important and sacred was the language in which the tradition was carried. Nothing was concealed; the bad was revealed as scrupulously as the good; nothing was evaded, nothing glossed over or gilded; all was set forth simply, with a sparing of words which brought the truth into simple, bold relief. The style of the tradition had long since been fixed; it had been hammered out as if in granite. No word in it could be changed, for the words were chosen and counted and handed over in form and number by the generations past, and there could be no adding and no taking away.

Not so, however, was it with the events of their own day which they entered into the chronicles.

From the day of his first contact with his brothers in Egypt, Moses had encountered those elements in Israel which sought to impose their hegemony on the people. There was to begin with the tribe of the Bnai Levi, which held itself apart, considered itself an exception, and proclaimed itself the ruling tribe. Korah, their elder and spokesman, had naturally looked upon himself as the man destined to lead the Hebrews out of bondage. It had also been part of his ambition to fill the office of the high priest; and when Moses held him at a distance, and raised to the first position among his aids his brother Aaron, and to the second Hur, Miriam's husband, Korah avenged himself by slandering Moses among the masses and undermining his reputation. Particularly did Korah seek to spread discontent by insisting that Moses was concentrating the government of Israel in his own family.

But the difficulties which were created for Moses by his family were greater than those which came from Korah.

Even in Egypt Aaron had already been dreaming of a priestly hegemony in Israel after the pattern of the Egyptian priesthood, with an ordered hierarchy, with rich treasure cities about the temples, and great wealth accumulated from field tithes and other taxes. In Aaron's plan the priesthood was to belong not to the entire tribe of the Bnai Levi, as Korah would have had it, but to the descendants of a single family, that of Amram, while the other Levites were to constitute a sort of temple slave body, the servitors of the priests.

Thus it came about that Aaron raised his sons in the spirit of a hereditary priestly order. Nadab and Abihu saw themselves as being, after their father, the founders of a sacerdotal dynasty, and from their youth on they gave evidence of a strong hankering for power and position. Jealous of their uncle, and even of their own father, they waited for the passing of the older generation, so that they might take over the leadership. But even during the lifetime of Aaron and Moses, these young men comported themselves toward the people as though the latter were still slaves. And indeed, since they regarded the Hebrews as the slaves of Jehovah, and they themselves were Jehovah's representatives, it followed that they stood toward the people in the relation of masters to slaves. They believed strongly that they were entitled to exact a head tax from every member of the congregation—naturally in the name of Jehovah. They also interpreted the laws and commandments of Jehovah—such as were traditionally accepted, or had been acquired recently—to their own advantage, as if it were the will of Jehovah that, having rid themselves of an ancient bondage, the Israelites should cheerfully take upon themselves the new bondage, that of a priestly dynasty.

Moses alone among the Bnai Amram was entirely free from ambitions of domination. He had but two passions, for which he was prepared to sacrifice himself, his family, his descendants. The first was Jehovah. The second, equally deep and overmastering, was his people and his desire to guide and direct it in such fashion that it should become the peculiar people in God's commandments, the model of justice and integrity. In the pursuit of these loves he neglected his wife and children.

He did not, when he passed through the Sea of Reeds, call to himself his son Gershom from Midian, to be his heir in the leadership, after the manner of Aaron and his sons. He took instead a total stranger, a young man of the tribe of Ephraim, Joshua ben Nun, whom no one had known heretofore, and made him his closest aid. The ambition of Moses was not to seize and to hold power, to transmit power to his sons, to fasten a caste on his people: it was to make the people a people of priests, a holy people.

He was thoroughly aware that the Bnai Israel would need a ritual and a mode of worship of Jehovah, and that this ritual and worship called for a priesthood. But it had never occurred to him that the priesthood would constitute a caste, which would live on the labor of the people, and to which the people would have to render up tithes of the field and the eldest of the flock: a caste with a great and costly sanctuary and a golden altar on which there would always be smoking sacrifices of sheep and of oxen.

After the victory over Amalek he had himself erected an altar of stones to Jehovah and had signalized there the marvels wrought for the people. He had not slain a sacrifice on it, though he knew well that the children of Israel would not give up the notion of sacrifices. The bringing of sacrifices was the only form of divine service which the world of that time knew. The lips of man were locked, and a heart overflowing with love and awe of God, finding no utterance in prayer, found it in sacrifice; but in *his* heart Moses believed that the desire of God was not for sacrifices, but for good deeds and a life of justice.

In the setting down of the first law which Moses proclaimed to the people in the name of God, the law which dedicated to God the first-born which opened the womb of the mother, whether it be a woman or a beast, conflict already arose between Moses and the priesthood.

Aaron and his sons, who took it upon themselves to work out all the laws of ritual and worship, interpreted the law to mean, simply, that every first-born, of woman or of beast, belonged to the priest, as the representative of God on earth.

"Brother Moses, does not the word of God in this matter mean that the first-born son who opens the womb of the mother belongs to the sanctuary as a slave, even as the first-born beast belongs to the altar as a sacrifice? And this immediately, as soon as we erect the tabernacle?"

"God said clearly to me that every first-born son of man shall be redeemed; and this only when we shall come to the land which is our inheritance."

"And to whom does the redemption money of the first-born belong, if not to the priests?"

"This I know not. I have no instruction from God concerning it. Give me time; I will inquire of Him."

Moses had always been cautious in the carrying out of God's will, scrupulous in every detail in obeying the voice he heard in his heart; he was more cautious and scrupulous than ever when it came to writing down the commandments of God, as well as the story of the wonders He had performed for Israel, his own part in it, and the part played by Aaron and the others. He was attentive to accuracy, he was concise, he confined himself to the factual incidents, courting no man. He created a council of scribes, the task of which it was to edit the chronicles, and the council called up as witnesses the participants in all events. Moses himself appeared before it and exerted himself to give an exact rendering of the words which he had received audibly from God, or through the voice in his heart, altering not even a letter. And thus the council of scribes heard the others, including Aaron, and even Korah, Dathan, and Abiram, on the subject of the slavery in Egypt. Miriam, the sister of Moses, had her share, too, entered into the chronicles. She told of the birth of Moses, and how Pharaoh's daughter found him in the Nile. The factual material which was collected by the council conformed not only in the matter of content, but in that of the style, so that it built up a continuity with the narrative which began with the creation and contained the lives of the forefathers. And when the scribes had completed the text, they brought it to Moses, who scrutinized it in the light of commands and revelations he had received from God; only when he was finally convinced that what was written was stamped with truth and was irradiated with the spirit of God, did he give permission to have it set down permanently in the Sefer-Torah, in the book of the teaching and the law, for all generations.

Moses was not alone, of course, in the production of a record of events. Korah and his group had their own version, while Aaron and his sons worked out various ritualistic laws which were aimed at the establishment of the priestly hegemony after the Egyptian model. But as long as Moses did not sanction them and did not declare them to be the word of Jehovah, they were not entered into the book of the law.

Moses appointed a second council which sat in his tent, the council of the interpreters of the law.

Recent as their liberation was, and brief their sojourn in the wilderness, though life was hard and the provision of food a daily problem, still, the mere living together of this great multitude created new and complicated problems which demanded immediate solution. There were weaknesses and passions which privation did nothing to repress, outbursts of greed, wild lusts, animal instincts, sexual corruption. There were some who had left Egypt with such an accumulation of wealth that even here, in the wilderness, they wanted to possess slaves. They hired themselves servants; they made usurious loans on utensils and articles of clothing. Many of the poor, envious of the richer ones, demanded that the wealth brought out of Egypt be declared war booty, to be divided share and share alike by all the congregation. When this demand was rejected, robberies ensued. There were cases of rape, against children as well as against women. Many of the Bnai Israel, proud of their descent, looked down on the proselytes among them as creatures of an inferior breed and behaved brutally toward them. On the other hand, Israelites would ape the worst characteristics and practices of some of the strangers, and there was a danger that the very roots of the people would become corrupted. After all, these were but recently liberated slaves whom Moses had led into the wilderness. The old discipline, enforced with the lash for many generations, had dissolved; here in the desert there were neither guards nor slave drivers, whip and rod in hand, to enforce order or obedience. The laws and commandments had not yet been proclaimed in their fullness; and, what was worse, there was no system for their introduction and enforcement.

They recognized and feared only one authority—Moses. They knew that Moses had the power to punish, with the rod of Jehovah which he held in his hand. And so those that had been wronged came, in fact, to his tent, to lodge their complaints.

He himself conducted the trials. He could not or would not appoint judges from among the sons of Aaron, who would have accepted only too eagerly, or from among the tribal elders. He could not bring himself to rely on others. The tribal elders would have inclined toward their own members, for the tribes were like large families.

Here, in the wilderness, Moses sought to anticipate the system of justice and righteousness which he hoped and believed the Bnai Israel would institute in the promised land. When he delivered decisions or sentences he kept steadfastly before him the moral perfection which was to be the norm of Israel in its own country. Without a definite code of laws, he grasped at the lofty spirit of the new order which he awaited from Jehovah at Mount Sinai; and because he alone could do this, he conducted all the trials in person, listened to all the complaints, rendered judgment, and exerted his authority to see that sentence was rigorously executed.

To some extent he leaned on his fragmentary knowledge of Babylonian law and the laws of some of the desert tribes, which were touched here and there with humane understanding, as for instance in the regulation of slavery. But what was at issue here was not the occasional individual decision, the righting of an individual wrong here and there, but the creation of a new order, God's order for His chosen people, which was to be a model for all other peoples; and what Moses sought was the universal principle and eternal guide for the Bnai Israel, to accompany them in their new land. With Joshua's help Moses sought out in the congregation the men who had received a training in the law and made them members of the new council.

Wherever the elders found a judicial ruling in one of the customs of the patriarchs, they naturally accepted it as a guide; where no indication or precedent existed, they examined the problem in the light of Babylonian, Egyptian, or desert usages. Moses weighed and compared the various laws according to their nearness to or remoteness from the spirit of the new order of justice which was his ideal. His individual judgments, too, were similarly grounded and motivated. Step by step he thus modeled a constitution which had in it the highest and noblest concepts of the world of his time and which incorporated both the purified traditions of the Hebrew tribes and the practices of other peoples.

He wrote down the law, but did not introduce it yet into the Sefer-Torah, or book of teaching. He was waiting for the supreme event, the revelation of the basic principles of justice at Mount Sinai, whereby all the laws would be re-examined and perfected and then proclaimed as the laws of God.

Meanwhile the individual cases absorbed all his time. He found himself unable to prepare the people for the immense moment. He was thoroughly aware that before he brought the Bnai Israel to the mountain to receive the law, he needed an apparatus of enforcement, so that the law, once given, could be guarded and applied. To this end it was necessary to find persons whom it was safe to place in authority and clothe with power, persons who would not abuse their position for self-advancement or conspire to impose upon Israel the hegemony of a group with dynastic ambitions. Moses was at a loss as to the method of choosing such persons, and he waited for an indication from God before he led the people to the mountain.

While Moses was wrestling with these problems of organization, a messenger came riding on a camel into the encampment and asked to be conducted to Moses; and when Moses set eyes on him he recognized him as one of Jethro's men.

"Thus says Jethro, priest of Midian," reported the messenger. "I, Jethro, thy father-in-law, am coming to thee, and thy wife and her two sons are with me."

Moses was suddenly smitten with shame. Ever since God had revealed Himself to him on Horeb, he had not known a moment's rest and had given no attention to his personal affairs. The land of Midian lay close to the desert of Sin; his heart had yearned toward Zipporah, his wife, for the faithfulness she had shown, for her willingness to go with him to Egypt; he was grateful to his father-in-law for the kindness he had lavished on him; he longed for his two sons, of whom the first-born, Gershom, carried in his name the memento of the father's homelessness and loneliness, while the second, Eliezer, signalized the father's trust in God; and for all this, he had not even advised them of his approach or invited them to come to him. Instead, it was his father-in-law who surprised him with a visit.

Moses hastened from the encampment with the messenger and went to receive his father-in-law and his family. They were already there, on the outskirts: ancient Jethro, in his white priestly robe, donned for the important occasion, bedecked with amulets, his head covered in token of his high office; behind him, his son Hobab, in the shepherd's mantle, the shepherd staff in his hand. And behind Hobab Zipporah sat on a small ass, her face now covered with a veil after the manner of the Hebrew women; it was thus that Rebekah had veiled her face when she went to meet Isaac. At her side stood the two sons, the older already a youth: Gershom and Eliezer. And they too were likewise dressed after the manner of Hebrews, with loincloths and many-colored smocks.

Moses loved his wife, and loved his children; for his father-in-law he felt reverence. He had learned much from old Jethro; nor had he forgotten the days when, a fugitive from Egypt, he had found shelter and security with him.

He made deep obeisance to Jethro, then embraced him and Zipporah and the children. His heart filled with joy, he conducted them into the encampment, and brought them to his tent.

Scarcely had the first greetings been exchanged than Moses launched into a recital of all that had happened in the long interval since their last meeting. He told his father-in-law of the manner in which God had compelled Pharaoh to release the children of Israel; of the splitting of the sea; of the travail and suffering of the Bnai Israel in the wilderness; of God's intervention to save them from starvation and thirst; and the attack of the Amalekites.

Jethro rejoiced for the grace which God had vouchsafed the Israelites and for the wisdom and greatness of his son-in-law. A priest, he praised and thanked the God of Moses, declaring Jehovah to be the greatest God of all the gods; and there and then he must bring a burnt offering and sacrifices to Jehovah, and he must do so on the altar which Moses had erected as a memorial of the victory over Amalek.

Then Aaron came and with him the most important of the elders, and even Korah, to greet and honor the father-in-law of Moses. Joshua and his young guard made all the preparations and set out tables before the altar. And in the presence of the chief men of the congregation the sacrifice was made, and they broke bread before God.

On the second day Moses invited his father-in-law to sit with him when he judged the people. Jethro was astounded to see the multitude which gathered before the tent in the early morning to bring their cases before Moses. One by one Moses heard them: light cases, such as might occur in any large congregation—quarrels, disputes, disorders, thefts; heavy cases, too—a case of rape, a case of a pregnant woman gored by someone's ox, and the like.

Most of the complaints had to do with the wealth which had been carried away from Egypt. Moses had long realized that the manner in which the Bnai Israel had indemnified themselves was not an unmixed blessing. In the scramble for possessions some had become rich, and riches provoked envy and hatred and led to other sins, to whoredom and all manner of injustice.

Moses did not differentiate in his treatment of light cases and heavy cases. He himself listened to the witnesses and to the defense; he himself issued judgment. The decisions he reached pleased Jethro mightily; he found them just and useful. Thus, Moses ruled that when a poor man had pledged his coat for a loan, the lender had to return it to him by nightfall, for it was the poor man's cover by night; wherewith was he to cover himself? But that Moses should take upon himself the settlement of such small cases, which might have been left to others, was displeasing to Jethro. Nor did he find it proper that the people should have to stand all day long in the frightful heat, waiting to be called up. Sometimes night would fall before a man could get a hearing, and then he would have to return the next morning. And on general grounds, what nonsense was this, that the leader of the people should himself conduct these trials, which were within the scope of any honest and decent representative? As Jethro saw it, it was not in keeping with the exalted status of Moses that he should be thus occupied; he would lose standing in the eyes of the people. Moreover, the strain was an impossible one. Jethro saw the drops of sweat gathering on the high forehead of his son-in-law; he saw his mantle becoming

223

soaked from the endless labor. And as it was with Moses, so it was with the people.

That evening Jethro unburdened himself to Moses:

"Thy judgments delight my soul, being just and helpful. God Himself has kindled the light of justice in thy heart. But the manner in which thou conductest these trials—that I must surely condemn. From morn to night thou sittest at thy task, from morn to night the people must wait on thee."

Moses unfolded his perplexities frankly to his father-in-law. He feared to share his authority with others. He told of the difficulties created for him by the Bnai Levi and by his own brother. But he was ready to listen to Jethro's counsel, knowing him to be skilled and prudent in these matters. For he remembered how, in Midian, his father-in-law had dealt out justice to his own people, according to his lights.

And Jethro warned him:

"This thing that thou doest is not good. Thou wilt surely wear away, both thou and the people; for this is too heavy for thee, and thou canst not do it alone. Hearken to my voice now, and I will give thee counsel. Thou must stand for God to the people, thou must be between God and them and bring them the laws and ordinances of God. Show them the way wherein they must walk, and the work that they must do. But the spreading and the teaching of the law, and the application of it, thou must leave in other hands. First, then, choose out of the people able and God-fearing and honest men, such as hate unjust gain, and make them rulers of thousands and rulers of hundreds, rulers of fifties and rulers of tens. The teaching of the law must penetrate throughout the people, it must reach to the humblest levels, to the hewers of wood and drawers of water. This thou canst accomplish, but not through the leaders of the separate tribes. Leave the tribes as they be, and create for thyself a special instrument for the execution of the law. Not the leaders of the tribes shall judge the people, but men appointed to that end; and give them the power to judge the people at all seasons. The great matters they shall bring to thee, but the small matters they shall judge themselves, according to the rules and laws and teaching which thou wilt give them in the name of God. Through them shalt thou keep thy hand over the people, and not through the leaders of the tribes, who, as thou sayest, will use the power either for their own tribes, or for their own families."

In Jethro's counsel Moses perceived the wisdom of long experience. He was aware that not a few of his own judgments had been deeply influenced by the recollection of Jethro's administration in Midian; but now his eyes were opened to a wider understanding of principle, and he saw in what manner he might prevent a sharpening of the feeling between the tribes, in what manner unify the people in the teaching of the law. Here was a way out of the difficulty which had threatened to pervert the teachings of God into instruments for the crooked intrigues of the tribal leaders.

It was God who had sent him this counsel through the lips of Jethro; and from that day on he threw himself impetuously into building up that apparatus of enforcement which he needed before he could lead the people to the foot of Mount Sinai.

CHAPTER FIVE

THE apparatus of enforcement which Moses rapidly brought into being did not break up the tribal system, which was far too deeply rooted and sanctified among the Israelites to undergo a sudden change. The Bnai Levi, too, remained in some sort of a privileged caste, even though they did not, for the time, have a special function; nevertheless, they were deprived of the dominion which they had exercised. In line with Jethro's advice, Moses constituted a new council of seventy, which he called by the ancient and honorable name of the elders of Israel.

The seventy were to be the interpreters and teachers of the law; with them, too, Moses was to take counsel in all weighty matters.

His brother Aaron he left, of course, in his high office of co-leader with himself: but he modified Aaron's position by associating with him a third figure, a representative of the tribe of Judah —his brother-in-law, Hur.

Other members of the Bnai Judah he introduced into the council of seventy; among them were Nachshon ben Aminadab, who had been the first to plunge into the sea at the time of the splitting, and Caleb ben Yephunneh. But the one that remained nearest to Moses, he whom he intended to make the heir of his leadership, was still Joshua ben Nun, of the tribe of Ephraim, who had conducted the battle against the Amalekites.

In the third month after the exodus from Egypt Moses began the approach to Sinai.

The Bnai Israel had remained till then in the wilderness of Sin. Moses now led them out of Rephidim, to the fruitful oasis of Nahal-paran, hard by the Sinai mountains. There rich streams descended from the heights; there were generous meadows for grazing; and clusters of palms threw a grateful shade—an ideal oasis for a large multitude. And now that the host was provided for, Moses left it under the supervision of Aaron and Hur and went into the hills, which lay a half-day's distance from the camp. He took no one with him, not even his servant Joshua. He had to be alone when he presented himself to Jehovah at the mountain.

Searching among the peaks, he soon found Horeb, where he had seen the burning bush and heard the voice of Jehovah. It was quite easy to recognize. Horeb was not a lofty mountain; it did not measure up to the towering masses about it, reaching into the heavens. The approach to the plateau which crowned it was made by a series of steep, cascading terraces; it was not one of the copper-ore mountains, but sandstone throughout, and its clefts sprouted desert shrubs and spare cactus. Surrounded by the monstrous peaks which thrust their savage bulk into the skies, it made an impression of tranquillity, modesty, and retirement.

Moses stood at the foot of the hill and lifted his eyes in awe and reverence, seeking a sign from Jehovah. There was nothing to be seen, and nothing disturbed the somber and oppressive silence. No vision appeared on the heights, and no leaf of shrub or cactus stirred.

Moses lifted his arms and called out in supplication:

"God of Abraham, Isaac, and Jacob, hearken to my voice. All things have happened according to the word Thou gavest our fathers, and Thou hast fulfilled the promise Thou gavest me on this spot. Thou hast freed the Bnai Israel from bondage, Thou didst give them bread in their need, and water to drink. Now I have brought them to Thy hill, that they may receive the commandment and the law, as Thou didst tell me in this place, Thou God of faithfulness and truth."

In the tremendous silence the prayer clamored and vibrated across the arches of the hills, and died down slowly.

Then he heard a voice calling from the height, the voice which had sounded from the burning bush:

"Thus shalt thou speak to the house of Jacob, and this say to the children of Israel. Ye have seen what I have done to the Egyptians, and how I have carried you on eagles' wings and brought you to Me. And now, if you will hearken to My voice and observe the covenant with Me, you shall be peculiarly My own among all the nations, for Mine is all the earth. And you will be unto Me a kingdom of priests and a holy people. These are the words which thou shalt speak to the children of Israel."

Joyously Moses returned to the encampment. He assembled the

elders and rehearsed before them the word of God, as he had been bidden:

"Of all the peoples of the world, which are all His, Jehovah desires to choose us as His peculiar people, a people of priests, a people of holiness, so that we may be an example to the other nations. We, the chosen people, are the first to acknowledge the one living God, and to take His law as the rule of our life, so that the world may see what is just and what is unjust, and from us learn the way to God. Will you take upon yourselves the yoke of this doctrine? Will you submit to the laws which God will give you, to be His holy people according to His desire?"

"We will accept all that God desires, we will obey all His words," answered the elders with one voice.

And Moses went on:

"Not for yourselves alone do you consent to obey God's commandments, but for your children, and your children's children; for not with you alone does He make the covenant, but with all who are with us today, and with all who are not with us today."

"We accept the covenant with God for our children and for our children's children, for all who are with us today and for all who are not with us today," answered the elders of Israel.

It was only then that Moses issued, in the name of God, the instructions concerning the mighty event which was to occur, three days hence, at Sinai, so that the people might know how to conduct itself and how to hold itself in readiness.

During this period the men and women were to abstain from each other. They were to sanctify themselves, and to wash their garments. For on the third day Jehovah Himself would descend upon the mountain in the eyes of the whole people.

So the children of Israel set about the preparation. Singly and in groups they came to the edge of the streams and washed their garments in the water cascading from the hills. But not their garments alone did they purify; it was as though the living waters were rushing through their souls, cleansing them of the stains of slavery in preparation for the third day. They knew now that the holy mountain would, on that third day, be fire from base to summit, and that they would not dare to approach it; man or beast that drew near it would be utterly consumed. And already they trembled at the thought of Jehovah's dread appearance, and they talked in low tones among themselves of the frightful experience which confronted them.

"They say Jehovah will bring forth not only a new order of the world, but a new creation. He will enfold all creation in His laws and commandments; the sun will shine, the earth will give forth its fruits, and the springs their water, in accordance with the order of His Torah—His law. A like portion will be given all men, no matter whether they sow a large field or a small; the harvest will be the same—even as it is with the bread which He causes to rain down from heaven," said humbly and trustingly an ancient elder, his eyes shining in his sunburned wrinkled face.

"They say He will restore the order of the world as it was in the six days of the creation. Man will not have to plow and sow; the trees will give their fruit untended, as it was in the garden of Eden when Adam and Eve lived there and had not yet sinned," said a second Hebrew, a long, lean, haggard figure, all skin and bones, with deep-set, dreamy eyes.

Thus they spoke among a learned group, steeped in the tradition of the tribe of Judah. Elsewhere the talk had a very different stamp.

"Who knows what burdensome decrees He will issue! Even before He reveals Himself on the mountain He already forbids us our wives. What will He do after? Perhaps He will forbid us entirely to multiply, perhaps He will want us to be like the angels," complained a burly, broad-boned son of the tribe of Dan, with a thick, tangled beard and a vast, hairy chest.

"Hast thou an alternative? Our forefathers sold us unto Jehovah as slaves. For when Father Abraham made the covenant with Him, he delivered us unto Him, with our wives and children, for evermore, to do His will."

"But are we not His slaves? Does he not feed us on His heavenly bread, and open up springs of water for us? And what does He desire of us? Have you not heard what Moses said, that if we only do His will, we shall become His children?"

"But why does he not give His doctrine, His teaching, His Torah to the angels in heaven? They do not need wives, and they need not eat or drink. They can live on His presence alone," insisted the Danite, waving his mighty arms excitedly.

"Scorpions in thy mouth and snakes in thine eyes, because thou blasphemest thy God; thy end will be as bitter as that of Pharaoh, or of Amalek. Hast thou forgotten the rod of Moses?"

"Today I may still talk; tomorrow, perhaps, I shall not be able to. Let me pour my heart out, then. Three days without a wife! And who knows what's to follow!"

In Korah's circle, too, they talked of the great event.

"The way of the world is this: first a people conquers a land, then it settles therein; later it sets forth the laws and commandments according to the manner of the life of those that dwelt there. But with us it is all topside-turfwise: before we have conquered the land which God has promised us, before we have so much as set foot in it, we are already given the laws whereby we shall live in it," said the sagacious Korah.

"Moses says that this is indeed the whole purpose of our liberation. Not for our own sakes did God redeem us, but that we might be the servants of His law. It is for the sake of the Torah that He brought us out of Egypt. That is, not for us, and not because of the promise He gave the forefathers, but for the laws and commandments which He has prepared for the land. We, and our wives, and our children are nothing! And the law, the Torah, is everything. Pharaoh held us as slaves in Egypt that we might build Pithom and Rameses; and Moses leads us into Canaan that we may be the slaves of the law which he is to give us," said Dathan.

"Law or no law—I only want to see him bring us into the land of milk and honey which we were promised. Thus far he has brought us not into a fruitful land, but into a stony wilderness."

"Did not God help Joshua to overcome the Amalekites?" asked a bystander.

"Who is Amalek? A rotten branch. But let him measure himself against the mighty cedars of Lebanon, against the Canaanites, the Hittites, the Moabites."

"As he conquered Amalek, so he will conquer all the enemies of God, of Israel and of Moses. . . ."

The new overseers of the people saw to the separation of the men from the women. They divided the families. The women and the younger children remained in the encampment, while the men and the older boys spent the night outside, on the rocky plateau. The next day Moses led them, in their shining garb, to Mount Horeb, and let them pass the second night in its neighborhood. The men and the older boys he placed on one side of the hill, the women with little ones on the other. It was the first time that the men and women had been separated from each other.

A great change had come over the countenance and bearing of this people. The three months of freedom in the wilderness had taken the cringing look out of their eyes, which were now the clear and open eyes of freemen. The ashen-gray, pulpy skin which had made their faces the faces of slaves had become firm and bronzed. Their limbs were no longer heavy and listless; they had taken on liveliness, energy, and elasticity. Black, curly beards adorned the faces of the men, and their heads were covered with mighty shocks of hair; and two long curls, the token of the Bnai Israel, hung down over their cheeks, one from each temple. More than one hairy chest was decorated with a golden stomacher brought from Egypt, or stripped from a dead warrior, Egyptian or Amalekite. With their finger rings and earrings, the emblems of freemen, with the precious Egyptian linens thrown over their shoulders, they looked, these slaves of yesterday, like a great assembly of one of the indigenous desert tribes.

No less striking was the appearance of the women. Their bodies were swathed in rich stuffs and multicolored robes; they were adorned with earrings, nose rings, and neckbands; with hair new-washed and shining eyes they stood erect, freed not only from the yoke of Pharaoh, but from that inner yoke which had oppressed their souls—row upon row of them, a fresh-plowed virgin field ready to receive the seed of God.

That night, as they rested in the enclosed circle of the hills, they already felt a vault settling over them—an arch composed of innumerable wings, of eagles or of angels. They were being drawn into the orbit of a new authority, they were being sundered from their surroundings; it was as if they were finding themselves in a vast sanctuary, of which the mountains were the walls; and they were unable to move from the spot. When the depths above them began to whiten, they saw a ponderous mass of clouds suspended over their heads; the sun did not emerge to disturb the brooding twilight; the summit of the mountain was enveloped by a black cloud which emitted coils of smoke, as though the mountain were standing over an abyss of fire. But they saw no fire; they saw only the smoke which, as it ascended, formed layer upon layer above the cloud. Now and again lightning flashes split the thickening gloom, played for an instant in the rolling smoke, and were extinguished. Thunder followed on every flash, reverberating with tremendous echoes. Then a ram's horn was heard, pealing ever more loudly.

A shudder passed through the hosts. But Moses commanded them to draw nearer. With beating hearts they crept toward the base; the clouds closed over them, and they were commanded to halt.

The smoke poured more and more heavily from the upper levels; and the ram's trumpet pealed more and more loudly.

Moses called up the mountainside:

"Jehovah! Jehovah!"

And a voice was heard answering down the slopes:

"Moses! Moses!"

Then the people saw Moses ascending into the thickest part of the cloud, ascending into it, and vanishing. After a brief interval he emerged and spoke to the priests who stood in the front; and he warned even them not to set foot on the mountain. He that did so would surely perish, for Jehovah Himself was now there.

The lightning and the thunder stopped; the ram's trumpet was heard no more. Intense silence fell from the skies and settled on all the earth. No leaf rustled anywhere, no bird lifted itself into the air. Nothing stirred on the ground or in the space above it; it was as if all creation had been petrified. And the terror which seized the assembled host in this stillness was greater than the terror which had been inspired in them by the lightnings, the thunder, and the trumpet peals.

Then a single voice was heard ringing out from the midst of the enveloped mountain:

"I am Jehovah, thy God, who brought thee forth from Egypt, out of the house of bondage."

The voice beat against the encircling summits and was dashed back into the valley; it was heard reverberating in the infinite distance, carried on the waves of the air, then brought back again by the dying echoes. So it sounded over the whole world, carried everywhere, across the deserts and seas and mountains.

And once again it was lifted:

"Thou shalt have no other gods before me . . ."

Again it pealed over the hills and through space, dwindling slowly into a vibrating like the strings of a harp.

232

"Thou shalt not make unto thee any graven image . . .
Thou shalt not take the name of Jehovah thy God in vain . . .
Remember the Sabbath day to keep it holy . . .
Honor thy father and thy mother . . .
Thou shalt not murder . . .
Thou shalt not commit adultery . . .
Thou shalt not steal . . .
Thou shalt not bear false witness against thy neighbor . . .
Thou shalt not covet thy neighbor's house . . ."

A long time passed before the voice of God sounded out the ten commandments from the smoking mountain. An interval ensued after each commandment. The voice waited until each commandment had been carried throughout the world and had reached every people; for the words were uttered not for one people alone, and not for one age, but for all peoples and for all generations until the end of time. And the ten commandments were a renewal of the act of creation; inasmuch as man and all else that lives issued from the first act of creation, so the continuation of life depends on the second act of creation, the giving of the law. And just as the first act of creation made a division between chaos and order, so the second act of creation made a division between good and evil, between right and wrong. From this day forth there would be a center of reference, a line of conduct, a standard whereby to measure good and evil in all the corners of the earth, for all men and for all generations until the coming of the great day of God.

When the lightning flickered through the dim twilight, followed by the rolling thunder, the Israelites fell on their faces; and they did not dare to look on the flaming mountain. They saw no more; they only heard. But the hearing was like a seeing. It was as if they saw the voice traveling through space; it was as if other peoples, other hosts of Bnai Israel, were assembled in other places, and for these hosts the voice paused and repeated the commandments; it was as if they saw these other peoples, who had issued from their tents, their caves, their cities and forests, and had likewise fallen on their faces before the voice of God. And, still without lifting their heads, they saw the fiery mountain from which God spoke rise into the air and hover over them. Wrapped in the blue-black clouds of smoke, the mountain rose higher and higher, till the clouds uncoiled from it and settled on the other mountains. Then

233

it seemed to them that they too were hovering between heaven and earth. They saw the world unrolled below them, and nations unknown to them even by name lay prostrate, and the voice of God wandered over them. And the voice broke upon the prostrate nations like a ray of light piercing a cloud. And suddenly the Bnai Israel felt that they were not alone; all space about them was filled; they were aware of a movement, a fluttering as of wings, a falling of shadows. These were the souls of all the ages, the souls of all men, whether then among the living or yet to be born throughout all time until the day of God: all the souls were there assembled when God descended in fire and cloud on Mount Horeb and gave His order to mankind and the world: and not a soul of all the generations of men was absent.

It lasted an eternity, it lasted an instant. It was an incident in human history not to be measured with the limited apprehension of man, but belonging to the province of the eternal and the infinite of Divinity. And therefore it is impossible to speak of the duration of the exalted episode. Only when the voice of God ceased from speaking did the world fall back into its framework of time and space; and only then did the Bnai Israel experience the fullness of fear. It was a peculiar dread of the ungraspable. They did not know where they were, whether on the earth or still hovering in space with God, held by an invisible power to the flying mountain; and they began to cry out to Moses:

"Speak thou to us, and we will hearken. Let not God speak! We die with fear!"

And Moses, closer to the mountain than they, called back in a loud voice:

"Fear not! God has come to prove you. Let His dread fall upon you, that you may not sin."

Then Moses departed from them and ascended into the cloud, that he might commune further with God.

The Bnai Israel had risen; they stood with hearts constricted, waiting for what was still to come. They saw Moses disappear into the cloud; they saw him, after a time, return, and approach the seventy elders and Aaron and his sons. He beckoned to them, he made them approach the cloud, as if he wanted them to enter, to behold the glory of God. But Aaron and his sons and the seventy elders bowed their heads and would not enter. Thereupon Moses entered again, alone, and lingered there. And the people still waited,

234

breathless with anxiety, to see what would happen, and to hear what they had to do.

A long interval ensued, and the host stood motionless. At last Moses issued again from the cloud and approached the people. Surrounded by the priests and the seventy elders, he took his stand on a rock and called out:

"These are the commandments which God has spoken to you. Will you accept them?"

And the whole people answered:

"All that God has spoken we will do."

Only then, after bidding them reassemble in the same place on the next morning, did Moses dismiss the people.

CHAPTER SIX

MOSES called together his scribes, bade them unroll the great parchment scrolls, and made them enter therein the words of God, even as God had commanded him.

He was preparing the book of the covenant which he would read forth to the people the next morning. He dictated not only the ten commandments which the voice of God had proclaimed—those commandments which were later to be placed in his hand, engraved on tablets of stone as the eternal testimony of the covenant between God and man. He had to set down also the laws and judgments which the Bnai Israel had received through the tradition from the fathers, likewise those laws which life itself brought forth, the laws which would guide the conduct of the Bnai Israel in the land which God had set apart for them. The ten commandments were above time and place, they were not peculiar to any one people, or any one way of life; they were given to all mankind for all times and for all circumstances. But simultaneously Moses issued a series of laws, in the name of Jehovah, designed to regulate the life of Israel in accordance with its peculiar destiny as a peculiar people, a kingdom of priests, which God would set up as an example to other peoples.

The ten commandments begin by eternalizing the principle of the one living God, both in affirmation and in negation. The one God cannot be spoken of as little or as greatest among the gods. He is the only God, and all others are idols. And thou art utterly subject to Him because thy fate is in His hand, whether it be thy will or not. He is a God of vengeance, and likewise a God of mercy. He will punish those that sin against His commandments, unto the second and third generation; but He will be merciful for thousands of generations to those that keep His commandments. He is therefore the God of order; for thy acceptance of Him comes not from thine own free will, but from the compulsion which He lays upon thee. Thou art subject to Him, and thou must conduct thyself according to His will.

The ten commandments affirm the principle of the Sabbath—not alone for God's sake, but for thine. Art thou a beast, that lives only to feed itself, and for which food is the aim of life? One day in seven thou belongest to God, thou becomest a part of Him. Thou makest pause in thy animal life to enter into a higher life.

The ten commandments affirm the principle of the family. They establish social laws not simply because these are a necessity for the existence of the community, as when they are devised and proclaimed by a king, being then changeable for another social order and another king. They are established and proclaimed in the name of God as eternal and unchangeable laws. If thou layest a hand on thy brother, if thou slayest him, if thou stealest, if thou bearest false witness against thy neighbor, if thou covetest thy neighbor's house, then thou hast sinned, not simply against society, but against Me, God: because man is sacred, and a part of Me, and is conceived in My image.

Then came the laws which the council had formulated under the guidance of Moses, those laws which had in part been taken from other peoples, or which Moses had learned of in the days when he dwelt with Jethro. But now they were reformulated and purified in the spirit of those high principles which were the foundation of the ten commandments; and thus improved they were introduced into the book of the covenant. Those that did not conform to that spirit Moses rejected. As always, he omitted his own name from the laws and proclaimed them in the name of God.

He had, quite early, conceded the need of a ritual for the Lord God Jehovah, for no people could dispense with ritual; it was the only known contact with Divinity. He rejected summarily the representation of God in any form or image, the common practice of all peoples. "Thou shalt make Me a simple altar. There, if thou wilt, thou mayest bring Me a sacrifice of sheep and cattle." Nor was any place chosen and specified: "But in whatever place I cause My name to be mentioned, I will come unto thee and bless thee." For the whole earth is the Lord's, and the whole earth, and no special place alone, is holy. "And if thou wilt make an altar of stone for Me, let it be simple, and not of hewn stones, and without steps to mount to it, but of natural stones, such as I have created."

It seems that Moses was forever haunted by the hideous recollection of the Egyptian slavery, in the midst of which he had grown up. He gave much thought to it; and an early law of his formulation sought to bring some order and human consideration into the system. He had also found support in the Babylonian law, which already treated slaves with a measure of humaneness. But the new principle which Moses introduced was the essential principle of the freeman.

For the time being he restricted the new principle to his own—to the children of Israel. The Hebrew could not really be a slave; he could only bind himself over to work for a certain time. After six years he had to be released, he and the wife he brought with him. It was only when the Hebrew renounced freedom of his own will that he could be degraded to the status of slave. Moreover, Moses added to the difficulties of keeping slaves by imposing new obligations on owners, making almost impossible the retention of Hebrew slaves. And the later interpreters of the laws added even to these difficulties, so that there arose a saying in Israel: "He that takes to himself a Hebrew slave takes a master to himself."

Moses expanded and interpreted the concept of the inviolable sanctity of the person as it is proclaimed in the ten commandments. "If a man come presumptuously upon his neighbor, to slay him with guile, thou shalt take him from Mine altar, that he may die." And "He that smiteth his father or mother shall be put to death."

If a man steal an ox or a sheep, and slaughter it, or sell it, he shall pay five oxen for the ox and five sheep for the sheep. If he have not the money, he shall be sold for his theft. But if the stolen ox or sheep or ass be found alive with him, he shall pay double.

If a thief come upon thee in the night and thou smitest him, so that he die, there is no blood guilt upon thee. But if the sun was risen, and it was day, and thou couldst have called for help, then there is blood guilt upon thee.

Certainly Moses, being human, could not altogether escape the influence of concepts reigning in his time; and therefore he proclaimed: An eye for an eye, a tooth for a tooth. But later interpreters of the law explained and mitigated it as meaning not literally an eye or a tooth, but the equivalent in compensation. On the other hand, Moses formulated a series of civic laws which are distinguished for their spirit of equity. These were the laws which no doubt sprang from the earliest life of the Hebrew herdsmen and shepherds; they dealt with damage which cattle might do to the property of neighbors. The laws shine like great beams of light in the darkness of those days and with their justice illumine even our own times.

Moses instituted a rigid discipline in family relations, strengthening the institution of the family for all time; he pronounced sentence of death against practitioners of sodomitic degeneracies, which were so widespread that many peoples regarded them as normal and in no way blameworthy: these degeneracies were deep rooted among shepherd tribes. Moses was profoundly concerned with the eradication of sin from among his people.

"He that sacrifices unto gods, save only unto Jehovah, shall be utterly destroyed."

"A stranger shalt thou not wrong, neither shalt thou oppress him; for you were strangers in the land of Egypt."

"Thou shalt not afflict a widow or a fatherless child. If thou in any wise afflict them—for if they cry at all unto Me I shall surely hear their cry—My anger will be kindled against you, and I will kill you with the sword, and your wives will be widows and your children fatherless."

"If thou lend money to any of My people, even to the poor with thee, thou shalt not be to him as a creditor; neither shalt thou lay upon him interest. If thou at all take thy neighbor's garment to pledge, thou shalt restore it to him at sunset. For that is his only covering, it is his garment for his skin. Wherein shall he sleep? And it shall come to pass, when he cries unto Me, that I will hear; for I am gracious."

"Ye shall be holy unto Me; ye shall not eat any flesh that is torn of beasts in the field."

"Thou shalt not utter a false report. Make not common cause with the wicked to be an unrighteous witness. Thou shalt not follow a multitude to do evil; and in a dispute thou shalt not testify only that thou mayest be with the majority; and thou shalt not favor a poor man in a dispute only because he is poor."

"If thou meet thine enemy's ox or his ass going astray, thou shalt surely bring it back to him again."

"And if thou see his ass lying under its burden, thou shalt refrain from passing by; thou shalt release it with him."

"And a stranger shalt thou not oppress, for thou knowest the heart of a stranger, seeing you were strangers in the land of Egypt."

"Six years shalt thou sow thy land, and gather in the increase; but the seventh year thou shalt let it rest and lie fallow, that the poor of thy people may eat; and what they leave the beast of the field shall eat. In like manner shalt thou deal with thy vineyard and thy oliveyard."

"Six days shalt thou do thy work, but the seventh day thou shalt rest; that thine ox and thine ass may have rest; and the son of thy handmaid, and the stranger, may be refreshed."

"Three times shalt thou keep a feast unto Me in the year. Seven days shalt thou eat unleavened bread, as I commanded thee, at the appointed time in the month Abib—for in it thou camest out from Egypt. And none shall appear before Me empty. And the feast of harvest, the first fruits of thy labor, which thou sowest in the field. And the feast of the ingathering, at the end of the year, when thou gatherest in thy labors out of the field. Three times a year all thy males shall appear before the Lord God."

"The choicest first fruits of thy land shalt thou bring into the house of Jehovah, thy God."

"Thou shalt not seethe a kid in its mother's milk—as the custom is among those that sacrifice to idols."

The next morning Moses appeared before the people already assembled at a little distance from the mountain. There was still a flicker of fire at the summit, and the smoke, still rolling, concealed the slopes. Moses now built an altar at the foot of the mountain and placed twelve pillars about it, according to the number of the tribes. And he sent, not the priests, but the young men of Israel, to bring burnt offerings and peace offerings of oxen to God. Then Moses took half of the blood and put it in basins; and half of the blood he dashed against the altar. He lifted up the book of the covenant and read it in the ears of the people; and when he had finished reading the laws and commandments he said, in the name of God:

"Behold, I send an angel before thee, to keep thee by the way, and to bring thee into the place which I have prepared for thee."

Moses was careful not to give the Hebrews so much as the slightest hint of a life after death, or of reward and punishment in the other world for good deeds and transgressions in this. He remembered too vividly all the abominations of the Egyptians, their cult of death and their enslavement of the living to the dead. He hated from the depths of his soul the idolatrous ritual of the death sacrifices. In the spirit of the ten commandments he called for a moral life without reference to reward in the world to come. Thou earnest no reward in fulfilling His commandments, for they are the condition for a full and healthy life here, on this earth; they will guard you from the manifold defects, from barrenness, from leprosy, from all the afflictions which come upon the idolators for sodomy and incest and other abominations. "You shall serve Jehovah your God, and He will bless thy bread and thy water; and I will take away the sickness from the midst of thee. None shall miscarry, nor be barren, in thy land; I will fulfill the number of thy days." This was the reward for a just life. "I will send My terror before thee," declared Moses, in the name of God, "and I will confound all the people to whom thou shalt come, and I will make all thine enemies turn their backs unto thee. . . . And I will not drive them out from before thee in one year, lest the land became desolate, and the beasts of the field multiply upon thee. Little by little will I drive them out from before thee, until thou be increased, and inherit the land. . . . Thou shalt make no covenant with them, nor with their gods. They shall not dwell in thy land—lest they make thee sin against Me, for thou wilt serve their gods—for they will be a snare unto thee."

The people stood in a dense multitude about Moses. On the one side the men, on the other side the women, with their little ones in their arms, and many big with child. He was as in the midst of an immense double sea: of beards, thick stranded like ropes, gray, brown, black beards; and naked breasts, naked arms. And all listened tensely, their breath coming and going through their quivering nostrils. Their hearts thudded with terror and joy in the exalted hour; and when Moses had ended the reading of the book of the covenant he lifted up the great parchment scroll over their heads, lifted it so high in his mighty arms that the script seemed to touch the cloud hovering above him. And it seemed to them again that the mountain of God had risen into the air and was suspended over them.

Then they raised their voices and shouted, each man outshouting his neighbor:

"All that the Lord has spoken we will do and obey!"

"We will do and obey!" rolled among the mountains and swept and vibrated through space, thousands of voices beating back and forth in waves.

Then Moses took the blood from the basins and sprinkled it over the heads of the multitude, and called out:

"Behold the blood of the covenant which God has made with you according to all these words."

And Moses turned to the people, embracing all of them in his glance, and stretching out his arms to them as if touching each one separately, saying:

"Today you all stand before Jehovah, your God—your chief men, your tribes, your elders, your overseers, all the men of Israel, your little ones, your wives, and also the stranger that is within your congregation, from the hewer of wood to the drawer of water. And thou shalt enter into the covenant of Jehovah thy God, and into the oath which He makes with thee; so that He shall establish thee as a people unto Him, and He shall be thy God as He has promised thee, and as He has sworn to thy fathers, to Abraham, Isaac, and Jacob. And not with thee alone do I make this bond, and swear this oath, but both with him that stands today before Jehovah, and with him that is not here today with us."

And as the tradition tells, not only they that stood before the mountain, but the unborn souls of all the generations to be, assembled and fluttering in that place, cried out with the Hebrews: "We will do and obey!" And the children still in the wombs of the mothers started up, and called, together with their mothers: "We will do and obey!"

Then Moses took Aaron and his two sons, the priests, and the seventy elders of Israel, and he led them—and this time they went with him—into the smoke of the mountain, that they might see where God's foot had rested. And it was like a paved work of sapphire stone, and like the very heavens for clearness. And God did not lay His hand on the nobles of the children of Israel, and they were not harmed. And the people rejoiced, and ate and drank.

Then Moses said to the elders: "Thus has God commanded me: Come up unto Me in the mountain, and I will give thee the tablets of stone, with the law and the commandments, which I have written." And Moses called his minister, Joshua, to go with him into the mountain. And to the elders he said:

"Wait here below for us, till we come back. And Aaron and Hur are with you; whosoever has a cause to plead, let him come before them."

And he took Joshua, and the people saw them ascending into the smoke. Then the people went back to their tents in the rich valley. And they saw God's glory resting on Sinai, for a devouring fire burned on it and illumined the land round about.

And Moses and Joshua had vanished into the cloud which surrounded the mountain.

And a day passed, and Moses did not appear. And a second day passed, and he did not appear. And thus a long time went by, and Moses did not appear.

CHAPTER SEVEN

AND the man Moses vanished, and was not.

Dazed, like sheep that had lost their shepherd, the Israelites wandered about the encampment staring dumbly at each other. Fear sat in their eyes. One thought obsessed all of them, though they did not dare to give it utterance.

"Did not Moses warn us not to come to the mountain—neither we nor even our cattle—lest we be utterly consumed? What, then, is to become of us? Who will lead us on our way from now on? Who will conquer for us the land which Jehovah promised us and for the sake of which He gave us His laws? Who will defeat our enemies? Joshua went with Moses, and he too has vanished. Yes, he left us Aaron and Hur and bade us go to them in case of need. But we do not see Aaron about, and we have no word of him. He sits in his tent, with his two sons, the priests, and they take counsel about something. As for the elders of Israel, they are new men, the people does not know them yet. And even Korah seems to be in hiding somewhere, and shows himself not in the encampment.

"Is Jehovah still among us? Is He still in the camp? From Him, too, no sign, no word now. Perhaps He has withdrawn into His heavens; perhaps He is hidden on Mount Sinai, which we dare not approach, lest we touch it and be utterly destroyed."

The children of Israel no longer remarked how God sent them their daily provision of heavenly bread. They had become so accustomed to the deposits of the white floweret crystals with the heavy morning dews, that they regarded them as being in the natural order of things, as having always been, as calling for no comment or wonder. They had utterly forgotten that there was a time when it was otherwise.

"And here we are locked in the round of a stony desert. Egypt we have left, but into the new land we are not yet come. And as to the peoples whose lands God has promised us—they know well enough that we are here in the wilderness, and that our footsteps are directed against them. They can assemble their hosts and fall upon us—and who will protect us? Who will lead us to victory? Who will take up our cause?"

These things were not said openly; but every man thought them in his heart; and the words were in their eyes, if not on their lips.

It seemed well to them to think these things. Only yesterday God had lifted them, with His mountain, into the heavens; today He had abandoned them, a flock lost in the wilderness, among caverns and desolation and wild beasts.

And Aaron sat with his two sons, Nadab and Abihu, in his tent, and they took counsel—not for the Bnai Israel, whom Moses had entrusted to their keeping, but for their own affairs, for the priesthood which Moses wanted to take away from them.

The plans and ambitions of Aaron had not changed from the day when Moses came to Goshen, and from long before. His life had been nothing but a preparation for the exaltation of the priestly hierarchy, and for his exaltation within it. He had always practiced bodily purification, such as became a high priest, ablutions and anointings and the like. It was true that he still retained his beard in its fullness, did not remove the hair from his head, or cut off the side locks which were traditional with the Bnai Israel. But his two sons, Nadab and Abihu, had shaved their heads, their faces, and their eyebrows, after the manner of the Egyptian priests. They sat, with their naked heads, opposite their father, and reproached him:

"Not of gold, and not of silver, did he say: but an altar of plain earth shalt thou make; and not of hewn stones, and with no steps of hewn stone to ascend to it. Nor dost thou need a special place for the bringing of sacrifices. 'Wherever I cause My name to be mentioned, I will come and bless thee.' That is, neither tabernacle nor sanctuary—nothing! And these are the means whereby he intends to maintain discipline among a people of slaves! By these means he intends to fill them with spirit and enthusiasm, that they may remain loyal to their God and fulfill His difficult commandments. Thus he hopes to train them to heroic deeds, to overcome those strong, settled peoples which have their own cults and rituals and ceremonies to inspire them, to maintain in them their religious ecstasy!" Thus spoke Nadab, the elder son.

"And without priests! No! Priests are not needed! Young boys he chose, from among the people, to make the sacrifices! Nor did he call thee to besprinkle the altar with the blood of the sacrifices; he

245

took it upon himself to fulfill the function of the priesthood. Nothing is enough for him. The government *and* the priesthood: he must have them both. Tell me, does God speak only to him? Has not God also spoken to thee? Did He not send thee together with Moses to Pharaoh? Thou wert the one—not he—to perform the miracles before Pharaoh. Thou wert the one to bring on the plagues which compelled Pharaoh to free the Hebrews. Thou wert his mouth, spokest for him. Does he not know that God had appointed thee for the priesthood, that he takes it away from thee in the eyes of all Israel?" stormed Abihu.

And Nadab took up the plaint again:

"Not a word concerning the priesthood did he let Jehovah utter from Mount Sinai! Not one command concerning ritual, or a tabernacle, or priests. And in the ten commandments not a word regarding sacrifices. And now that he is with Jehovah on the mountain, he will assuredly see to it that the very office of the priesthood shall be removed. What will then become of thee? And what will we do?"

"He took a stranger, a lad from the tribe of Ephraim, not his own son, and not a son of his brother, and made him his nearest helper. He brings him up to be his representative, and he made him the commander of the host in the battle against Amalek," continued Abihu.

"And thou sayest not a word! Thou acceptest everything from him and sayest not a word!" complained Nadab bitterly. "Not thee did he take with him on Mount Sinai, but a stranger. And soon he will thrust thee away altogether, and thou, and we thy sons, will be among the smallest of the people, among the hewers of wood and the drawers of water."

Aaron did not move. He listened to the plaints and reproaches of his sons and remained silent. It cut him to the heart to hear them speak thus against his brother. The pain of it was seen in his features, yet he did not bid them be silent or even interrupt their complaints. The same thoughts had been in his own mind, and his sons had only uttered what he had felt but had not given speech to. For this was his brother, this was Moses, and Aaron struggled with his own bitterness. And in the end his feelings grew too strong for him, and he said:

"Yes, yes, all these things you say are true; but it is Moses, the man of God, to whom God has appeared. True, often I do not understand him. I argued with him: 'If God bade thee command the

Bnai Israel to borrow the gold and silver and raiment of the Egyptians, it was not because He desired to make the Bnai Israel rich. His intent was that the Israelites should keep the gold and silver and precious stuffs for His great and magnificent tabernacle, which it is His purpose to erect.' And I rejoiced when I saw the Bnai Israel spoiling the Egyptians. And at the sea, when the waves threw up the dead Egyptian horsemen, with their golden breastplates, I said to Moses: 'Thus it is that Jehovah sends us the gold which we shall need for the sanctuary, for the altars, the shovels, the pots, the basins, and all the other vessels for our worship.' When, with your help, I worked out the ritual of the priesthood, so that thereby the children of Israel might feel the glory of God, and honor Him and fear Him, I wanted Moses to enter it into the book of the covenant, when he was preparing it for the reading to the people. But his answer was that God had commanded him to come up to Him on the mountain; there God would entrust to him the Torah; and there and then Moses would ask God concerning the ritual, and he would himself bring down all the commandments and statutes concerning the service of the priesthood. Therefore, my advice is that we do nothing, but wait until Moses comes down from the mountain, bringing with him the word of God concerning us."

"Too late! It will be too late then!" cried Nadab. "The people are restless. Moses has vanished. They are looking for a leader to take them into the promised land. The people have gold and silver, and they want a god, one who will rejoice with them and with whom they can rejoice, a god whom they can see, feel, dance around, have in their tents—yes, even carry on their throats. They will bring their gold and silver to Korah, I say, and he will set up a worship for them, and he will become their priest, not you and not we."

"And who knows whether Moses will bring down from Sinai any statutes and commandments relating to the priesthood and the service," said Abihu. "Has not thy brother declared in the name of Jehovah that this whole people is composed of priests? 'You shall be to me a kingdom of priests and a holy people.' Moses needs no priests, and he needs no sanctuary. He brought to the children of Israel a flaming fire on a mountain, thunder, and lightning. The people wants a god to rejoice with, like every other people. But instead of a god, Moses gives the people harsh and difficult commandments, which the people cannot fulfill."

"Not I say it, but the people. Go out into the encampment, and hear them. 'Moses has given us an invisible God! We want to see our God, as all the other peoples do. We want to rejoice with Him, not be afraid of Him.' The children of Israel cannot live with nothing but laws and commandments. They must have a god whom they can see and hear. The god must live in their midst. He must have his sanctuary among them. Jehovah may live in the heavens, among the flames on Sinai; but there must be someone who shall, side by side with Jehovah, be a god for Israel. This god must have his tabernacle, his place, among the people; and the people must come to him, bring him its sacrifices and rejoice with him and with his priests, who will speak for the god to them, will represent him and celebrate his festivals."

"But Jehovah told us from Sinai that we shall have no other gods beside Him," answered Aaron. "I fear to fall into sin against Jehovah and against Moses."

"Moses is not among the living, and thou wilt take his place. Thou wilt take this matter before Jehovah, and He will sanction it."

Aaron meditated and could not make up his mind.

Meanwhile, from day to day, the people became more uneasy. Day after day they looked for Moses, and Moses did not appear. They assembled before Aaron's tent and demanded Moses of him:

"Where is Moses? Why does not Moses return?"

Aaron was at a loss for an answer. He put them off. Moses would return tomorrow. But the morrow came, and there was no sign of Moses. He would come the next day. But there was no Moses the next day either.

The multitude turned to the second deputy left behind by Moses —Hur. Hur, the brother-in-law of Moses and Aaron, was a very old man. He tried to soothe the multitude with words: Moses had gone up to Jehovah; he was with Jehovah on the mountain, and there God was giving him His Torah, His law. Moses would return; he was expected daily—they must have a little patience.

"No!" they answered. "If Moses has not returned by now, then he will never return. All this means but one thing: God has taken Moses to Himself."

They bethought themselves of their old leaders, the Bnai Levi, and turned to the head man, to Korah, who had been their representative before Pharaoh in Egypt.

248

"Come! Be our leader," they said. "Be our leader, as thou wert in Egypt, before Moses appeared among us, for the man Moses has disappeared, and is no more."

But Korah, shrewd and farsighted, perceived at once the dangers of the situation. The Israelites in their growing panic were capable of the wildest things; they were preparing to throw off every vestige of the discipline which Moses had laid upon them. Korah decided that under the circumstances his best course was to hold off, remain at a distance, and let Aaron and Hur face the turbulent multitude. Let them bear the responsibility, before Jehovah and Moses, for the follies which the Israelites would commit in their despair. He, Korah, would thus remain the only leader uncompromised by events; to him would then fall the office to which he was entitled as the eldest of the Bnai Levi—the office of the high priesthood. On the other hand, if Moses was actually no longer among the living, as the masses believed, then who would take over his place before God if not he—Korah? As far as the people was concerned, he had an excellent pretext; he was a demoted leader. And it was this role that he proceeded to play.

"Who am I, that I should take the place of Moses? I am now but one of the people. See, Moses has left his deputies to look after you, members of his own family. Go, then, to his brother Aaron, and to his brother-in-law Hur. He has appointed them, and they are now your leaders. Let them tell you what lies before you."

And to the Bnai Levi Korah said:

"Hold yourselves off from the people, and do not tell them what to do. Not you were appointed by Moses to carry on, but men of his own flesh and blood. Let Aaron and Hur advise the people now."

And so, bewildered and increasingly frantic, the people went daily from one tent to the other, and there was no one to bring them the word of Jehovah.

The days passed, and the weeks, and the man Moses had vanished and was not.

One morning the seer Balaam came riding on his little ass into the encampment of the Israelites. From man and beast dangled innumerable icons and figurines. This time Balaam was accompanied by someone—a black Negress. She carried in her arms two naked children, who had their lips glued to the nipples of her mighty breasts, which hung down like sacks. Running along by the side of the black woman were children of various ages: mother and children, too, were adorned with figurines and teraphim.

All the icons, figurines, and teraphim were in one likeness, whether modeled in clay or stamped on tablets with hieroglyphics: the likeness of a calf.

Balaam and his companions came to a halt in the midst of the encampment opposite the tents of Dan, the stormiest and most rebellious of the tribes. He called out:

"He that would increase the fruit of his loins, let him come hither! He that desires increase of his flocks, let him approach!"

They began to assemble, the tall, hardy, broad-shouldered, stiff-necked Bnai Dan. They came out from under their black tents and encircled the seer and the Negro woman and children. They stood about him and scratched their thick-tangled beards and stared with wide-open eyes.

The icon-covered seer bowed to the circle of men:

"Peace be unto you, sons of Dan. A kinsman was your father to me, in the days of Jacob. We are of one blood, then, you and I. Your mother Bilhah was nothing less than a daughter of our tribe, by my brother, the king of Zohar. According to your descent, it is you who should have the birthright among the tribes of Jacob. For Rachel was the most beloved wife of Jacob, and so Bilhah was second only after Rachel in the eyes of Jacob. But your brother Levi snatched the birthright away from you."

"Who art thou, and whence comest thou, stranger?" asked the Bnai Dan.

"Who I am? Ask the stars, and they will tell you. My name is written among them as the revealer of the destinies they wield. Whence I come? From all the four corners of the earth. My home is as much above as it is below. My eyes and my mouth suck the light of the stars, though my feet tread the earth. He whom I bless, he is blessed; and he whom I curse, he is cursed. 'Balaam' men call me. 'The seer,' the stars call me."

"And those teraphim that thou carriest, what are they good for? Wherein is their power?" asked one of the bystanders.

"What they are good for? Oh, ask your fathers, and they will tell you; inquire of the past generations, and they will make you wise. From the land whence you came, the land whither you go, he came. Canaan is his home, and Calf is his name. He is the god of shepherds. He multiplied the seed of your father Jacob and increased his flocks when he served Laban the Aramean for his wives. Bilhah, your mother, brought him into Jacob's house; and when Jacob left Laban the Aramean, Rachel stole him from her father and hid him under the saddle of her ass, for he is also the god who opens the wombs of women and multiplies the seed of the husband. He is the god of your fathers, and he is also your god, for you will be shepherds, like your fathers. He will increase the seed of your loins and enlarge the number of your sheep."

"Scorpions in thy mouth and sand in thine eyes! The god of our fathers is Jehovah, and He is our God, Who has just given us His laws by Moses, His servant," cried one man in the circle.

"Jehovah! Jehovah! Jehovah! I know him," said the seer, thoughtfully, and shook his head. "He is a God of slaves, and you are freemen today. He is a God of poor folk, who have no oxen and no flocks, no gold and silver: but today you are rich. We have heard how you took away the wealth of the Egyptians, their gold and silver, and their earrings which you wear, their golden chains and their neckbands: free, rich men are you today. You have stripped and spoiled the Egyptians. But what shall you do with your gold and silver, with your flocks and herds, serving a God who is jealous of every pleasure which rejoices the heart of a man, a God who makes a slave of man, and binds him in the chains of His laws and commandments? What did He do with you when He called you to His festival at Sinai? He separated you from your wives and held you apart from them for three days. Is it thus that one celebrates the festival of a god? Be counseled by me, and make yourselves a festival for the god Calf: he will shower blessings upon you. You will know then what rejoicing means, what dances are, and how one drinks. Not to mention the matter of the women. For you are the manly vigor of the god. Look well at his virility—" and he pointed to the male organ of the Calf. "He will pour strength and manhood and power into your loins, and make you as he himself is. Bring your women out! Let them gaze on the god of fruitfulness. Merely looking on him they will become submissive to you; their breasts will fill with milk, their bosoms rise and fall with desire; their bellies will writhe with eagerness to receive your seed; their wombs will open, and they will bear you men-children, muscular and manly as the god himself. And as your wives, so will your sheep and cattle be, hee-hee-hee. . . . Call your wives out, and they will prove themselves yielding, as yielding as the cow is to the leaping bull. That, I say, is a god for freemen such as you are."

"Deborah! Miriam! Mafima! Fiha!" In agitated tones the men called into the tents; and one man, with red ears and blazing eyes, pulled his wife from the tent and pointed to the Calf on the images:

"Look closely, women, look closely! Just the sight of it will make you conceive!" cried Balaam. "Barren our sister was—" and he pointed to the Negro woman—"barren, accursed. Her womb was closed, sealed with seven seals. Her husband was prepared to send her away. And one of the images hung about her neck cured her and made her fruitful. Look at the springs of milk which the god has opened in her breasts. Look at the fruit of her belly. Nothing but twins, and all of them male; all of them bursting with strength, as the god himself is. Buy these teraphim, women, an unfailing charm for fruitfulness."

And in but a little while the men were tearing the rings from the women's ears, and exchanging them for the seer's Calf images to hang upon the women's throats.

"Israelites! Israelites! What is this you are doing? Bethink yourselves of Jehovah, and of the covenant He made with you! Remember the ten commandments which God declared to you! Remember the words of your response: 'All that God has spoken we will do!' Remember the Torah which Moses is now receiving from God on Sinai!" screamed an old man, with eyes that shone from a setting of bones, with a white, trembling beard, and skeletonlike arms which he lifted from his withered body as he pushed his way through the throng.

It was Hur, the ancient. Someone had run to him, had told him that an idol-worshiping priest had brought his images into the encampment. And old Hur had hastened breathlessly to the tents of the Bnai Dan. He arrived as they were hanging the images about the necks of their wives, and he went from woman to woman, tearing the images down.

Balaam broke into cackling laughter, and the saliva spurted from his toothless mouth:

"Laws and commandments! The Torah of Jehovah! Yes, to many, many peoples did Jehovah offer His laws and commandments. He sent messengers to the Egyptians, the Canaanites, the Hittites, to all of us. We would have nothing to do with the Torah

252

—none of us. And at last he found you, the dupes, the gullible ones, the fools!"

"Idolater! Abomination! Villain! Out of the encampment, abomination! Carry him forth!" And the ancient leaped like a youth at Balaam, and, tearing the images from him, threw them on the ground and stamped on them. "Out of the encampment, defiler!" He lifted his fists at Balaam.

"I am going, I am going," said Balaam, collecting the images. "But I will return. You clever sons of Dan! Do not let yourselves be sold again as slaves to Jehovah. You are free men, rich men, sons of freedom, who deserve to rejoice with their god!"

"To your tents! Moses will come, and he will punish you with his rod," cried Hur to the Bnai Dan.

"Moses will return no more. His coffin was seen in heaven, over Mount Sinai. Jehovah has killed him," called out Balaam.

"Who saw the coffin of Moses? How knowest thou that Jehovah slew him?" demanded the Bnai Dan.

"The soothsayers of Egypt have seen the coffin. I will bring them hither. You shall hear it from their mouths."

"Out, abomination! Out of God's encampment!" shrilled old Hur, and with flailing arms he pursued Balaam on his donkey.

Like a beast of prey which trails a flock in the wilderness, concealing itself in caves and gullies by day, and falling on a straggling victim by night—so Balaam had attached himself to the Israelites since the time they had left Egypt.

He was not the priest of some particular cult or god. He was a seer and counselor for every kind of idol worship; and the seekers of idolatry came to him in times of difficulty or perplexity. He was a man of hot imagination and strong emotions; he was susceptible to trances, and when transported by one he believed himself to be possessed of a spirit. Then he would have visions, and prophesy. But he was before all else an expert as a curser, and it was chiefly as a dispenser of maledictions and imprecations that he served peoples and idolatrous cults. Peoples went to war with each other on the strength of his curses. When the leader of a host was preparing an attack, he sent for Balaam and hired him to place the interdict of his anathema on the enemy, crippling his arms and paralyzing his strength.

Balaam believed in all the demons and worshiped all the idols.

But like Jethro he also believed that there was a higher Spirit over all the gods, He that was called Jehovah. But contrariwise to Jethro, he would not submit to the authority of Jehovah and would not worship Him among the local gods. He rebelled against Jehovah, in the name and for the benefit of the other gods. He knew that the Eternal God had declared war on the other gods and was therefore a deadly threat to their existence; and he did all that lay in his power to undermine the authority of Jehovah and to weaken Him.

The greatest defeat he had ever suffered had been the conversion of the Israelites by Moses to the worship of Jehovah; and he was mortally concerned with creating a rift between the people and its leader. A shrewd knower of men, Balaam had foreseen that Moses would encounter enormous difficulties in putting into practice the laws and commandments; and he waited, waited for the propitious moment when he would be able to steal like a fox into the garden which Moses had planted for Jehovah. He had foreseen the day when the Bnai Israel would grow impatient and rebellious, prepared to throw off the yoke which Jehovah had placed on their necks. That would be his opportunity.

And the day came when Moses vanished into the cloud on Sinai; when the Bnai Israel became confused, restless, and distracted; when the intrigues over the priesthood divided the camp, setting Aaron and his sons against Korah and his followers, adding to the panic created by the protracted and inexplicable absence of Moses. Already with the proclamation of the ten commandments on Sinai, with their preamble which sounded the death knell of idols, Balaam had carried the alarm to all the priesthoods; and a breath of terror had passed across the priestly hierarchies, and, not less, across the rulers of the peoples whom Jehovah was preparing to drive from their land, to make room for the Bnai Israel.

Balaam also had his spies in the encampment, recruited among the mixed multitude which had accompanied the Israelites out of Egypt. From them he learned in detail of every incident, of every turn of affairs; and when he received the first reports of the despair which took hold of the Israelites with the vanishing of Moses, he called together his friends among the priests of the cults and took counsel with them. Their decision was to send a number of idolatrous priests into the encampment with the help of the spies, and so to work on the confusion, so to enhance it, as to drive the Israelites into the arms of the gods.

254

Balaam was as good as his word. He returned to the encampment, as he had promised old Hur. Driven out at one gate, he returned by a dozen others. And at every return he brought with him new testimony of the power of his gods and the weakness of the rule of Jehovah, which was now tottering to its fall.

He brought into the encampment two celebrated magicians of Egypt, Yanes and Yambres, who were in fact said to be his sons. In their fantastic, star-embroidered robes, in their towering headgear, they showed their magic arts in a hundred different ways among the Israelites. They pointed to the stars, and read into them all manner of predictions; they showed the Israelites the Heavenly Cow, which reigned above in the night, as the sun reigned by day; they outlined the scorpions and lizards and beasts which reveal themselves in the constellations; and they persuaded the Israelites that they could see the coffin of Moses floating in the sky above Mount Sinai.

"See! See! There it floats—the ark in which Jehovah has concealed Moses. Do you see? Just such a coffin as the one in which you carry Joseph's bones from Egypt. There it is, hanging over Sinai. Beyond all doubt, Jehovah has slain Moses, as He does all that come too near to Him, for He cannot tolerate that a man, or even a god, should meet with Him face to face."

"Yes! It is indeed so! Moses warned us not to touch God's holy mountain, lest He slay us."

"Then our lives hang by a hair. For how can a man of flesh and blood avoid moving Jehovah to anger, one way or another, and forfeiting his life?"

"Who can stand in His presence?"

The spies whom Balaam had sown among the mixed multitude became active in spreading the report throughout the camp:

"Moses has been slain! Jehovah consumed him as a lion consumes a sheep. We have seen his coffin floating in the sky, above Mount Sinai."

A wailing went up from the camp: "Moses is slain! Jehovah has slain him!"

And Israel became like a whore: but yesterday standing under the bridal canopy with Jehovah, today prepared to receive all comers, all offers of idols and idolatry.

Balaam next brought into the encampment his friend Naaram, a priest of the goddess Ashtoreth. A beautiful, tenderly nurtured youth was Naaram, with a young, neatly curled beard, with a painted face, eyes ringed with kohl, blue-tinted lips; but he was garbed like a woman, he had the breasts of a woman, and he spoke in a shrill, feminine voice. He came in a carriage filled with Ashtoreth images carved in wood; and four naked girls, with thin golden chains over their sex, drew the carriage. And he presented to the Bnai Israel the goddess with the spreading hips, with the dove pressed to her overflowing breasts:

"Here is the goddess of love. For those that believe in her she unveils all the hidden mysteries of lust, all the delights of desire, whether for man or woman, of love for the flesh of others, of love for one's own flesh. Those who become her followers and adepts she blesses with the blessing of double sex, so that they become equally serviceable as men or as women."

Balaam went so far as to introduce into the camp of Israel his friend Bors, priest of the god Moloch, a man with a naked, swollen belly, great hairy hands, thick lips smeared with blood, and a large, hideous blood sign on his forehead. This priest presented the image of his god to the Israelites—a figure with an animal head and double horns like those of an ox protruding from a human face: the gaping mouth displayed the fangs of a wild beast. The belly of the idol, which was swollen, like the belly of the priest, had a slit which revealed the fire always blazing inside.

"My god is the god of storm and thunder. But he is likewise the god of rain and dew. When he feels in his mouth the soft, delicate flesh of a child; when his tongue is refreshed with the sweet taste of flowing blood, and his teeth close crunching on a marrowy bone; then he grows gentle and mild, and he sends the drizzling rain which makes fruitful not only your fields, for the growing grain, but likewise the cattle in the stall, and the wives in your embraces."

The Hebrews, for all their long enslavement in Egypt, had never lost the traces of the bright heritage of their forefathers. Their essentially healthy natures were unresponsive to the corrupt and refined lusts of the double sex which was the gift of the goddess Ashtoreth to her followers. Still less were they tempted by the fetid pleasure of hearing the god Moloch crunch the bones of a sacrificed child. But as against these things the instinct of reproduction, of begetting and multiplying, which had remained powerful within them even in Egyptian days, drew them to the cult of Calf. The Calf image tempted them, where the foul Moloch god and the barren lusts of the Ashtoreth left them cold. Children! Yes! The multiplying of the flocks and herds—that too! They desired nothing, they would hear of nothing, but Calf.

And suddenly the throats of the men and women throughout the camp were adorned with little hanging images of Calf. In vain did Hur, together with certain members of the tribe of Judah, threaten them with the memory of the avenging rod of Moses. It was as if the Calf cult had entered into their blood through a magic philter, overcoming all reflection and reluctance. Even the more thoughtful among them yielded to the infection. Elderly men and women who but a little while back had been shouting at Sinai: "All that God has spoken we will do" were now to be seen parading in the precious ornament of the Calf image.

Like apes which, seized with terror in the darkness of night, take refuge in the frenzy of copulation, so did the Bnai Israel, captured by the Calf cult, find in the lusts of the flesh respite from their perplexity and wretchedness. But the Calf idol swiftly became something more than a provocation to lust; it took on the character of a rescuer and savior; it would liberate them from the desert; the god who had led them out of Egypt would lead them into the land of their fathers.

In a blind confusion of lust and of panic terror which lust could not wholly overcome, they swarmed to Aaron's tent. There they stood, young men and elderly men, men with thick, curled black beards, and men with white beards and lack-luster eyes; men with powerfully arched chests; and men whose enfeebled bodies had never recovered from the slavery under Pharaoh. There were Hebrews and non-Hebrews; there were faces burned by the sun, and faces black from birth. There were women with tousled hair and uncovered breasts—young breasts, like apples, and breasts that were like empty water skins. And all of them, men and women, young and old, were shouting and protesting, were demanding, with outstretched arms and angry eyes:

"Rise, and make us a god to go before us, for the man Moses who brought us out of Egypt is gone—we know not what has become of him."

This was what Nadab and Abihu had been waiting for. They said to their father:

"Here is thy opportunity to show Moses that dry laws and commandments are not enough to nourish a people. A people must have a tabernacle, a sanctuary, an altar, a hierarchy of priests; it must have festivals and dances, song and freedom—else it will make itself a Calf image. Do thou make them a Calf image."

And Aaron agreed.

To the men in the multitude he said: "Take the big earrings from the ears of your wives and sons and daughters, and bring them to me."

They obeyed him; they snatched the earrings from the women folk and the young ones; they added their own earrings; they threw them in a heap at Aaron's feet.

Then there was a searching in the camp for men skilled in metal-work and woodwork, and under their hands the images began to emerge. The trunk of a twisted tree became a Calf with exaggerated organs of sex. A fire was lit, the golden ornaments were thrown into the melting pot. The smiths hammered and stamped, the sheeted gold was poured over the Calf image: a coarse and clumsy figure it was, the head being that of a calf, its lower parts those of an ox.

Aaron himself, the high priest, took a hand in the work.

Even before the image was completed a multitude, most of them of the strangers, under the lead of Balaam's infiltrated men, were chanting:

"This is thy god, O Israel, who brought thee forth from Egypt!" And while they looked at the image in the making, they kissed and fondled the figurines dangling round their necks.

And now Aaron perceived that things had gone too far, and the people was being carried away in drunken acceptance of the Calf idol. His intentions had been otherwise. He had played for time. Perhaps on the morrow Moses would return. Before he left he had mentioned something about a period of forty days on the mountain —the period was drawing to its close. Meanwhile, with these thoughts in mind, Aaron bade them erect an altar, and again he put his hand to the work, he and his sons. The day was drawing to a close—the day had been won. Too late now to begin festivities.

"Return betimes tomorrow!" he said to the people. "Tomorrow the festival to Jehovah will be held."

The festival to Jehovah! He would make it a festival to Jehovah! He would, if need be, bring the Calf idol into the service of Jehovah. This was his comfort and his self-vindication for his seeming betrayal of his trust.

"To your tents!" he cried again. "The festival will be held to-morrow."

But the people would not budge. They would have their festival now. Many had lain down about the completed image, as if to guard it. The festival must begin now—and extend into the night.

Fires were lit under the starry sky, and groups of delirious men and women circled about them in dance, crying out wildly. The flames increased, their lurid light was thrown up at the underside of the cloud that hung over Sinai. A terrible and oppressive spirit emanated from the massive bulk of the cloud: it was as if invisible hands, clenched into angry fists, extended down from it, stupefying the desert. But the Bnai Israel remarked nothing of this. They kept their eyes averted from the mountain while they leaped and screamed in the intoxication of their new worship, and unobserved by them the majesty of Jehovah rested on the vast desert spaces.

The night was inundated by an immeasurable shamelessness. It was as if all the black demons, all the idolatries and abominations had assembled in the encampment of the Israelites to fight the last, decisive battle with Jehovah. From among the tents of the Bnai Israel drunken voices ascended. Men defiled women in the open, under the stars, and committed all manner of abominations. Maddened by the lusts which the Calf god had set loose in them, they broke through all restraints and prohibitions; they erased from their hearts every law that blood, inheritance, tradition, and the glory of the fathers had sustained in them during the years of their slavery. It was as though the Bnai Israel had gone wild with the desire to avenge themselves for all the humiliations and sufferings to which God had condemned them in the long period of their Egyptian bondage.

And there was no one to put a restraining hand on them. Fear of the mass frenzy paralyzed the new leaders, the councilors whom Moses had set up as the new elders of Israel. They hid themselves wherever they could to escape the notice of the intoxicated multitude. Korah and his followers, who knew the people, and who even at this pass might have had some influence over them, deliberately held off, to incur no responsibility. "Aaron and Hur are the leaders," they said. But they were not altogether easy as to their decision; for when they saw Aaron himself, the brother of Moses, the next in line before the Divinity, apparently taking the lead in the uprising, even putting his hand to the making of the Calf god and

259

the erecting of the altar, they said to themselves: "Who knows but what there is some purpose in all this?"

And so the congregation of God was delivered over by its leaders into the hands of the Evil One.

The only one to make a stand, to interpose himself between the Bnai Israel and the Evil One, hoping, with his feeble body and blazing faith, to serve as a barrier between them, was Hur, the second deputy appointed by Moses.

When Aaron consented to take a hand in the pouring of the gold for the Calf god, he sent for Bezalel, the grandson of Hur, who had been known in Egypt as a master goldsmith and architect of palaces. But Bezalel could not be found; Miriam had concealed him in a cave; and she, together with Hur, her husband, sought out Aaron, threw themselves at his feet, and pleaded with him:

"Aaron, Aaron, thou art the oldest in the house of Amram! What is this thing thou doest?"

"It is the will of the people," answered Aaron. "I will not oppose their will, lest they tear me to pieces."

"Is it not better to be slain than to fall into sin against God?" asked Hur.

"God is good, and He will forgive us. Moses will plead for us."

But Nadab and Abihu, who were present in Aaron's tent, became impatient with the intruders: "Get you gone from here, old people; get you gone."

Miriam and Hur went in search of Korah. They found him at length and said to him:

"Korah, Korah, thou art the elder of the tribe of Levi. Arise, and save Israel from the jaws of the Evil One. Thou and the Bnai Levi."

"He who betrayed the Israelites to the Evil One, let him save them. Thou, Hur, thou and Aaron are the leaders. We are the excluded ones—" and Korah pulled to the curtain of his tent.

Then Hur ran to his own tribe, the Bnai Judah. He woke from their sleep Nachshon ben Aminadab and Caleb ben Yephunneh, the leaders, and said to them:

"Come out with me, you sons of Judah, to whom it will be given to rule over the Bnai Israel, and hold them back from worshiping the Calf god, lest they lose thereby their birthright among all the peoples of God."

They answered: "Our time is not yet come. Let those take the splinter out from the flesh of the lion who have put it there. We cannot make whole that which Aaron has broken."

And now, perceiving that there was no one to hold back Israel from sinking into the abyss, Hur said: I will put my own body as a barrier before Israel, to prevent him from falling."

And he went and stationed himself at the gate of the encampment, to hold the people back from approaching the Calf god.

In the meantime the morning star had arisen; at his rising the heavens were flooded with fire and blood, and the blue-white clouds were edged with crimson.

And the Bnai Israel came out of their tents and ascended the rocky terraces to seek and collect their daily nourishment.

And on this day God did not diminish their bread, and they gathered it, an omer for each man—for they found it waiting for them as they had found it on the yesterday, and the day before. And they gathered it in their baskets and carried it into their tents.

And soon they came forth for the festival. They came by families, with their wives and daughters. And they were adorned with all the finery that God had given them, with all the spoils of Egypt: they shone in golden chains, in chaplets set with rubies, sapphires, and amethysts, in jeweled stomachers, earrings, finger rings, and bracelets. The women had covered their nakedness with blue-dyed silk, with fine wool and delicate linen; their heads were crowned with mountain flowers, and at their necks, hanging down and dancing between their breasts, were the little images of the Calf god. In their hands they carried baskets of manna, God's bread, to bring as an offering to their new idol. And they marched in high, festive mood. The flutes shrilled before them, the cymbals clashed, and they advanced with dancing steps, singing to their new god.

At the gate of the encampment two weak old arms blocked their way, and an ancient, feeble breast opposed them like a shield. Two blazing eyes shot fiery arrows at them, and a voice which seemed to be issuing from some deep cavern, a voice which had wrestled there with evil and with death, threatened and pleaded:

"Brothers of the house of Israel! Remember the oath which you swore to Jehovah! Remember the holy covenant which you made with Him. Go not to the idol! Go not! Jehovah is your God."

"Out of the way, old man, lest you be trodden underfoot," they answered.

But the old man would not budge. He stood his ground, he took hold of their limbs and their clothes and impeded their progress.

"Remember the covenant which your forefathers Abraham, Isaac, and Jacob made for your sakes with Jehovah!"

"And if our forefathers sold us as slaves to Jehovah, shall we forever remain so? Today we are freemen."

But the old man clung to them frantically, held on with unnatural strength to their limbs and clothes, still arguing fiercely:

"God made you a chosen people, to be a light to the peoples of the world, so that from you salvation and redemption might come. . . ."

He did not finish his plea. They flung him down, trod him underfoot, did not even take the trouble to push his body aside, but marched straight over it.

They came before Aaron, who was already waiting at the altar. And he brought a burnt offering and a peace offering before the Calf god, which stood glistering in the sunlight.

And they stuffed their bellies with food, and swilled, and made merry; and the sound of their laughter and rejoicing went up to heaven.

But from heaven a voice was heard, the voice of a woman, filling all space with lamentation and weeping. It was the voice of Mother Rachel which was heard in the heights, mourning over her children.

For that day was a day of Satan; and all the evil decrees, the persecutions and tribulations which the children of Israel were to encounter and endure throughout all the ages to come, were written down and sealed on that day.

CHAPTER EIGHT

AFTER forty days and forty nights Moses came down from the mountain. At the foot he found Joshua, his servant, who had been waiting for him.

And when Joshua beheld Moses coming out of the cloud which covered the mountain as far as the base, he closed his eyes. He was afraid to look into the face of Moses. For it seemed to him that he did not recognize his leader and teacher. Moses was covered with a dense growth of long, white hair, white eyebrows, and a white, spreading beard, and from the midst of this white growth his mighty countenance radiated light like a sun. His giant frame was concealed under a white mantle which blazed like silver in the sunlight. In his arms, held high, he carried the mystic stone tablets on which flickered, in fiery letters, the ten commandments.

He was silent when he rejoined his servant, silent as he walked with him, remote from his surroundings. He was wrapped in a mysterious cloud of his own, as if he were still in that ineffable world where he had wrestled with angels and demons for God's word. But there did not rest upon him that spirit of exalted joy which Joshua had thought to encounter; instead, there was a meditative sadness. The face shining amidst the white hair was melancholy and immobile—darkness in the midst of light.

Joshua felt that Moses knew something had happened in the congregation, hence the heavy concern which weighed upon him. But Joshua was afraid to ask; he was even afraid to look straight at him. He only knew that by his side strode a man who had for forty days and forty nights sojourned in the heavens with God and the heavenly hosts and who now carried in his arms the tablets on which the fiery letters had been inscribed by God's own hand. And in the eyes of Joshua this man was transformed into an angel of the Lord, and he was afraid of him.

And Moses remained silent, guarding within what God had said to him.

263

For God had said:

"Go down; for the people which thou broughtest out of Egypt has become corrupt."

Moreover, God had proposed to create a new people from the seed of Moses himself, saying: "I will make of thee a great nation."

But at once, in the heavens, Moses had replied that he did not want to be the father of another people; his desire was toward this people, the children of Abraham, Isaac, and Jacob, which God had brought forth out of Egypt with a mighty hand. "And why should the Egyptians say, for an evil purpose didst Thou bring them out of Egypt, to slay them among the mountains? Not for them, and not for me, but for Thee, for Thy name, Thy glory, and Thy oath, which thou hast sworn to Thy servants Abraham, Isaac, and Jacob."

And in the heavens Moses had damped the first fires of God's anger. God had repented; He would not annihilate this people. He would not bring upon it the evil which He had intended in His first hot fury.

Nevertheless, Moses did not know what God's intention was: would He bring the Bnai Israel into the land which He had promised them, or would He not? And Moses was heavyhearted in his uncertainty; but he concealed his thoughts and spoke no word of them to Joshua; and the two went on silently side by side.

When they had left the last foothills and arrived on the stony plateau, they heard the shouting and the tumult re-echoing from the valley of the encampment.

Joshua, tense with the feeling of the approaching danger, said: "A sound of war comes up from the camp."

"No; I do not hear the voice of those that shout in triumph, nor the voice of those that cry in defeat. It is a sound of singing I hear," answered Moses.

And he marched on, holding tight to his breast the stone tables on which glittered in flame the letters of the ten commandments, graven on both sides by God's graver of fire. He pressed them tight to his breast as if he sought in them shelter and counsel against the hour of need, and his silence boded evil.

They came at length to the rim of the rocky plateau whence the steep slope led into the encampment. And Moses saw them: in the multicolored robes thrown loosely about them, they were dancing a wild dance about the Calf god, which glittered on a high altar. He heard clearly now the wild shrieks, the singing, the howling, and the ejaculations. And he remained standing on the rim of the plateau. He put his face against the edge of the stone tablets and stood thus a long time, like an image hewn in stone. Then his body started convulsively into life, as though lightning had struck it. He lifted the tablets and flung them heavenward with all his strength, as if to say: "Return to the place whence you came!"

The tablets fell and were shattered, and the fragments began to roll down the slopes into the valley. The echo of the crash beat back from the valley and against the mountaintops, wandering into distant spaces. It was as if a cry of pain had issued from the letters on the tablets, as they ascended again to heaven.

With mighty footsteps Moses descended into the valley, leaping like a youth from crag to crag in the impetus of his fury. Joshua, following, was left far behind.

And like a whip of flame Moses cut his way into the camp, flinging to right and left with his mighty arms the startled revelers. They knew him at once, and panic spread swiftly among them. The dance was arrested, the voices stilled, heads were suddenly bowed, and bodies sank to the earth.

Moses did not utter a word. In his white-blazing mantle he strode through to the altar. With his own hands he took hold of the abominable image, flung it down with mighty force over the heads of the worshipers, so that it fell asunder, then cast the pieces into the fire which burned on the altar. The wooden parts of the image were consumed, the gold melted. Then Moses spoke: he bade them take the melted gold, mix it with the ashes of the consumed wood, grind the mixture between millstones, and cast the dust into the pool formed by one of the cascades descending from the hills.

Then he commanded Joshua: "Drive them to the pool, and make them drink of the water, like whores!"

The people started away in terror. The water was poisoned with the dust and ashes of the idol. Their bellies would swell up if they drank. They turned and refused, and sought to flee to their tents. But Joshua and his young men surrounded them, drove them back, compelled them to stoop and drink of the water.

Moses saw Aaron standing by the altar. Him too he should have compelled to drink of the poisoned waters, with the rest of the idol worshipers. But he contained himself. He only drew near to Aaron and asked wrathfully:

265

"What did the people do to thee that thou shouldst have brought this great sin upon them?"

Aaron, white with fear and trembling from head to foot, bowed his head in shame and began to stammer:

"Let not the anger of my lord be hot against me. Thou knowest the people, that its inclination is evil. They came to me and said: Make us a god which shall go before us, for the man Moses, who brought us out of Egypt, is gone, and we know not what has become of him. And I said to them: He that has gold, let him take it off. And they gave me the gold, and I cast it into the fire, and there came out this Calf."

A bitter smile came over the lips of Moses, as if he had tasted a poisonous root; he could not but smile at his brother's childish excuse. He looked at Aaron contemptuously and asked:

"Where is Hur?"

"Hur is dead. They trampled him to death when he attempted to hold them back from their idol worship."

The face of Moses became darker still, his eyes clouded over, and his breath came heavily:

"Where are the elders, the elders of Israel?" he demanded, harshly.

It took a little time before Joshua and his young men could find and drag out from their hiding places a handful of the elders.

"Why did you let this great sin fall upon the people? Why did you not hold them back?"

"We were afraid that they would do with us what they did with Hur," answered the elders, trembling.

Moses looked at them in disgust. "You were afraid! Ah, Jehovah, Jehovah, the fault is mine! See to whom I entrusted the Bnai Israel!" The note of sorrow changed again to anger. "Drive them into the midst of the people!" he commanded. "Their sin is as great!"

Then Moses turned and looked at the multitude lying scattered on the plateau; and suddenly he perceived the figurines of the Calf god hanging from the necks of the men or dangling between the breasts of the women. And there were not a few among them who, lying naked on the ground because they had cast off every vestige of clothing in the wild dance about the idol, were fondling the foul images even at this moment—fondling them, kissing them, as if imploring them for rescue from the hand of Moses and the wrath

266

of God. And at this sight there was awakened in Moses such anger as he had not known till then.

This was not the people for whose sake Jehovah Himself had come down from heaven! This was not the people with whom He had made a covenant! Not the children of Abraham, Isaac, and Jacob, but a hideous slave rabble without discipline and without law. "It is Aaron who has brought them to this wild condition, Aaron and the elders to whom I entrusted them." And his anger flamed up still hotter in him, so that suddenly he sprang away from the altar, leaped to the gate of the camp, and thundered:

"He that is with Jehovah, let him come to my side!"

There ran toward him the sons of the tribe of Levi and gathered about him.

"This is the word of the Lord God of Israel. Let every man take up his sword and go through the camp from gate to gate, and find the guilty, and slay them, every man his brother, and every man his companion, and every man his neighbor."

This was the word for which the Bnai Levi had been waiting. They knew the people, they knew the leaders and the guilty ones, they knew everyone who had a part in the setting up of the abomination. And they went through the camp, dragging out men and women, young and old, to the slaughter. And soon the bodies of the dying were rolling on the plateau, and their blood ran between the stones. The air was filled with shrieking and lamenting and the sound of the death rattle. And when the execution had been completed Moses said to the Bnai Levi:

"This day you have consecrated your hands to the Lord, because you have not spared your own sons and brothers. Through you may blessing come."

Then he went to his tent, to meditate on what was to be done.

There he found Miriam, whom Bezalel had brought to him. She had covered her snow-white head and her shriveled body in the black mantle of widowhood. She bowed before Moses, but he approached her, embraced her, and said:

"My sister Miriam! Thy brother Aaron has slain Hur. Thy husband's blood is on his head."

"Son of Amram, I have come to implore thee for my brother Aaron."

"I know not yet what is to be done with him. I shall inquire of God."

"But thy brother Aaron knows well what thou shouldst do with him. He has come to the door of thy tent with his clothes torn, with ashes upon his head and a rope about his neck. And thou shalt do with him what thou hast commanded the others to do with their brothers and sons. Arise, son of Amram, and slay thy brother, as the others have done."

Moses paled. Miriam had put into words what had been in his thoughts. It had indeed been in his mind to deal with Aaron as with the other worshipers of the idol. Hearing the words now explicitly from his sister, he took fright at his own intentions. In that instant there rose before him the image of his brother, as he had stood with him before Pharaoh, and with the rod which God had given him had wrought the miracles: his brother Aaron, his companion in God's mission.

He started out of his painful meditations and said: "Where is he?"

"He stands at thy door, awaiting thy judgment."

"Go, bring him in, Bezalel," commanded Moses.

When Aaron entered he threw himself at the feet of Moses, stretched out his hands and cried:

"My lord and master, do with thy servant what seems good in the eyes of God, for thy servant has sinned greatly against his God and his people."

And Aaron remained lying with his face to the earth.

Moses stared down at the torn clothes, at the ashes, at the rope about his brother's neck, and his heart contracted with compassion. It occurred to him on the instant that as he would deal with Aaron, so God would deal with His people. How could he implore God's mercy and forgiveness on Israel if he could not show mercy and forgiveness toward his own brother? But what of the others? What of those brothers whom he had ordered to be slain by *their* brothers? The question harassed and burned him; it was as if a white-hot spear had been thrust into his flesh. No—he could not resolve the question. He would bring it before God; and as God decided, so he would act. But meanwhile his brother lay at his feet in the raiment of a son of death. This was Aaron! This was the Aaron whom God had shown him in heaven, in a vision, robed in the raiment of the high priesthood! He bent down to his brother, lifted him from the earth and said:

"It is not becoming that thou, who wert prepared to conduct the

268

service before the All Highest, shouldst wear the clothes of a son of death." And he made his brother sit down by him and said, in anguish, but without anger:

"Aaron, Aaron, what is this that thou hast done?" And he repeated: "What did the people do to thee that thou shouldst have brought this great sin upon them?"

"I did it for Jehovah and for thee," said Aaron.

"For Jehovah thou didst erect an altar to the idol?" asked Moses, his anger starting up again.

"As thou hearest," answered Aaron, and he spoke more confidently now. "Yes, for Jehovah and for thee, in order that Jehovah might see how the people thirst after Him. The people demand that God shall be among them, shall be in their midst, that they shall see God, hear Him, and know that He goes before them. The people live in everlasting fear. These were slaves in Egypt whom thou broughtest into a stony wilderness. The sun burns above, and under their feet the earth is copper; for their bread they must look to heaven, for their water to the crags. Surrounded forever by enemies, who await the chance to destroy them, the Bnai Israel are forever in terror. They are in terror lest they commit a sin and the heavens will cease to rain bread, the rocks will cease to send out water, the enemy will descend on them. Therefore they must know, see, and hear the presence of God in their midst, feel that He guides them always with His own hand, and not only through wonders and miracles, with thunder and lightning from the mountaintop. And when thou, brother Moses, didst close thyself off with thy God in the cloud, remaining there many long days, the people felt itself lost, without strength, without guidance. They came to me and demanded that I make them a god. Had I not done it, they would have slain me, as they slew Hur. And they would have turned to Korah. Korah would have done their will. And had he once acquired power over the people, it would have been much harder for thee to win them back to Jehovah. For Korah would not have made the Calf god as I did, who declared a festival for Jehovah. He would have made the Calf god for its own sake, so that he might thereby win dominion over the people."

Moses listened to all that his brother had to say and turned the matter over in his mind. He knew only too well Korah's ambitions, his lust for the priesthood which would have made him the ruler of the people. And surely there was some satisfaction in this—that

269

the Bnai Levi had not participated in the sin and had responded to his call and had carried out his command. It was not good that he should have been forced to slay three thousand from among the host, though the Bnai Levi had received their meed of praise for the act; and even less desirable was it that he should have had to call upon them, upon the Bnai Levi, to vindicate his leadership. And worst of all would it be that he should have to transfer the priestly dynasty to Korah. Yet it seemed to him that he had no alternative.

He betrayed nothing to Aaron, but said: "Thou sayest that the Bnai Israel had no one to lead them when I went up the mountain to God. Did I not leave them the commandments which God gave them from Sinai? And did they not all answer with one voice: 'All that the Lord hath spoken we will do and obey'?"

"Son of Amram, have I not warned thee time and again that a people cannot live with laws and commandments alone? A people must have something more. It must feel that God is with it, in it, among it. And if it cannot unite with its God by meeting Him face to face—for no one shall look upon God and live—then it must at least reach out to Him through a service for Him. It will come before God and cleave to Him through the sacrifices which it brings. And not in every chance place can this sacrifice be brought to Him, but in a special place designated for Him, so that the people know that God is there. We are not able to grasp the infinite. We cannot image forth the invisible. And even as our feet must rest upon the ground, and our bodies must find themselves in some limitation of space, so must our imaginings turn to a designated place which our eyes can see. Therefore the people must have a tabernacle, in which it knows that God rests: an altar, upon which alone the sacrifice can be brought; and a priest whose office is from God, and who alone has been chosen and sanctified for the fulfillment of this sacred mission. The people is rich, the people has gold; the people desires to build a home for its God, so that God shall always be in its midst. We have with us our kinsman Bezalel, on whom God has poured out the spirit of craftsmanship. He has studied the arts and crafts among the Egyptians. He is skilled in the making of many things, working in gold, and silver, and copper, in the chiseling of stones and the cutting of wood, and in every craft. Command the people that they redeem themselves from the sin of the Calf god with their gold and silver, with the silks

270

and woven stuffs of their wives, with their ornaments and precious stones—all that they took from Egypt. And create a tabernacle for Jehovah which shall be far more beautiful, far more majestic, far richer, than any of the sanctuaries of the Egyptians. And let this tabernacle be with the people, and let it go with the people. And when the Bnai Israel will see the tabernacle in their midst, they will know that God is with them, and they will fear to sin against Him, and they will rejoice in His presence among them, and will be filled with contentment because of His glory and splendor."

Moses listened long and earnestly, and was silent. Then at last he said:

"Aaron, Aaron, thou hast brought a great sin upon the people, and hast defiled it in the eyes of Jehovah. Jehovah must first purify the people from its uncleanliness, free it from its sin, and free thee, too. I know not what God's intention is now toward His people, or toward me, and I can do nothing alone; I cannot speak yea or nay, I cannot turn to the right or left, for good or bad, until I have been shown His will. Therefore go home, and wash thyself, and eat bread. Tomorrow we shall know what is to be done."

Moses did not sleep that night. He lay awake upon his couch, and Joshua his servant sat at the door of the tent. And Moses prayed in his heart, and revolved in his mind the words of Aaron. Far otherwise had been the intentions of Moses toward his people; he had dreamed of very different foundations; he had not wanted anything but a pure ritual to express their relationship to God; and the bond between them and God was to have been the heart in its purity. He had not succeeded. He began to perceive that Aaron was right. The people was too young, too unschooled, to attain to that high level of pure union with God through the will alone. Perhaps it was best, then, that the people which had failed and fallen in the making of an idol, should rehabilitate itself by the creation of a tabernacle, and that Aaron, who had occasioned their impurity by his service before the Calf god, should purify them by his worship before Jehovah.

In the morning Moses had the people assembled, and he stood up in their midst and said:

"You have sinned greatly. And now I will beseech God, and it may be that he will forgive you your transgression."

He returned to his tent and withdrew behind the inner curtain. And his servant Joshua stood at the entrance of the tent and let

271

no one approach, so that he might not be disturbed in his prayer. And Moses threw himself upon the earth, and lifted his hands, and cried:

"Jehovah, Jehovah! Hear me!"

He waited in great anxiety of spirit, not speaking again until he felt that Jehovah was hovering above him, and heard his voice. Then he said:

"I am not a man of speech, neither was I gifted with speech yesterday or the day before, and I know not how to pray to Thee. I beseech Thee, instruct me how to address Thee, and hearken to my supplication and my cry."

And after a while he continued:

"This people has sinned a great sin. It has made itself a god of gold. And now, incline Thine ear to my prayer. If Thou wilt, forgive this people; and if not, blot me out, I pray Thee, from the book which Thou hast written."

And Jehovah answered him:

"He that has sinned against Me, him will I blot out of My book. And now go, lead this people to the place of which I have spoken unto thee. Behold, My angel shall go before thee. Nevertheless, in the day of My visitation, I shall visit their sin upon them."

And this message of Jehovah to Moses was transmitted to the people, and they mourned.

And God appeared to Moses again and said:

"Speak to the children of Israel and say: A stiff-necked people are ye. If I come up one instant among you, I will consume you. And now, take off your ornaments, and I will consider what is to be done to you."

Then the children of Israel stripped themselves of their ornaments by Mount Horeb.

And Moses did not do as God had bidden him. He did not lead the people forth from this place. He only took his own tent and had it carried a distance outside the camp, far from his own. He wished to be alone with God. And he called his tent *Ohel Moad,* the tent of revelation, so that the people might know that there God revealed Himself to him. And to this place came every man who sought God.

Then it happened that when Moses went from the camp to the tent of revelation all the people came forth and stood, each man before the entrance of his tent. And they kept their eyes on Moses, and whispered fearfully among themselves:

"He goes there now to meet with Jehovah."

And when Moses entered the tent, a pillar of cloud came down and rested before the entrance, and a voice was heard issuing from it. And the people seeing the pillar of cloud before the tent bowed themselves down, and worshiped, each man at the door of his tent, and they said:

"Surely now Jehovah speaks face to face with Moses, as a man speaks with his friend."

And Moses came and went between his tent and the camp, but his servant Joshua, the son of Nun, never left the tent.

And the people knew that Moses communed with God concerning them, and they were afraid of His anger. But they were also reassured in the knowledge that they were not abandoned and that Moses was interceding for them.

And still Moses did not cause the host to move from this place.

He stood in his tent, and the pillar of cloud was before the entrance. And he spoke to the pillar of cloud as a man speaks to a man; and a voice answered him out of the cloud.

"Thou hast commanded me to go forth from this place and to bring the people to the land which Thou has promised to their fathers; but Thou hast not let me know whom Thou wilt send with me. Yet thou didst once say to me: 'I have chosen thee to know Me by My name, and thou hast found grace in Mine eyes.' Now, therefore, I pray Thee, if I have found grace in Thine eyes, show me Thy ways, that I may know Thee. And behold, this people for which I plead before Thee, it is Thy people, too."

And God answered Moses out of the cloud:

"My presence shall go with thee and I will be with thee."

But Moses would not content himself with these words. He stood his ground stubbornly even before Jehovah; he would not cause the congregation to move from this place. It was as though he was intent on testing Jehovah, so that he might know how far his power and authority went. And he said:

"If Thy presence go not with us, in the sight of all of us, carry us not up from this place. For how shall it be known that I have indeed found grace in thine eyes, I and Thy people, if not by Thy presence among us? How else shall the world see that we are separated to thee, I and Thy people, from among all the peoples on the face of the earth?"

And God yielded to Moses, and His voice was heard from the cloud:

"This thing too, that thou askest, I will do. For thou hast found grace in My sight, and I have known thee and distinguished thee by My name."

And in this moment of deep and mystic communion with God, Moses was seized with a fierce desire to look direct on the glory of God, this God upon Whom all his life and ways and work were founded. And he prayed:

"I beseech Thee, show me Thy glory!"

And God answered him: "I will make all My goodness pass before thee, and I will utter before thee the name of Jehovah; and I will be gracious to those on whom I bestow My grace, and I will be merciful to those on whom I bestow My mercy. But My face thou canst not see, for no man shall see Me and live. And now, hew thee out two tables of stone, like the first, and I will write upon them the words which were upon the first tables, which thou didst break. And be prepared in the morning, and come up in the morning on Mount Sinai, and present thyself to Me on the summit. And no man shall come up with thee, nor let any man be seen throughout the mountain."

CHAPTER NINE

ON this occasion Moses decided to leave Joshua with the congregation, knowing that it would be secure in his care.

He arose with the first glimmer of light, and taking with him the two tablets which he had hewn out the night before, he began his lonely ascent of the mountain.

When he left the plateau of Mount Horeb and came on to the slopes of Sinai, he was astounded by what he saw about him. Had God transformed the landscape for him, here in the heart of the copper mountains, and laid down for him a pleasant path of tender herbage? On either side of him little brooks tumbled out from the midst of the hills. The standing pools were rimmed with a green growth of plants, some of them familiar to him, others quite unknown. And everywhere he saw growths of myrtle. The spiral-shaped buds spread out in a mosaic tapestry; and out of the buds were wafted sweet perfumes, like the perfumes of all manner of precious herbs.

It was not simply that the plant life here was different from that of the wilderness; it was rather as if the whole order of nature had undergone a transformation. He beheld trees which stood out like mighty arms from the mist-filled clefts of the hills, their roots mantled with moss and their bark with creepers bearing incense-fragrant buds and leaves. The pungent aroma of ginger, the pepper-sharp touch of cloves, the thick, heavy breath of jasmine, issuing from the depth of the tangled growth, mingled with the tender exhalation of the maybells and the virginal perfume of the violets which clustered on the green banks of the gaily tumbling rivulets and the tranquil pools. The higher he climbed, the more fantastic became the perfumes which the winds carried to his nostrils. And the trees multiplied—trees that were familiar to him, and trees that were quite unknown: the bark-encrusted cedar, the somber, earnest, stone-hard acacia, the hot-breathing palm, and the cool needle pine; he saw the cold, severe oak adorned like a bride by the red and white oleander; their knotted roots were interwoven

275

like the veins of a single body in the rock from which they sprang, and their branches, heavily mantled with crisp leaves spread out like the fingers of a man's hand, were joined and intertwined aloft; their pleasant natural odors mingled with each other as though they flowed from the same leafy source; and it was as if nature had made, here on Mount Sinai, a rendezvous for all the varieties of her creation.

Still ascending, Moses came into a little wood where the trees, towering in straight perpendicular lines, made a shadow with the wide canopy of their intertwined branches, from which creepers depended like the tendrils of the vine. The trees resembled the acacia, but he was astonished by the solidity of the trunks. Neither in Egypt, nor in any of the lands he had visited, had he seen acacias with trunks of such girth. They were less like trees than like mighty structures, each standing apart, and all at regular intervals from each other. Their bark was chiseled, here finely, there in deep clefts; the leaves resembled laurel; and where the wood showed it seemed to be firm and filled with sap. Beneath them reigned shadow and tranquillity. Moses marveled to find in this place trees of such massiveness and compactness; he was accustomed to the soft, barklike body of the palm and the netted, sievelike tangles of rushes. It must be, he reflected, that here the north and south of God's nature had joined hands on His mountain.

Sweet and pleasant was the stillness of the place, and he sat down to rest under a tree, the stone tablets by him. Then suddenly he felt as it were a wave of deepest purification sweeping through his body; he was being sanctified, as if the silence were of waters dedicated to his ablution. There went out of him the need of food and drink, and he was aware of lightness, as if he had grown wings and could fly.

With the sense of increasing purity came also an increasing awe, and he thought: "Surely God is in this place."

He heard footfalls—a leaping, not a walking; and before he could look round a young ram came bounding from a covert. The instant it perceived Moses it became motionless. Thus it stood a while, as though reflecting, then approached him with graceful, dancing steps, stretched out its horned head, and licked his feet with its moist tongue.

Moses stared down at the animal. It was an image of cleanness. Drops of water glistened on its hide, as if it had just come up out

276

of a pool. Its head was crowned by curving horns, and it lifted its dumb eyes to Moses. There was such moving purity, innocence, and simplicity in its glance that Moses impulsively placed his hand on its head and caressed it. And the skin was smooth and warm to the touch, so that Moses said to himself:

"Such a skin is a fitting cover for the tabernacle of God."

And it seemed to him that the animal understood his words, for it looked up at him with an expression of love and gratitude.

In the days when he served Jethro, Moses had heard tell of a legendary acacia tree from which flowed such delicate incense perfumes that whosoever breathed them was cleansed of all sinful thoughts; and among such trees, the legend told further, there lived a young ram.

"Of acacia wood will Jehovah build His tabernacle, and it will be covered with the skin of the ram."

He rose and ascended still further and came into fields of snow. He had known that on the heights of the Sinai range, in the clefts which the sunlight did not reach, the snow remained unmelted; but it was a new thing to him that at this time, midsummer, the whole mountainside should be covered with snow. And the snow was of such freshness that it seemed new fallen; for it was spotlessly, brilliantly white, as if radiant clouds had settled on the ground and gently covered it. A cool cleanness breathed on him, as though he were again being purified, and this time of all sorrow. And it seemed to him that God was purifying him from the sin of the Calf god, which he, the leader of the Bnai Israel, shared with the people; it seemed to him that he was being cleansed of sin and sorrow before he reached the summit of the mountain, the place of his meeting with Jehovah.

And still he ascended, from level to level. The incense had breathed on him, the dewy snow had washed him. Now it was the winds that blew through his flesh. And the higher he ascended the more completely he was disgarmented of his human and earthly nature. It was as though his external self, his body, were falling away from him like a robe, and he was becoming pure soul, freed from all earthly needs.

A glorious vista opened before him. The horizon was no longer locked in by the mountain walls. He stood on the summit of the world. Below him the copper-tinted peaks flickered upward out of their settings of snow: golden pillars on silver foundations. And above them hung the blue-dazzling heavens. It seemed to Moses that God was showing him the image in which the tabernacle was to be built: golden pillars on silver bases, the copper peaks rising from the snow fields.

The world lay at his feet. In the blue distance he could discern the two giant arms which embraced the tremendous mass of Sinai, two reaches of water cleaving the sands, and pointing in two directions, to two different worlds: one toward the Red Sea, toward Egypt and Goshen, the other toward the wilderness of Sin, the Dead Sea, and the promised land; one toward slavery, the other toward freedom.

And now the silence grew more intense. Moses saw a turning cloud descending from heaven; it turned and curled and descended tornadolike, it wrapped him about, it lifted him and carried him; and he found himself in a hollow on a mountain peak rising golden out of the snowfields, opposite the peak on which he had been standing but a little while before.

He looked about him. The arching stone above him shone with an inner light. From where he sat he could see mountain peaks, the sky, and the distant arms of the sea below. To one side stood a table with the shewbread on it, and near it a seven-branched candlestick of pure gold shone brightly; and there was a curtain in blue, purple, and vermilion hanging in the air, like a flame, and concealing something from him.

The curtain parted and he saw two mighty wings, wings unattached to any body or shape; and the wings overshadowed an ark, and smoke rose from between the wings, thickening and rolling together until the wings were hidden from his view.

And Moses called out:

"Jehovah! Jehovah!"

Then a hand was placed on his eyes, and he beheld nothing. But he heard a voice issuing from the cloud:

"Jehovah, the Lord God, is merciful and gracious, long-suffering, and abundant in goodness and faithfulness; keeping mercy for thousands, forgiving iniquity and transgression and sin; but He will in no wise clear the guilty, visiting the iniquity of the fathers upon the children, and upon the children's children, unto the third and the fourth generation."

And Moses bowed his head to the earth and worshiped, saying:

"If I have found grace in Thy sight, let the Lord God go among

278

us, for it is a stiff-necked people; and pardon our iniquity and our sin, and take us for Thine inheritance."

And the voice answered:

"See, I make a covenant. Before all thy people will I do wonders, such as have not been in all the earth, nor in any nation. And all the people among whom thou art shall see the work of the Lord, for it is a terrible thing that I will do with thee."

Then the hand which had been placed on his eyes was removed, and he saw a fiery likeness wrapped in cloud passing before him and vanishing. And Moses fell face to earth and cried out:

"O Jehovah, Jehovah, merciful and gracious God, long-suffering, slow to anger, abundant in goodness and faithfulness, forgive Thy people, for Thy people sinned against Thee without intent."

Then God opened before Moses an aperture into the future, and He made pass all His goodness before him, and Moses beheld the things that are to be until the end of all days.

There passed before him the righteous of all the generations: those that serve God with their wisdom, and those that serve Him with leadership and skill; likewise those upon whom God brings His spirit to rest, those to whom it is granted to suffer and die for His name's sake, and those to whom it is granted to spread His name through the world.

Then God revealed to Moses the price which would be paid by those that believed in Him, by those that guarded and held sacred the words uttered by the lips of the prophets. And God unfolded before him the age-long road of the martyrs across the generations, the bloody road traversed by those who obeyed His commandments, the record of the long war between the followers of God and the followers of the idols.

And Moses saw the tormented body of a holy man lying on a wooden board; and by his side lay the holy scroll of the Torah, just such a scroll as Moses himself had written. And soldiers stood over the man and harrowed his flesh with iron rakes; they flayed the skin off the raw flesh, which spouted blood; and the holy man, with eyes fixed starkly on heaven, uttered, joyfully and blissfully, the words which were written in the book of the covenant: "Thou shalt love the Lord thy God with all thy heart and with all thy soul and with all thy might."

Then a hand drew aside a curtain from the sky, and he saw generation after generation of the martyrs, and heard the cry of

"Hear, O Israel!" which went up from all the corners of the earth. He saw dungeons filled with instruments of torture; racks, and thumbscrews, and foot blocks, branding irons and nail-loaded lashes. He saw men and women consigned to the flames of gigantic pyres; and from amid the blazing pyres went up the cry of "Hear, O Israel!" And not only the martyrs from among his own brothers were shown him, but those from among other peoples, all martyrs who suffered for their belief in the one God, and for their fulfillment of His commandments. And he saw and heard the false prophets who spoke for false gods, and the priests of the idols who committed abominations in the name of God.

And Moses took a fiery stylus and incised the commandments on the stone tablets: "Thou shalt have no other gods before Me. ... Thou shalt not take the name of Jehovah thy God in vain. ..."

But God did not release Moses yet. Other mists were torn asunder, other curtains parted, and still the future defiled before him.

He saw the reign of evil triumphing on the earth. He saw the innumerable slain. The earth was covered with blood, as though it consisted of one gigantic, oozing wound. The bondage of Egypt was as nothing compared with the bondage of the reign of evil. He saw hordes of ghastly ruins of men and women tugging at wagons, splitting rocks, uprooting trees, laboring convulsively under the lash: and he saw their counterpart, the bloated bodies of those whose nourishment was human blood; he saw the revelries, the mad excesses, the gorging and swilling of the slave masters. He saw multitudes being driven with swords and clubs into blazing ovens, and forever the cry went up from them: "Hear, O Israel!" And with this cry on their lips they surrendered their bodies to the flames.

And Moses cried out to God:

"It is enough! It is enough! I can look no more! I am but flesh and blood!"

And God answered, and said:

"Look, and see, and hear, so that thou mayest understand, and feel, and know how to write My laws."

And Moses took up the burning stylus and incised upon the stone tablets:

"Thou shalt not kill."

And his heart was filled with a great, sorrowing indignation, and he took upon himself again the oath of eternal war between God and Amalek from generation to generation, until all trace of Amalek should be destroyed from under the heavens, and evil should be wiped off the earth.

But God opened before Moses other vistas, and he saw nations and peoples scattered afar over the face of the earth, singing a song of praise to God and glorifying His name. And the song went up from regions of snow and from green valleys, from the borders of great seas and from inland, wooded places, from mountaintops and from lowlands. Everywhere God's name was glorified and exalted, and everywhere, in all tongues, the chant of adoration ascended. It was as if the words which God had spoken to Moses had been carried to every corner of the earth, and had sounded in the ears of each people in its own language.

And in the languages of all the peoples Moses incised on the stone tablets the words: "I am the Lord thy God, who brought thee out of Egypt, out of the house of bondage."

From all the earth the echo returned:

"I am the Lord thy God, who brought thee out of Egypt, out of the land of bondage."

Now there swam down from the zenith an island of green. Edged with incandescent light, it floated gently till it hovered over against the earth; and on this mist island Moses saw a little clearing of tender and restful green by a peaceful pool, and on its bank a flock of sheep. And he saw a wolf and a lamb lying down together and a child leading them.

And Moses rose to his feet, and called out into the far future which God had revealed to him in the opening of the heavens:

"With all those that are here now, and with all those that are not here now, God makes a covenant today."

And he took the oath of faithfulness, and he wrote down the words on the tablets, for the whole earth is Jehovah's and His glory is over all lands.

And thus Moses sat at the entrance of the hollow forty days and forty nights. Neither bread nor water passed his lips. And God made to pass before him all His goodness. And He showed him all the martyrs and all the saints, both of his own people and of the other peoples, who were to spread the word of God throughout all nations in all tongues; and those that were to die for His name's sake, whether of the Hebrews or of the gentiles; and those that in quiet retreats would glorify the name of God through their knowledge, their meditation, and the work of their hands. And God caused Moses to see and hear all the prophets who would arise before Jehovah, whether of the Hebrews or of other peoples, bringing to men the love of God and the joy of serving Him, whether they did so with the spoken or written word, or with the music which exalts and liberates the hearts of men and draws them toward God. And Moses heard the singing which is an adoration, and the singing which is supplication; he saw and heard all those who would search out God's laws and interpret them so that righteousness might be multiplied; and those that meditated on God's works and brought them to perfection. He saw and heard all those that have their portion in God, who are His partners in creation, who are blended with Him in His works—blended in a great Oneness.

And Moses rose and sent his voice through space and time: throughout the creation, from end to end of the All, for all ages till the last day, for all souls, whether on earth with him or yet to be, for all men of all races and all colors, living then or yet to live on the face of the earth: and he called:

"Hear, O Israel! The Lord our God, the Lord is One."

And when the forty days were ended Moses came down from Sinai bearing the new tablets on which he had inscribed the ten commandments of God.

And he did not know, when he descended with the tablets, that the skin of his face shone from God's holding speech with him. And Aaron and the children of Israel, seeing the radiance from afar, were afraid to come near him. And Moses called Aaron and the rulers of the congregation, and made them approach, and he spoke with them; and he gave them in commandment all that God had spoken with him on Mount Sinai.

And when he had ended speaking with them he covered his face with a veil. Thereafter he would remove the veil only when he went before God to speak with Him; but when he came out among the children of Israel he covered his face again.

CHAPTER TEN

THREE things Moses brought down from Mount Sinai: the ten commandments inscribed on new tablets; Jehovah's command to wage a war of annihilation against the false gods of the lands which the Bnai Israel would occupy; and the model of a tabernacle, the place of the assembly of the people before God, the tent-like sanctuary which the Bnai Israel were to carry with them throughout their journeyings in the wilderness until they would reach their land.

The instructions for the portable sanctuary were given him in the precisest detail, according to the model which was shown him. It would rest, not on permanent foundations, but on a series of thresholds, and its various parts would fit and dovetail into each other and be held together by rings, hooks, and staves. And not the forms alone were to be faithful to the original model, but the materials of wood and metal, the woven stuffs, the precious stones for the adornment of the vessels, the curtains, and the coverings, and the jeweled workmanship of the breastplate and the ephod.

A call went out to the congregation in the name of God:

"Bring an offering to the Lord, from every man who gives it willingly and with his whole heart, setting it apart for the Lord: gold, silver, and brass; and blue and purple and scarlet wool, and fine linen and goats' hair; and rams' skins dyed red, and skins of the sea *tahash,* and acacia wood; oil for the light, spices for anointing oil and for sweet incense; onyx stones, and stones to be set in the ephod and in the breastplate."

And the people brought the offerings. Men and women drew off their earrings, finger rings, and neckbands of various designs; great and rich was the offering, the endless spoils of the Egyptian women, the extorted recompense for the hundreds of years of slavery. Rows of baskets were placed at the feet of Moses and Aaron, filled with blue and purple and scarlet stuffs, linen, and goats' hair—freely offered for the building of the sanctuary.

283

Moses sent men with axes to hew down the massive acacia trees he had seen on the upper slopes of the mountain. He sent hunters into the Sinai woods to catch the rams, and fishermen to the shores of the Red Sea for the legendary otter-like *tahash,* the skin of which, according to God's command, was to furnish the outermost covering of the tabernacle.

Sinai itself, rich in copper and silver ores, supplied metal for the thresholds and vessels. And there were among the Bnai Israel coppersmiths, workers in silver, and gold beaters who had labored for the Egyptians. There were also gifted women skilled in the spinning of the finest linen and the weaving of the most precious stuffs of purple and blue, as well as in the embroidering of the stuffs with cunning designs of birds and beasts.

But the most gifted and most skillful of the craftsmen in the congregation, subtlest in the production of marvelous vessels in gold, silver, and copper, was young Bezalel, son of Uri, son of Hur, of the tribe of Judah—Miriam's grandson. He had studied under the foremost goldsmiths of Egypt and even as a boy had been instructed by Pharaoh's master of the jewels. To the gifts which he displayed almost as a child he owed his escape from the mud pits.

To him, on God's command, Moses entrusted the direction of the building of the sanctuary.

Bezalel chose as his chief assistant a companion with whom he had worked in Egypt, Aholiab, of the tribe of Dan, who was cunning above all others in the weaving of figures into purple stuffs. Between them Bezalel and Aholiab tested and chose the workers for the sanctuary, and Moses put in their charge all the gold and silver and fine cloths.

Soon there was an oversupply of all the materials needed for the building of the tabernacle according to the plans, and for all the ornaments, vessels, and furnishing. Morning after morning the Bnai Israel brought, from every corner of the encampment, armfuls of stuffs, baskets of metals, caskets of jewels, and rare herbs and ointments. And morning after morning new craftsmen came pleading to be given a share in the labor; for all were eager to have a hand in the putting up of the sanctuary, the first dwelling place which God would have on earth. At last Bezalel and Aholiab reported the oversupply to Moses, and Moses sent word through the encampment: "It is enough: the material and the workmen suffice for the building of the sanctuary!" And only then did the people cease from bringing their wealth and the offer of their services.

Under a shelter of palm branches stood the rows of spindles and looms. Young and old women spun the thread of goats' hair and wove the curtain for the tabernacle, the old teaching the young. The curtain was not single and of a piece; for since the tabernacle would be dismantled and reassembled, and moved from place to place, one curtain consisting of eleven parts woven together, each part thirty cubits in length and four in width, would have been too heavy. The curtains were therefore joined each to each with fifty loops and fifty copper hooks, and became one covering.

And the women talked as they worked:

"How different from the old days of slavery, when we sat in the dark, weaving nets for Pharaoh's fishermen!"

They remembered well the time of bondage, the forced labor, the overseers standing over them with the lash; they remembered how, if a woman grew faint with the heat, or with overwork, she felt at once on her flesh the sting of the lash. Here the work was done as a free-will offering, in the midst of joy and laughter. They were weaving the covering for God's sanctuary: Jehovah would dwell there, would rest in their midst under this covering. Many were the women who begged to be given their portion in the work; and Bezalel and Aholiab had to arrange turns for them, so that as many as possible might share the privilege.

Not far removed from the spinners and weavers stood the tanners and hide dressers, naked-breasted men, their shocks of hair, their beards and earlocks in wild disorder, their faces streaming in the heat: but the work went forward swiftly and gaily. They scrubbed the hides of the rams which the hunters had brought them from the slopes of Sinai, they dipped the finished skins in the vermilion dyes. These rams' skins too would be fitted together to make a covering, a covering on top of a covering, and the one beneath would be of goats' hair. For there would be four coverings in all for the sanctuary: one of the finest spun linen, blue and purple and vermilion, which would be on the inside; then one of goats' hair, above the linen; then the rams' skins above the goats' hair; and last the *tahash*. Each covering was made in separate parts, and the parts were put together with copper hooks, edge to edge. And the outside covering of *tahash* skin, which reflected the sunlight like burnished copper, enchanted all who looked on it with its mystical beauty.

The coverings were the outer protection for the tabernacle against the winds and sandstorms of the wilderness. But the innermost covering would be the exposed ceiling of the tabernacle within, and it was woven with especial attention and care in a sheltered place. There, too, the most skillful of the craft weavers among the women produced the door hangings and the vestments which Aaron and his sons would wear at the services. Ten inner hangings were being woven of the most delicate, gossamerlike linen, and into the airy fabric were infused rather than worked figures of mystical cherubs in their own blue coloring. But the background blue of the hangings was like a drift of clouds, edged with vermilion and twinkling as with stars. The ten sections of the curtain, one section linked to the other with blue loops drawn through gold rings, made a twilight in the sanctuary—a silence and repose such as falls on the earth with the first glimmer of starlight; and over this silence brooded the outspread wings of the cherubim on the ceiling curtain.

Bezalel directed the workers in metals, the makers of the vessels and instruments and furnishing which were associated with the sacred service; the spinners and weavers, the makers of the curtains and coverings and hangings, were under the direction of the master craftsman Aholiab. The first was of the noble tribe of Judah; the second, of the despised tribe of Dan, the guiltiest among the tribes in the matter of the Calf god. It was as if in these two representatives the tribes were reconciled and made equal—as if in the presence of God there was neither great nor small among the tribes of Israel.

A great change in regard to the nature of the sacred ritual had set in since the incident of the Calf god, as far as both the will of God and the conceptions of Moses were concerned. In the harmony of this change it was as if God was more yielding to the desires of Moses than before the idolatry; and one might have said, if it were at all permissible to say such a thing, that the conceptions of Moses guided the commandments of the Eternal.

Before the incident of the Calf god Moses had declared, in the name of God, that God desired neither gold nor silver. "An altar of earth shalt thou make unto me. . . . And if thou wilt make Me an altar of stone, thou shalt not build it of hewn stone. . . . And in every place where I cause My name to be mentioned, I shall

286

come to thee and bless thee." After the incident of the Calf god Moses brought down from Sinai the complete plan for a sanctuary, a tabernacle in the form of a golden house. True, it would not be a great house, and it could be dismantled and reassembled at will. It would be thirty cubits in length, ten cubits wide, and ten cubits high. But the pillars, hewn from the massive trunks of the acacias brought down from Sinai, and square cut, with a height of ten cubits, and a width of a cubit and a half, would be covered with gold back and front. The pillars would be settled into sockets in the silver thresholds, two sockets under each pillar. Twenty such gold-covered pillars, or posts, set side by side, touching, would make one long wall of the tabernacle; opposite them twenty more pillars would make the second long wall. The western wall would consist of eight gold-covered pillars, every pillar set into the socket of two thresholds.

The walls were to be fastened to each other with gold bolts shot through the middle of the posts; and above, the pillars were to be held together by gold rings.

On the eastern side, over the entrance to the sanctuary, would hang a curtain of costly weave. Like the other curtains in the sanctuary, this one would be knotted and woven of linen, and of blue, purple, and scarlet wool; it would hang from golden rings over five gold-covered pillars in sockets of brass.

The golden sanctuary, the ornament of Israel, with its four coverings, was to stand in the center of a court a hundred cubits long and fifty cubits wide. The two long sides of the court, and the shorter western side, would be set with silver-covered pillars in sockets of brass—twenty pillars on each long side, ten pillars on the short side, with one socket to each pillar. Hangings of fine linen work would run along these three sides, drawn on rings. On the eastern side, at the entrance, there were to be three silver-covered pillars in brass sockets, and a curtain twenty cubits wide, in blue, purple, and vermilion wool, and in fine-spun linen. The hooks on the pillars about the courtyard were to be, like their holders, of silver, and the sockets everywhere of brass. Thus, from without, it would seem that the sanctuary with its flaming golden walls was rising out of a sea of molten silver.

Infinite in variety and endless in detail the work looked at the outset. A large area was set aside for the smelting and metal working, separated from the encampment by a hedge of thorns and palm branches, and roofed over with matting to shield the workers from the fierce desert sun. There the fires blazed, the metal seethed in the white-hot crucibles.

And now it became apparent that the great outpouring of free-will offerings would not suffice for all the golden coverings of the pillars, the vessels of the service, and the other furnishings of the tabernacle. Moses now had to make a new levy on each male in the congregation above the age of twenty, a tax of the weight and value of half a shekel, a redemption and ransom from the sin of the Calf god. "The rich man shall not pay more, nor the poor man less, than half a shekel." Moreover, the number of half shekels paid into the sanctuary would reveal the number of men above the age of twenty in the congregation. Thus the levy would serve a triple purpose, as a payment to the sanctuary, a redemption from sin, and a census of the people. Payment was made in gold or silver, in stuffs and in spices, to the value of the weight of half a shekel. And thus the additional material was obtained, the additional precious metals and costly cloths; for the tabernacle consumed, insatiably ravenous, the wealth of the Bnai Israel. And it was well that this should be so, for the riches taken from the Egyptians belonged to Jehovah. The golden cups, jars, chains, stomachers, crowns, and helmets, the silver-covered stools, tables, ewers, and harness—all, in brief, that had been taken from the Egyptians, was thrown into the crucibles; and more than one ornament of high craftsmanship was thus melted down into raw material for the sanctuary—the gold and silver in separate crucibles.

Copper ore was mined from the Sinai fields, and, mingled with other metals, yielded varieties of brass. Only the raw material could be molten. The vessels and instruments of the sacred service could not be poured out in molds; they had to be hammered out with stone mallets. On huge anvils, or on natural rocks, the gold leaf for the pillars, the hooks, the rings, the bolts, the staves, were beaten out by skilled workmen under the close supervision of the master craftsmen.

In their section, the woodworkers carved out the solid pith from the bellies of the acacias; they measured with tapes of rope; they hewed the pillars with razor-edged axes; they chiseled the exact forms of the wooden inner parts of the gold-covered bolts, rings, and hooks.

Woodworkers on one side of the field, copper smelters on the other, and in a third section the gold beaters. And from every section there ascended the ringing, hammering, thudding, and hissing of their multiple labors. Pots and basins, fire shovels and ash shovels, incense burners and copper containers, sieves and washing pans, carriers, hooks, staves, hoops of gold, silver, and copper, horns, and crowns were shaped and hammered out in the countless work stalls dedicated to the sanctuary.

And the great architect of the whole, the master of all the crafts, sat in his tent taking counsel with his chief assistants, master craftsmen like himself; and with his own hands he produced the intimate vessels of the service, the most sacred of the implements of the sanctuary. Not without meaning was his name Bezalel—"in the shadow of God." For God's shadow rested on him and filled him with the divine grace of the artist.

All the arts were fused and united in his masterpieces. In his craftsmanship he sang out the song of creation before God; and in every vessel which he created he renewed the inspiration of his contact with the highest spheres.

Bezalel did all his work in continuous consultation with Moses. Moses would describe to him the vision of each sacred vessel and instrument as it had appeared to him on Mount Sinai; and Bezalel worked from the description. And Moses, watching his youthful eyes, saw them filled with that incandescent light which had issued from the throne of God. Indeed, it was as if those eyes were fixed across space on some recess in the heavens, and there, in the divine light, he saw each vessel and instrument even as Moses had seen it.

He came at last to the noblest and most exalted of all the furnishings of the sanctuary—if that could be called furnishing for which, indeed, the whole sanctuary was being created—the ark, which was to hold the tablets with the ten commandments which Moses had brought down from heaven, the covenant, the conditions of the bond between Jehovah and Israel.

He carved out the body of the ark from a single block of wood, and lined it inside and outside with the finest gold. The highest reach of his imagination went into the creation of the covering for the ark; for this would serve as the throne and mercy seat of Jehovah, when He would speak to Moses. Ark and covering were to be deposited in the Holy of Holies. And there would be nothing else in the Holy of Holies: only the ark with the two tablets of the law within. Thither Aaron would come once each year, on the Day of Atonement, to implore God's forgiveness on the sins of Israel.

The roof of the ark Bezalel made of pure gold, a heavy mass laid over the ark; and he hammered out two cherubim, two vast, mystical birds which cast the shadow of their wings on the ark. Between the wings, between the faces of the cherubim—for they confronted each other, face to face—the divine Presence of Jehovah, the *Shekhinah,* would rest.

Now this was an extraordinary circumstance: only a little while before, God had issued the commandment to Moses concerning the making of images; and Bezalel in turn had been most rigidly commanded by Moses: "Not after the manner of the Egyptians, or of other idol worshipers, shalt thou make the house of God!" There was to be no image of man or beast, no likeness of a living thing. And here Moses suddenly ordered that images of cherubim be made and set within the curtain which covered the entrance to the Holy of Holies.

Into the structure and spread of the cherubim, into the lines of the forewings, Bezalel infused all the tenderness, the sweetness, the compassion, and the mother love of a bird brooding over its chicks. At the same time he threw into the severe main curve of the wings the suggestion of mingled fear and combativeness which is evoked in the mother by her little ones, when, twittering in her shadow, they seem to say: "Shelter us under thy wing." The feathers, which were all softness and caresses toward the little ones, were like knife-edges, like sharp claws, toward a possible intruder or enemy, outwardly the fury of the protector, inwardly the sanctity and gentleness of love. But what kind of faces was he to set on the cherubim? —for faces they must have. Surely not the faces of eagles, with the hooked, combative beaks of eagles; and not the bearded faces of men, either. A later tradition asserts that Bezalel set upon the cherubim the faces of two young and innocent boys, in whose dewy glances shone the purity of a stainless youthful love, for these two faces were to symbolize for ever the reconciliation of God and Israel after the sin of the Calf god.

But the most difficult task confronted Bezalel when he came to the making of the candelabrum which, according to God's command to Moses, was to carry the eternal light in the sanctuary.

In an astounding way, Moses had completely forgotten the form of the many-branched candlestick, shining, a single glitter of gold, in the vision on the mountain. He remembered neither its proportions nor the details of its ornaments. He only knew that it had seven branches and that there was a light in every branch. He tried several times to recall the inner image which had once been so vivid. He even climbed up the slope of Sinai again in the hope that the vision would flash back upon him; and there were moments when it seemed that he had captured it again. But they were illusory; the suggestion of an image started up suddenly—and was as suddenly withdrawn.

In the end he relinquished the task entirely to Bezalel, bidding him follow his own imagination.

And Bezalel hammered out the candlestick from a single block of gold of the weight of one talent. The base and central stem suggested a tree trunk on firm-spreading roots, and the six arms, three to a side, the branches of the tree. Between the branches he set little almond-shaped bowls, the mouths of which were like tender buds, on which a dewdrop hung, like a tear on the eyelid of a young child; and from every bowl a flower issued. And when the seven branches of the candlestick were lit, the flowers and the teardrops were also illumined. And not only light issued from the candlestick into the eyes of the beholders, but a spirit of purity, which stole into their hearts and sanctified them for prayer; for the stem and the pipes were not only like a tree trunk and branches, but also like a man lifting his arms in prayer to God.

When Moses saw the candlestick which Bezalel had hammered out from a single block of gold, he cried out:

"This is the form of the candlestick as God showed it to me among the flames on Mount Sinai."

From among the sacred vessels of the first sanctuary it is the form of the *menorah*, the seven-branched candlestick, which has accompanied the Bnai Israel on their millennial journeyings. The *menorah* and the tablets of the law have remained the holy symbols of the Bnai Israel unto this day. For if the tablets represent the law of God, the form of the *menorah* represents prayer to God.

The *menorah* brings Sabbath and festival into the Jewish home; it removes the traces of the workaday week from the wrinkled face of the Jewish mother and puts upon her head the crown of the Sabbath. And it shines, across immeasurable seas of tears, from the day when Aaron first kindled it in the tabernacle, to our own day.

291

At length the great moment came for the dedication of the sanctuary. It was the first month of the second year after the liberation. For eight days the tabernacle had been open, and the cloud within which dwelt the Presence had descended and covered the Holy of Holies, where the tablets rested in the golden ark; and the glory of God filled all the sanctuary.

A whole week Moses spent in rehearsing with Aaron and his sons the ritual of the offering of sacrifices on the brazen altar which stood at the entrance of the sanctuary; and of the burning of incense on the golden altar in the middle of the sanctuary for the shewbread and the Menorah. For seven whole days Aaron and his sons sat in the tabernacle, studied the bringing of the sacrifices, and sanctified themselves for the service. On the eighth day of the first month of the second year after the exodus, Moses called together all the elders and the congregation about the court of the sanctuary.

And he led forth Aaron and his sons and washed their hands and feet from the brazen ewer which stood at the entrance gate of the sanctuary court. Then he clad Aaron and his sons in the ordained raiment which Bezalel had prepared in accordance with the directions of Moses. He placed the tunic over his brother, and then the girdle, and then the robe and the ephod, with the girdle of the ephod, from the ends of which hung down pomegranates worked in purple wool, and golden bells; and the purpose of the golden bells was that the people might hear when the high priest entered the Holy of Holies, for none but the high priest might enter there. He placed on Aaron's breast the breastplate, which, like the ephod, was wrought in gold, in blue wool and purple and vermilion, and in spun linen, with four rows of precious stones set in it: the first row was ruby, topaz, and carbuncle; the second, emerald, sapphire, and diamond; the third, ligure, agate, and amethyst; and the fourth, beryl, onyx, and jasper. On every stone was incised the name of a tribe in Israel. Then Moses put the headpiece on Aaron, and on the headpiece the holy crown of pure gold, on which was engraved the device of a seal with the words: "Holiness unto God."

The sons of Aaron too he clad in the tunics of linen and in girdles, according to the prescribed ritual.

Then Moses said to Aaron:

"Approach now the altar, and bring thy sin offering and thy burnt offering, and do atonement for thyself and for the people."

And Aaron drew near to the brazen altar and slaughtered the bullock of the sin offering, which stood prepared for him. And his sons, who stood behind him, scooped up the blood of the bullock into basins and handed them to the high priest. Then Aaron dipped his finger into the blood and touched the horns of the altar.

Then Aaron's sons brought to him the other sacrifices of the day, and Aaron performed the ritual according to the instructions he had received from Moses. And parts of the sacrifices he laid out on the altar, and other parts his sons carried away to the outside of the encampment, as Moses had taught them.

Then Moses and Aaron went forth from the sanctuary to the people outside, and Aaron lifted his hands over the people which stood about the sanctuary, and he blessed them with the blessing which God had given through Moses. And he blessed the children of Israel for the first time with that blessing which has become the benediction of all peoples unto this day:

"The Lord bless thee and keep thee;
The Lord make His face to shine upon thee
and be gracious unto thee;
The Lord lift up His face upon thee and bring
thee peace."

And when Aaron uttered the words of the benediction a ray of light fell from heaven upon all the people that stood about the tabernacle.

Within the sanctuary a flame appeared over the altar and consumed the parts of the sacrifice that lay upon it. And the people without saw the flame descending from heaven and lighting on the altar, and they uttered a jubilant shout, and fell upon their faces.

When Moses and Aaron went back into the tabernacle, they saw that the whole interior was filled with a sacred, brooding smoke; and the vessels of the service seemed to be swimming in the cloud; the Menorah twinkled with its many lights on the outspread arms; the manna of the shewbread glittered like precious stones, and the staves of the ark made the dividing curtain stand out in two curves like the breasts of a young woman. The cherubim on the sanctuary covering threw a shadow with their wings, and stars shone down from the covering itself.

But for Nadab and Abihu, the two oldest sons of Aaron, all this was not enough. They wanted to raise a denser cloud, they wanted to help out Jehovah; and they did that which Moses had not prescribed. Each one of them took a censer, and placed incense on it, and brought strange fire before God. And they lifted up their smoking censers in order to fill the sanctuary with incense. And a fire came out of the altar and consumed them on the spot, and they died before the Lord in the sanctuary.

Then Moses spoke to Aaron and said:

"This is what God meant with the words: 'I will be sanctified in those that come near me, and before all the people will I be glorified.'"

And Aaron was dumbstruck.

Then Moses called Mishael and Elizaphan, the sons of Uziel, Aaron's uncle, and commanded them:

"Come near, and carry your brethren from before the sanctuary out of the camp."

And they carried the burned men out in their coats, as Moses had commanded.

And to Aaron, and to his two younger sons, Eleazar and Ithamar, who had remained with their father in the sanctuary, at the service, Moses said:

"You shall not let your hair grow, and you shall not rend your clothes and mourn for your brothers; but the whole house of Israel shall bewail the burning which God sent upon them. Nor shall you go out from the door of the tabernacle, lest you die. For God's anointing oil is upon you."

And they did as Moses bade them.

And therewith ended the dedication of the sanctuary.

CHAPTER ELEVEN

SOON after the dedication of the sanctuary Moses drew up a full and exact accounting of the gold, silver, copper, precious stones, and precious stuffs which the Bnai Israel had brought as offerings, and of the various uses to which they had been put. Even with regard to him the masses of the Bnai Israel could not refrain from giving utterance to their suspicions in popular catchwords and witticisms.

When he had completed the accounting he turned once more to the problem of organization.

The fact that neither the Bnai Levi nor the elders had been able, by persuasion, or in the last resort even by violence, to prevent the people from making the Calf god, convinced him once for all that it was necessary to introduce a new discipline, a military discipline, deriving its authority from Jehovah. As he now perceived, the Bnai Israel could best be controlled through the elders of their separate tribes; and it was to this ancient system of divisions that he therefore decided to return.

According to God's commandment he had carried out a counting of all the males above the age of twenty years in each of the tribes. And in further fulfillment of the commandment he had designated an elder for each tribe. For the tribe of Reuben, Elizur, the son of Shedeur; for the tribe of Simeon, Shelumiel, the son of Zurishaddai; for the tribe of Judah, Nachshon, the son of Aminadab—and so throughout all the tribes. And to every tribe he appointed a standard, or banner, with its special device; and for every tribe he designated its own place in the camp about the sanctuary.

The men above twenty in every tribe were the "hosts"—all that were able to go forth to war; and the name now given to the head of the tribe was "prince." The entire host of the Bnai Israel was divided into four camps, with three tribes to a camp. Every camp had its own standard, under which it rested; and in addition, each tribe raised its separate banner, with its peculiar emblem. These

emblems were the pictorial representations of the individual blessings which Jacob on his deathbed distributed among the fathers
of the tribes. They were wrought in the colors of the twelve precious
stones which were set in the breastplate and ephod, one jewel for
each tribe.

The princes of the tribes signalized their assumption of office by
the bringing of offerings to Jehovah.

First they provided six closed wagons and twelve oxen for the
transportation of the tabernacle when that should be dismantled
for travel. Every two tribes contributed one wagon and two oxen.

Moses turned over the wagons and the draft animals into the
keeping of the Levites. Two of the wagons went to the Bnai
Gershon, with four oxen; four of the wagons, with eight oxen,
to the Bnai Merari. These were the two Levite families whose duty
it was to transport the tabernacle when the camp of Israel moved.
They were under the command of Ithamar, the son of Aaron. The
vessels of the sanctuary were, however, to be carried separately, and
they were assigned to the Levite family of the Kohathites.

The princes celebrated their assumption of office a second time
by the bringing of sacrifices to the sanctuary. Each day, for twelve
days in succession, the prince of a tribe performed a dedication of
the sanctuary, and the day was named after the relevant tribe. The
honor of the first day was given by Moses not to the tribe of Reuben, which had the right of the first-born, and not even to the tribe
of Levi, which was distinguished now by the religious birthright,
but to the aristocratic tribe of Judah, and to its prince, Nachshon,
the son of Aminadab, who had been the first to plunge into the
waters at the dividing of the sea.

Nachshon ben Aminadab's offering was a silver platter of the
weight of one hundred and thirty shekels and a silver bowl weighing seventy shekels, both filled with fine flour mingled with oil, for
a meal offering; in addition, a golden bowl weighing ten shekels,
filled with incense. For sacrifice he brought one young bullock, one
ram, one lamb of the first year, for a burnt offering; one kid of
the goats for a sin offering; and for a peace offering two oxen,
five rams, five he-goats, and five lambs of the first year.

And after the manner of Nachshon ben Aminadab's offerings
and sacrifices, each prince of a tribe brought his offerings and sacrifices. Twelve days the celebrations lasted, according to the number

of the tribes, and every day an elder of a tribe was anointed a prince in Israel.

The Levites, who in the Egyptian days had been the overseers of the Bnai Israel, were now wholly consecrated to the service of the sanctuary. From the age of twenty-five to the age of fifty every Levite had to do actual service in and about the sanctuary. At fifty he was relieved of his formal duties; nevertheless he remained with the sanctuary "to help his brethren in the maintaining of order."

Now the duties of the Levites consisted of serving in the sanctuary, guarding it, preserving the purity of its vessels, and transporting it from place to place; they were placed completely under the authority of Aaron and his sons in all that pertained to the relations between the Bnai Israel and the sanctuary. They were the servitors of the priests in their manifold work; they removed the ashes from the altar and washed away the blood; and they were charged with seeing to it that the sacrifices brought by the Bnai Israel were without blemish, according to the law.

The Levites were considered in some wise the first-born of Israel. And since every male offspring that opened the womb of the mother belonged to God ("For to Me belongs every first-born among the children of Israel, whether of man or beast . . . from the day on which I slew all the first-born in the land of Egypt"), Moses, in the name of God, declared the Levites the servants of the sanctuary, which was God's. He dressed them in white tunics, and had them remove the hair of their heads and their beards, that they might be recognized as the temple slaves; and Aaron performed over them a ceremony of atonement, and dedicated them to the sanctuary service.

Nor was the service of the priests confined to the sanctuary ceremonial. The priest was also a healer among the Bnai Israel. They came to him with whatever sicknesses appeared in the camp; but more especially the priest was concerned with any form of contagious sickness, with inflammations of the skin, boils, fluxes, issues, and, above all, leprosy. He diagnosed the sickness according to well-defined symptoms, decided whether it was curable or incurable, contagious or innocuous, and prescribed accordingly. The contagiously sick, who endangered the health of the camp, were isolated until their condition was no longer a public danger. On being declared healed by the priest, they brought a purification offering to the sanctuary and returned to the camp. The Levites also assisted the priests in controlling and caring for the health of the Bnai Israel.

To provide the means for the support of the priests, and of an entire tribe which was consecrated to the sanctuary, Aaron and his sons instituted an immense ceremonial system for the bringing of sacrificial offerings. For every minor infraction of the general laws or the laws of purity, the Israelite was compelled to bring a sacrifice; and as this was both an atonement and the confession of a sin, overt or covert, intentional or unintentional, the forms and conditions of the sacrifice were various. There were the sin offering, the purification offering, the peace offering, the burnt offering, the meal offering; and they consisted of their proper varieties of large and small animals, fowl, meal, or oils; of oxen, cattle, sheep, kids, doves. Part of the sacrifice was burned on the altar; but in most instances this was a minor part of the offering. It might consist of a sprinkling of blood, or of the fat, or the kidneys. The remainder, the meat of the oxen, sheep, and goats, the oil, the fine flour, was appropriated by the priests and the Levites. Later, Moses instituted also a regular tax or levy for the support of priests and Levites: the tithe of the harvest, the redemption or ransom money for every first-born male child in Israel, and the sacrifice of every first-born animal offspring.

In order to surround the bringing of sacrifice with a religious aura, the priests elaborated a complicated ritual to which every separate sacrifice had to conform with scrupulous exactitude. They prescribed what was due on every ox or sheep or goat; what parts were to be burned as offering to God; what parts should be seethed and be given to the priests. They laid down rigid rules as to who might and who might not eat of the flesh of the sacrifices, who might and who might not remove the ashes and blood from the altar. The ritual was published in such form as to seem to have issued from the one almighty God, the Creator of heaven and earth.

The cry of protest against the priests was later to be heard from the lips of the prophets. In the name of God they lifted their voices against the sacrifices: "To what purpose is the multitude of your sacrifices to Me, saith the Lord. I am full of the burnt offerings of rams, and the fat of fed beasts; and I delight not in the blood of bullocks, or of lambs, or of he-goats." The best sacrifice to Him was the humble and broken heart—so sang the sweet singer of Israel. The later generations replaced the sacrifices by prayer. But if God did not need the sacrifices, the priests and Levites did; and the sacrifices were brought for them, not for Him. For without the sacrifices they could not have maintained a whole slave tribe in the service of the sanctuary.

While Aaron and his sons elaborated the ritual of the sacrifices and the ceremonial of the sanctuary, Moses delivered to the Bnai Israel, in the name of God, a great codex of laws which laid the foundations of Jewish morality, formed the character of the Jewish people for all the future, and instilled into it the strength and endurance to confront all the countless calamities which history was to visit on them.

Moses set himself two objectives. The first was, to create a civilization for a people in the making, and for the land in which it was to live. At the moment the land was still possessed by its native population. This native population was sinful and idolatrous, given over to the wickedness of Sodom. Therefore God would drive it forth from its habitation to make room for a people dedicated to holiness, a people charged with the building of a civilization which was to be a model for all mankind. To this end, God imparted to Moses laws and statutes and commandments and instruments which were to be instituted when the Bnai Israel were settled in their land, and which were to guide them into that order of life which God desired to create through them.

Meanwhile, however, the material for this divinely planned creation consisted of recently liberated slaves, in whom still lingered the traits which are the eternal stigmata of slavery. Quite apart from the rabble, "the mixed multitude," which went up with Israel from Egypt—a confusion of peoples steeped in idolatry and always apt to slide back into their original condition—quite apart from these, there were among the Bnai Israel themselves many elements which had assimilated toward the lowest and coarsest of the Egyptians. The tribe of Dan, for instance, manifested a strong inclination toward idol worship. For the Bnai Dan the Calf god, with all the abominations linked to its ritual, was easier and more natural than the high moral level on which God desired to place them. Even after the frightful denunciation of the Calf god, they did not cease to hanker after it, and even to worship it in secret. Many of the women of the tribe had Egyptian husbands, who went up with them out of Egypt as part of the mixed multitude. Among these the family life had a tendency to sink to the Egyptian level; and they were tainted with whoredom and filth, which made them easy victims of various idolatries.

The conversion of these slave elements into a people fit to take upon itself the high commandments of Jehovah was a gradual process. Moses found it necessary to issue a series of hygienic and sanitary regulations for the protection of the health of the camp; and he had to clothe them with the authority of direct commands of Jehovah, for mere regulations would have been ignored. Even so elementary a matter as the disposal of human ordure had to come under the heading of a divine command. An iron discipline surrounded these regulations, and their contravention was a provocation of the anger of the Lord. To maintain such a discipline, to ensure obedience and order in the camp, there was needed a religious organization; and it was this function that the tribe of Levi served.

There were misdemeanours and transgressions, such as blasphemy, and cursing in the name of God, for which the Levites themselves administered punishment. There were also crimes for which the punishment was death by strangulation.

A great change had come over Moses with the incident of the Calf god. He had realized that only a rigid discipline and a castigating arm could induct this people into the mission which God had assigned it.

He began to issue, in the name of Jehovah, laws which were to govern not only the relations of man to man, and the relations of man to God, but the bearing of a man toward himself, the maintenance of personal purity and cleanliness, even in the matter of what might and what might not be eaten—all this in order that it might be "a holy people."

It is not clear why Moses prohibited, as food for the Bnai Israel, certain animals, certain fish, and all kinds of creeping things. It may be that he was guided by certain hygienic principles. It may be that the hot climate called for a special dietary regimen. It may also have been that the passionate hankering after flesh, among healthy men whom the watery manna could not sate, alarmed Moses, and he feared that they would take to eating frogs and other reptiles, with consequent dangers of poisoning. And all these prohibitions he issued in the form of commandments, carrying the full weight of the authority of Jehovah.

The prohibitions were, however, decided on with the help of his council; and they issued the list of the forbidden things, "every creeping thing that creepeth upon the earth," and "whatsoever goeth upon the belly," sea creatures without fins and scales, and various animals. There cannot be any doubt that Moses and the council had a wide knowledge of the dangers of poisoning, of skin diseases, and of other sicknesses inherent in certain foods in that climate. Moses had led out of Egypt a people of workers accustomed to eating the frogs and other reptiles which swarmed in the Nile, as well as the meat of animals pastured in the rich meadows of the Delta; and they remembered the good, juicy taste of flesh, they longed to feel between their teeth a crackling, marrowy bone, to suck out the delicious softness of some sea creature. After their long diet of manna they were ready to swallow indiscriminately all kinds of reptiles, worms, locusts, scorpions, spiders—whatever living thing they could lay hands on. To Moses the physical purity of the people was close-linked with its moral mission, and he was determined to guard at all costs the health of the Bnai Israel.

But all these laws and regulations concerning diet and personal hygiene and public health had a more than temporary purpose in their effect on the character of the people, on its behavior and its psychic condition. The enunciation of the principle that every living creature belongs to God, that therefore one is forbidden to slaughter it merely in order to eat it; that it may be slaughtered only as a sacrifice to God, and its flesh enjoyed only under certain circumstances: all this infused into the Jewish people a humanitarian attitude toward God's creatures. The beast is God's; its blood may not be consumed, for the blood is the life, and life is God's. From this conception sprang later a series of laws relating to man and beast. It was forbidden to muzzle the ox when it trod out the corn; the beast of burden shared with man the Sabbath day of rest; and a man could not eat or drink in the morning before he had given food and drink to his beasts. And until this day shehitah, the Hebrew mode of slaughter, is the most humanitarian way of killing an animal for human consumption; for by shehitah the animal is dedicated not to man, but to God.

A powerful influence on the character was also exerted by the dietary laws. By putting certain restrictions on his appetite, they disciplined the life of a man. And concerning the laws of purification there is the saying of the great Rabbi: "Dead bones do not make unclean, and water does not make clean; but it is a decree from heaven, and we must observe it." The laws of purification were as a rampart about the Bnai Israel, keeping out the floods of idolatry, filth, and dissoluteness which surrounded them. They were promulgated in order that the Jewish person might remain in unbroken contact with God. "For whom do you purify yourselves?" asked the great Rabbi Akiba. And he answered: "For God."

It is our belief that all the laws of foods and of purity which Moses issued were intended to safeguard the Bnai Israel from poisoning, as caused by unsuitable nourishment, and from contagious diseases, as caused by uncleanliness. On these grounds he decreed that not only was the eating of unclean creeping things forbidden; it was forbidden likewise to come in contact with a carcass or any other unclean thing. That they might become a holy people in the spirit, the Bnai Israel had to be trained in the ways of physical well-being, too. It was to be a sound and healthy people which would enter upon its mission in the promised land.

Now while these regulations seemed, therefore, to bear the stamp of a temporary purpose, relating to the transition time in the wilderness, Moses also issued a series of laws which were to be the permanent order of Israel in its own land, laws designed to crystallize the "holy people." These laws shine with the light of an eternal significance; their spirit of ordered justice, their profoundly moral formulation, have caused them to take root in every civilization down to our own day. They are valid for us today as they have been valid for every civilization touched with the spirit of God through the utterances of all his prophets.

Moses introduced into the life of the Bnai Israel the principle of the seven-year cycle of the Sabbatical year, and the fifty-year cycle of the Jubilee. Every seventh year the earth rested, even as man and beast rested every seventh day. It was a difficult agrarian innovation, the uses of which were not understood until later. The principle of the Jubilee signifies that the earth is the Lord's, and that a man is entitled to its use only for a specified and limited time.

Moses warned the Bnai Israel against imitating the Egyptians and the Canaanites in their customs, laws, and behavior. "You shall keep My statutes and My judgments, which if a man do, he shall live in them."

And what were the doings of the Egyptians and Canaanites, against which God warned the Bnai Israel so sternly?

These peoples were given to incest, to the sexual union of the closest blood relatives. There was no law in Egypt against the marriage of brother with sister, and none in Canaan against the union of mother and son. Nor was it an unusual thing among these peoples that a father should violate his own daughter, or that a man should lie with an animal. And from these practices degeneration resulted, and they brought forth cripples and witless creatures and all manner of monsters.

And now the prohibition was issued, once and for all. A strict line of demarkation was drawn in the matter of such unions between members of the same family; and out of this demarkation a new family bond was to emerge, a bond made sacred by the purification of sexual relations. The new family bond would become the standard for all mankind, to such a degree that men would wonder how it could ever have been otherwise, and would ask who it was that had introduced the prohibition of such unions between the members of a family.

"The nakedness of thy father and the nakedness of thy mother—that is, the knowing of them in sexual union—shalt thou not uncover; she is thy mother; thou shalt not uncover her nakedness."

"The nakedness of thy father's wife shalt thou not uncover. The nakedness of thy sister, the daughter of thy father, or the daughter of thy mother, whether she be born at home, or born abroad, thou shalt not uncover."

"Thou shalt not give thy children to Moloch."

"Thou shalt not lie with a man, as with a woman; it is an abomination."

"Neither shalt thou lie with any beast to defile thyself therewith; neither shall any woman stand before a beast to defile herself therewith; it is confusion."

"Defile not yourselves in any of these things: for in all these things the nations are defiled which I cast out before you. And the land has become unclean, and I visit upon it its iniquity, and the land itself vomits out its inhabitants."

"Whosoever shall commit any of these abominations shall be cut off from among his people. . . ."

"Ye shall be holy; for I the Lord, your God, am holy."

"When thou reapest the harvest of thy land, thou shalt not wholly reap the corners of thy field . . . thou shalt leave them for the poor and the stranger. I am Jehovah, your God."

"Ye shall not steal, nor deal falsely, neither lie to one another."

"Thou shalt not defraud thy neighbor, neither rob him: the wages of the hired man shall not stay with thee overnight."

"Thou shalt not curse the deaf, nor put a stumbling block before the blind, but shalt fear thy God."

"Thou shalt not hate thy brother in thine heart; thou shalt rebuke thy neighbor, and not bear sin toward him. Thou shalt not avenge, nor bear any grudge against the children of thy people."

And finally, the utterance which has become the foundation of all relationships between man and man in our civilization:

"Thou shalt love thy neighbor as thyself. I am Jehovah!"

And in order to make it clear that "thy neighbor" did not refer solely to a brother in Israel, it was strictly enjoined that the same law should apply to the stranger as to the homeborn. For, immediately following the admonition: "Thou shalt rise up before the hoary head, and honor the face of an old man, and fear thy God," came the words:

"The stranger that dwelleth with you shall be unto you as one born among you, *and thou shalt love him as thyself.* For ye were strangers in the land of Egypt. I am the Lord your God."

Among the fundamental or basic laws of Moses, there was one which might seem to have been issued on hygienic grounds; but it is a law which has had the profoundest effect on the making of the Jewish family. It is the law which forbids the husband to be with his wife during her menstrual period.

During the time of her purification, for some days before and after the period, the law, which was afterward formulated in all its details, forbade the husband any kind of intimacy with his wife, on peril of incurring the sin of the gravest impurity. He was sternly enjoined to respect her state of body and mind, and not to force himself upon her in the days of her psychic crisis. The interval assigned for the purification restricted the privilege of the husband to not more than two weeks in the month; and when the wife issued from under the cloud, cleansed and purified by her husband's thoughtfulness for her womanhood, she was irradiated with love and gratitude toward him; and she was then like the ripe grape filled with wine. And standing before him, she was renewed for him in her virginity.

This ancient, tender, and delicate law of denial during the woman's periods infused a strange freshness and beauty into Jewish life, like the winds laden with the odor of new blossoms blowing through the days of the Pentecost. Out of this ceaseless purification the Jewish family developed the strength to withstand those tribulations which are the portion of all life, and those which fell with particular heaviness on the Hebrew people.

305

CHAPTER TWELVE

THE blue-silver cloud which throughout these days had hovered above the tabernacle finally lifted. It was the signal for the departure.

Two heralds stationed themselves before the sanctuary and began to blow on the silver trumpets which Moses had had made for them on God's command. At first they blew long, single blasts, calling together the leaders and elders of the tribes. To these Moses issued the instructions for the order of the march. Then the trumpet calls changed to a continuous and mighty pealing which rang through the entire encampment. When the hosts were ordered and assembled a final burst announced the instant of the setting forth.

When the Bnai Israel left Egypt, they had resembled a stormy and swollen river bursting its banks and pouring over the fields. The progress from Goshen to Sinai, along the reach of the Red Sea, had been devoid of system or discipline. The tribes were mingled; they carried with them, at the moment of the exodus, nothing more than the ark which contained the bones of Joseph, and the loads of gold, silver, and precious stuffs which they had "borrowed" from the Egyptians; to these had been added, later, the booty gathered from the Egyptian horsemen drowned in the Sea of Reeds.

How different was the pageantry of their departure when the tribes set out from Sinai in the direction of the promised land!

Mount Sinai is like a mighty mother breast, rising between the two arms of the Red Sea, one of which reaches toward Egypt, the other toward the Jordan. The first march, along the Suez arm, was the march from slavery into freedom; the second, along the Ezion-geber arm, was the march from freedom toward the destined land.

But Sinai might also be seen as something other than a breast between two arms. It was a womb, which had given birth to a people. Slaves had streamed forth from Egypt to the mountain; from the mountain a people marched away—the people of Israel:

306

a people equipped with the fundamental laws of a new world order, graced by God with the supreme benediction of election and separation, adorned with the crown of the ten commandments and the book of the covenant.

It was a people that marched in strict military formation: at its head the first threefold host of the tribes of Judah, Issachar, and Zebulun, under the leadership of the elder and leader of Judah, Nachshon ben Aminadab. Behind Nachshon ben Aminadab strode the elders of the associated tribes, Nathanel ben Zoar and Eliab ben Helon. Over each tribe fluttered its individual banner.

When the first threefold host had drawn from the encampment, the trumpets began to sound again. Then the Bnai Gershon, of the tribe of Levi, the carriers of the sanctuary, set forth.

On the six wagons which were the gifts of the elders of the tribes, the entire sanctuary was laid out in sections: the gold-covered pillars, the thresholds, and the multiple coverings. One wagon also carried the young grandchildren of Aaron, the High Priest—the blossoms of the priesthood, as they were called. They were few in number, these descendants of Aaron, and much care was lavished on them, so that they might grow up without any physical defect which might unfit them for the sacred services. Dedicated as they were to Jehovah, they were regarded as part of the sanctuary itself, and were carried with it in one of the wagons pulled by a group of Levites of the Bnai Gershon who, because of the holiness of their task, went barefoot.

The tabernacle was followed by the threefold host of Reuben, Simeon, and Gad, under the leadership of Simeon, on whose flag was the legend: "Hear, O Israel, the Lord our God, the Lord is One."

Then came the supreme sanctity of the Bnai Israel: the ark, which contained the ten commandments and the book of the covenant—the ark, which stood in the Holy of Holies, and on the cover of which, between the cherubim, Jehovah's spirit rested.

The bringing forth of the ark from the Holy of Holies was a high ceremony performed by Aaron and his sons. While the tabernacle was still assembled, the priests entered the Holy of Holies and covered the ark with a shining cover of pure blue. Then they took up the golden carrier staves which were passed through the rings, and carried the ark into the open; there it was transferred to the hands of a chosen family of the tribe of Levi, whose duty it was to carry the utensils of the sanctuary on their shoulders.

But it was not to the Bnai Korah, the most distinguished family in Levi after the Bnai Amram, that this distinction fell; it was allotted to the family of the Bnai Kohath.

This family occupied a special place among the Levites. On the command of God Moses had assigned to it the most sacred of the tasks. Its commander, Eleazar, the son of Aaron, a man of gigantic build, with a magnificent face, a thick-woven black beard, and great, luminous eyes, marched at the head. He carried in his arms the golden cruses containing the delicate oil, prepared according to a specific recipe, which Aaron used for the eternal light of the *menorah*. Distilled laboriously from rare incense plants which blossomed only here and there in the wilderness, this precious liquid was guarded with the closest attention. The service of the sanctuary had to be resumed the moment the Hebrews rested from their journeying; the eternal light had to burn always before God; and to the commander of the Bnai Kohath was entrusted the carrying of the oil when the host was in motion.

Behind the elder came the young Levites of the family, powerful youths in white, new-washed robes, with the staves of the blue-covered ark on their shoulders. The carriers in front walked backward, with their faces to the ark.

Immediately after the ark came the holy vessels of the sanctuary, all covered with blue cloth: the *menorah,* the shewbread table, the basins, cruses, fire shovels—each borne separately on the shoulder of a white-robed Levite. The long line of carriers ended with Moses and Aaron and their sons, who, as members of the Bnai Levi, marched with their tribe. Moses led a group consisting of the seventy elders of Israel whom he had elected, of Joshua, his aid, and of the heralds and trumpeters and signalers who transmitted his directions to the host, called the pauses in the march and its resumption, and assembled the elders of the tribes to hear the commands of Jehovah.

Thus the tribes marched under their banners and standards, and the devices on these symbolized the blessings which the patriarch Jacob had distributed among his sons, the fathers of the tribes, as he lay dying; so that it seemed as though the tribes marched under the shelter of the blessings. Judah at the head: "Judah is a lion's whelp," Jacob had said: "The scepter shall not depart from Judah, nor the ruler's staff from between his feet." And in the bearing of Judah's leader, Nachshon ben Aminadab, there was already the bearing of the kings who were to come from this tribe. Men apart were these sons of the tribe of Judah, unbroken by slavery. Who would have thought that the overseers' lash had ever descended on these bodies? Faithful these men were—the first to leap into the sea, the first to march out to war. A lion is Judah, and a lion flutters on his sky-blue standard. "His eyes shall be red with wine. He washeth his garments in wine, and his vesture in the blood of grapes."

Behind Judah, in the same division of the host, marched Zebulun and Issachar. In the Bnai Zebulun one glimpsed the future fishermen and men of the sea. A ship adorned their banner. Jacob himself had foretold their calling: "Zebulun shall dwell at the shore of the sea, and he shall be a shore for ships." Zebulun marched with his brother Issachar: "Issachar is a large-boned ass; he saw a resting place that it was good, and he bowed his head to bear." The sages of later ages said: "He bowed his head over the book, for the Bnai Issachar were to be men of learning; they were to find the land of the Torah, and the resting place of wisdom. And Issachar was to enter into partnership with his brother Zebulun: Zebulun was to work for him, provide him with nourishment, while Issachar bowed his head over the book and studied the lore of God." Therefore the banner of Issachar was dark, and it bore the emblems of the sun and moon. Out of the tribe of Issachar were to come the sages who would scrutinize the ways of the stars in heaven and the laws of the measurement of time.

So tribe followed tribe. The color of Dan's standard was that of the sapphire, and its emblem was a serpent. "Dan shall be a serpent in the way, a horned snake in the path, that biteth the horse's hoof, so that his rider falleth backward." Dark-skinned men, with white teeth and curly hair—a shepherd folk were the Bnai Dan, exposed to the burning rays of the sun. All the vices of the shepherds of Egypt had passed into the Bnai Dan: a horned snake in the path of Israel was Dan. All too easily they slid back into idolatry, which they had learned in Egypt; they were the first to worship the golden calf; their palates longed for the flesh of kid seethed in its mother's milk—and in this was a hint of the goddess Isis, whom they had worshiped secretly in Egypt: mother and child are one, the mother is the child and the child is the mother, the unbroken continuity of fertility. The wrath of Jehovah and the hand of Moses would fall heavily upon the Bnai Dan, to smite the idolatry from their hearts. They were the first to bear upon a standard, like a universal symbol, that benediction which has provided every one of us, to the last man, with the buttress of hope in the hour of need: "I wait for Thy salvation, O Lord."

The third threefold host was headed by Ephraim, and included the tribes of Menassah and Benjamin. With Dan marched Asher and Naphthali.

"Arise, O Lord, let Thine enemies be scattered!
Let Thy foes flee before Thee!"

With this chorus and battle cry, which the Levites lifted up and in which all the marchers joined, the Bnai Israel drew away from Mount Sinai.

The command to march in military formation applied only to the youth of the tribes. The old people, the women and children, together with the cattle, the sheep, and the asses—in their midst the baggage and the folded tents—came after the youth; they were guarded by swordsmen and bowmen under the command of the captains of hundreds and the captains of tens. And beside the captains were the Levites, to instruct the Bnai Israel in the laws and to enforce the commandments, in order that the new discipline, introduced by Moses in the name of Jehovah, might be maintained among the multitude.

The wandering host stirred up a gigantic cloud of dust in the wilderness. Floating above them, as if carried by the wings of invisible angels, the cloud was like a covering and shield over the heads of the Bnai Israel. In the day it was like a smoking pillar which led the way, and in the night it shone like a pillar of fire.

It was another type of wilderness into which Moses now led the Bnai Israel; and it was with another aim and purpose. Approaching Sinai, he had hastened his footsteps at God's command; and he had known whither he was leading the tribes. Between the Sea of Reeds and Sinai he had not reckoned with the possibility of hostile attacks. His path had not lain through populated areas, hostile or even neutral: the Amalekites had been an unexpected incident. But the second half of the route to the promised land, between Sinai and the Jordan, presented many obstacles. Here the hosts of Israel would be exposed to frequent attack.

He wanted to avoid a clash with those peoples concerning which God had told him that their lands had been given to them as an eternal heritage. He knew, however, that though some of the neighboring peoples were of the kindred of the Bnai Israel—such, for instance, were the descendants of Esau and of Lot—and might have been expected to show friendship and understanding, nevertheless the dread rumor of the wonders God had wrought with His people, and of the promise He had made them, had spread universal alarm. Moses therefore expected both open and concealed hostility. Nor was he acquainted with this part of the wilderness. He did not know where the oases lay, or the river beds which sustained a certain amount of vegetation. He therefore asked his brother-in-law, Hobab, who knew these parts well, to accompany him as guide and promised him a share of the gifts which God held in reserve for the Bnai Israel. But Hobab refused; he preferred to remain with his own, in his own country.

It would seem that the bearing of Moses toward his wife's family, his failure to admit even his own sons to high privileges in the priesthood or in other spheres of leadership, had resulted in a certain embitterment. In the face of Hobab's refusal, he fell back on his own resources. Three days before the departure from Sinai he sent out the carriers of the ark and the sanctuary, accompanied by a military guard, to find the next resting place for the host. He provided them with a sign: when they would see the cloud descend and rest on the ark, they were to know that this was the place which God had chosen for the next pause. There they were to erect the tabernacle and prepare to receive the Bnai Israel, which followed at an interval of three days.

But these provisions turned out to be futile; in spite of all that had happened, human nature reasserted itself. On the second or third occasion of the renewed march through the heavy sands of the wilderness, the ancient murmuring rose again in the camp, and again Moses felt rebellion in the air. It was rebellion not simply against the toil and discomfort of the march, but against the entire system of laws which he had instituted at God's command: the laws of family purity, the laws of sexual continence, the laws of dietary cleanliness. And once again the tribe of Dan and the mixed multitude were the first to relapse into the evil ways which they had brought with them out of Egypt.

"What else will he forbid us? Perhaps the next command will make it a sin to sleep with our own wives! Perhaps there shall be no more multiplying!" they murmured among themselves.

During one of the pauses a bearded Abyssinian who was crawling through the sand looking for a lizard to eat, raised his voice in overt protest. "And what is it all for?" he cried. "For the thin, slimy stuff which we are given every morning as our day's provisions? I tell you it's already crawling out of my nose. Before one has even tasted it, it is gone, it has vanished."

Another, emboldened by his words, took up the plaint. "Twenty years I lived with my sister-wife in Egypt. She bore me many children, sons all. We made our little hut out of the Nile mud, and there was not a word spoken against us. And here comes a man, a messenger sent by Moses, and commands me, in the name of Jehovah, to send my wife away from my tent. I dare not live with her; I dare not touch her. She is unclean to me. 'Who is Jehovah, that I should listen to Him?' I asked. 'What has He done for me?' Pharaoh commanded me—yes! But he also gave me food. What does Jehovah do for me?"

And a third responded:

"And so thou art forbidden to sleep with thine own sister. But art thou permitted with another's? Has not this same Jehovah commanded through Moses, and Moses through his messengers, to refrain from touching our wives when their time is on them? When has such a thing been heard before? Not to touch thine own wife, when thou desirest her!"

"The very thing I have said! We shall be forbidden to breed and multiply! As our food is, so shall our multiplying be!"

"But all he knows is to issue laws and commandments: this thou mayest not, that is forbidden thee, and the other thou shalt not touch. No crabs, no turtles, nothing that lives in water unless it have both fins and scales. And the first-born of thy house, from thy son to thy sheep, thou shalt give Me, for it belongs to Me. Soon He will take our lives away. I tell you, men, do what you like with me—but it was better under Pharaoh. There at least we knew what we had. Here we have nothing. Tomorrow he can take away even that nothing—or forbid us to enjoy it."

"He sits there in his tent with his men and keeps on inventing new prohibitions," and the speaker pointed toward the tent of Moses.

The wilderness in which the Bnai Israel now found themselves was harsh and forbidding in the extreme. The surface of the Sinai plateau had been covered with a hard layer of reddish stone; but the mountain springs and the melting snows of the summits had hollowed canals into the lower levels. And even when the channels ran dry, when they became choked with stone, the mere sight of them was a kind of refreshment to the eye of the desert wanderer; and it seemed to him that his ear caught the echo of murmuring waters. However brief and meager the flow might be in the winter months, the streamlets still left the sign of their fruitfulness on the rest of the year: the water soaked through, it softened into loam the sandstone beds and left behind a thick dampness; here and there, in obscure holes, tiny pools remained; here and there an alluvial deposit worked its way into the cracks of the stones, and broke into a mossy green; here and there sprang from the heart of the granite an acacia, a cactus bush, familiar and unfamiliar plants, some of them eatable, substitutes for the homely radish, the sturdy onion, and the stinging garlic.

But ever since the tribes of Israel had descended the slopes of Sinai they had been lapped in sandstorms. The entire stretch here was one reddish sea of fine sand, across which moved sand waves, like the gigantic scales of leviathan. The sun was half eclipsed by a sand cloud which rose from under their feet; the rays struggled to break through the dusty net. There was sand grit in their manna. Whatever they took into their mouths, they tasted only the grit, which crackled between their teeth. They ate sand; they breathed sand. The sand powder settled on their eyes and their lips.

From the door of his tent at the foot of the hill on which the tabernacle was raised, Moses let his eye pass over the tents of the Bnai Israel casting their shadows on the blinding glitter of the sand waves in every direction. It was as though the hosts of the Lord had descended and covered the levels of the wilderness. Countless they were: and all of them were dependent, for food, for drink, for their very lives, on the one living God.

Now that they were in the wilderness of Paran, they no longer lacked water. At this time of the year the rivulets opened on the

313

sandy heights, flowed into the deep-cut channels, and fell into the valley where the children of Israel lodged.

Falcon-eyed, Moses could see in the distance how the Bnai Israel were clustering, like ants, about the water holes and water channels. Singly and in groups they crawled on all fours, sniffing, licking the damp sand, thrusting their fingers into every opening, pushing the sand aside. Moses knew only too well what it was they longed for, what it was they sought: a leaf, a spear of grass, a cactus spike, a thorn—anything rather than the monotony of the manna, with its thin, sickly sweetness dissolving on the palate; anything rather than the interminable dreariness of the sticky liquid, the very sight of which had become loathsome to them. Even a locust or a grasshopper was like a mirage of fresh waters in their imagination; and their eyes lit up at the thought of a frog or a lizard.

The great events of Sinai had been in vain. The thunders and the lightnings were forgotten. The eyes of the Bnai Israel no longer found delight in the sanctuary, with its gilded pillars flickering on the hilltop. They even looked with indifference on the thick blue cloud sending out flickers of white fire from its edges. Hunger had eaten away every feeling of awe and pride, every human response to divinity, and had left, like a festering sore, one longing, and one longing only: and that was to sate that hunger with food into which they could sink their teeth in wolfish bliss.

On the road from Egypt to Sinai they had not been tormented thus by their hunger. For a time the manna had allured them with its newness and freshness; its mysterious appearance and disappearance had stirred their curiosity and wonder. Besides, in the early days of their exodus, when such things were not yet forbidden them, they had helped themselves to the reptiles and water creatures which they found on the shores of the Sea of Reeds. They had also been filled with the expectation that at Mount Sinai a new order of things would begin for them; the manna was but temporary nourishment which Jehovah vouchsafed them until He had brought them to His mountain. Thence, after giving them the Torah, God would carry them on eagle's wings to the promised land. But now, as they plodded toward the promised land, the hankering for plain human food overwhelmed both their spiritual gains and their material hopes. The desert which they were traversing was utterly devoid of animal or vegetable life. A single coat of overlapping scales covered the surface of the earth—sand waves of a petrified sea. In vain did they seek, sniff, scrutinize the earth, in vain they dreamed of at least an earthworm, a little snake, a lizard crawling in the clefts—something to swallow in defiance of the commandment. There was nothing but the insipid, sticky manna falling with the dews—a stuff which melted on the tongue before the famished palate could get the taste of it; the teeth had nothing to take hold of, the stomach remained empty; their insides were cold and hollow, the machinery of the body fell into disuse. As the manna came, so it disappeared, leaving behind no aftertaste of human food.

Moses was thoroughly aware that he could not long retain control of the Bnai Israel with the thin diet of manna, which only served to sustain their lives. He had led out of Egypt a race of workers, men, not angels—men who, like all living creatures, needed earthly food. Moses, the captain of Pharaoh's hosts, and Moses, the leader of the Bnai Israel in the desert, knew what human beings were. He knew that a man was dependent on his animal wants. But his faith was in Jehovah; he had believed that Jehovah would change the nature of this people, which He had brought forth from Egypt in the midst of so many wonders. Had not the Bnai Israel been brought forth precisely because they were separated from the rest of the human order, were they not the subject of a special election, and thereby the chosen people? Had they not also been placed in a special category by the very wonders which had been wrought with them? Was not Jehovah their earthly father as well as their heavenly God? He it was who had set the destiny of the Bnai Israel. He had liberated them from bondage not in the manner of other liberated peoples, but by His own strong arm, with signs and miracles; and he had sustained them many months—almost two years—in the uninhabitable wilderness.

God had given them a Torah—laws not for angels but for men of flesh and blood. He had given them statutes and commandments which they were to institute when they came into their land. All these laws concerning seed, and heave offering, and tithe, the ten commandments which Jehovah had proclaimed from Sinai amid thunder and lightning—these were neither for angels dwelling in heaven, nor for the nomadic robber tribes which haunted the deserts and lived on the booty of sword and bow: they were laws for a normal life in a secured land, which God had promised their

315

forefathers. Soon they would reach the borders of the land and leave the wilderness behind them for all eternity. They would settle in the land which had been assigned to them, which He had chosen for the patriarchs from of old. He would drive out the idolatrous inhabitants, and He would lead the Bnai Israel into the heritage of the fathers; and they would live there according to his Torah and His commandments. They would become the chosen people, the people of the election, a light and a radiance to the rest of the world. And here they were, carrying with them the sanctuary; here was the cloud hovering over the sanctuary, where God rested among them. What other people had experienced such unimaginable greatness? For what other people had He performed such miracles and marvels as for the Bnai Israel? What did it all mean, then? Given all this, were they indeed incapable of controlling their lust for earthly food, could they not repress their hankering after meat and greens for another month or two, till they reached the rim of the wilderness, where the settled places began? Here they were, close to the borders of Edom. Ever since Jehovah had come to rest among them, it was indeed as if He had carried them on the clouds of heaven, bringing them rapidly to the frontiers of their own land. Why did they lament? Why did they bay like wolves? But a little while, and they would be in their land, and everything would be well with them.

CHAPTER THIRTEEN

BUT things became worse rather than better. The murmuring of the people rose until the sound of it reached the tent of Moses. He sent out Joshua ben Nun to go through the camp, and in a little while Joshua returned in the company of the leader of the host, Nachshon ben Aminadab.

"It is the mixed multitude again," reported Joshua breathlessly. "They are stirring the people up, they are playing on the hunger of the people. They conjure up all those green things which they have not seen for so long. They talk continuously of the flesh of living things, and speak contemptuously of the manna, so that the people loathe it the more."

"They have infected the people with lust of meat as with leprosy, harping forever on pots of flesh which they used to eat in Egypt," added Nachshon ben Aminadab. "And the leprosy of their lust spreads and spreads. It has reached also the warriors of the tribes; among the warriors, too, there is an angry murmuring. They want a man's ox meat, not a child's milk. I cannot control them."

"And this—after Sinai! This in the presence of the sanctuary, and on the very borders of the promised land," said Moses, heavy-heartedly.

"But it is the sanctuary itself which has awakened their appetite for meat. The sacrifices which they see upon the altar, the sight of the blood, the odor of the burning fat which reaches their nostrils —they do not stop talking of the sacrifices which God demands of them. They want sheep for themselves, and cattle, and oxen, like the priests."

"Where shall we find all the sheep and cattle to sate such a multitude? Do they not see that the manna is only for the time being, during the days of their sojourn in the wilderness? Soon we shall reach inhabited land, where they will be able to sow, and to pasture sheep."

"But I say again, it is not the Bnai Israel which revolt against

317

Jehovah and thee. It is the mixed multitude: Abyssinian slaves, children of Cush, and sons of Liberia; offspring of Asiatic tribes and even Egyptians who have accompanied us out of their land— strangers who are not of the seed of Abraham. It is they who incite the people. I have always warned against them," said Aaron, who had entered with his son Eleazar, both in their priestly garb. "The children of Abraham are filled with the faith of Abraham, the awe of Isaac, and the humility of Jacob, in the presence of their God. The descendants of the forefathers have the virtues of the forefathers. But these strangers who came up with us must be driven out of the encampment. They must be separated from the children of Israel, they must be made the hewers of wood and the drawers of water."

"Jehovah has commanded us not once but many times that there shall be one law for us and for the stranger, and that we shall love the stranger because we were strangers in Egypt. Those that came up with us are even as we are: it was not us they followed after, but Jehovah; it was not in us they believed, but in Jehovah. They are even like us, under the protection and the law of Jehovah," said Moses, firmly.

"And how do they observe the laws of Jehovah? Did they not almost stone the elders when these came and told them, in the name of Jehovah, to put away their sister-wives? They drove off with staves the messengers who told them that it was forbidden to live with a sister or mother as one lives with a wife," returned Aaron, obstinately.

"But who are the elders of Israel that the Bnai Israel shall listen to them? Did they hold back the Bnai Israel from the worship of the Calf god? By no means. They hid in holes, for fear that the people would stone them if they interfered. Those that cannot risk their lives for Jehovah cannot be the messengers of Jehovah."

Aaron was stricken dumb. He let his head sink when Moses mentioned the golden calf, and the others did likewise.

"No! The Bnai Israel are right in not listening to the voice of the elders. A new council of elders of Israel must be formed, a council which the people will trust, to whose voice it will listen. Come, let us go to them," said Moses, and he turned to Joshua.

"Moses, my teacher, go not out into the camp."

"Why?"

"The spirit of the people is hot. They are capable of committing an outrage."

"Better that they sin against me than against Jehovah. Follow me!" And Moses went out.

"Brother Moses, shall I go with thee?" asked Aaron.

"Thy honor is greater than mine," said Moses. "Stay in the tent. Thy priestly garb, in which thou doest service before Jehovah, must not be stained."

When Moses came into the camp he was not marked. In vain did Joshua and the others call out: "Moses is among you!"

They did not look round; it was as if he had never been their leader. They were otherwise occupied.

Before the curtains of their tents the Bnai Israel sat, their heads sunk, and talked with longing of the foods they had been wont to eat in Egypt. Moses saw a mother, surrounded by her children, crawling on all fours among the tents, like a desperate hen with her little chicks, and nosing the garbage-covered sand.

"Thou seekest in vain," her husband called out to her. "What thinkest thou—that thou are still in Egypt? The sweepings outside the tents there could furnish us with kingly meals. Here thou wilt find only gritty sand. The manna leaves no trace even in thy bowels. It comes unseen, and so it vanishes."

"Egypt, sayest thou? Ah, if I had only the onion skins I threw out daily for the fowl, if I had only the bones which I threw to the dogs, if I had but the peelings of the garlic—"

The husband, a tall man, lean as a wanderer's staff, wagged his goat beard at her: "Ah, do not put me in mind of it, the water runs from my mouth!" He wiped the slaver from his lips. "Oh, those days! When you felt the stab of desire here, under the heart, and you could pick up something and bite into it, deep, deep. . . ."

"Woe to us, that we let ourselves be talked into leaving such a dear, dear land as Egypt, with its fish in the river and bread in the baskets," wailed another woman, "to follow Moses into such a wilderness."

"What? Wouldst thou perhaps return to Egypt, to knead mud and make bricks without straw?"

"Is it so bad to work? We worked, indeed, but at least the bite of bread was certain. When thou camest home from work, thou knewest what awaited thee—meat, fish, bread, garlic, onions. What

319

awaits thee here? That drop of sweet snow, which melts on the tongue before thou knowest its taste."

"But, brothers in Israel, children of Abraham, Isaac, and Jacob, all this is but a passing thing, until we reach our own land. Think of the laws and commandments which God has given us. It is for a rich land, a fat land, that these laws and commandments have been given," called out someone in their midst.

"Oh, true, Moses has indeed given us laws and commandments. But what can we do with laws and commandments? Eat them? Would that he had given us bread, rather, plain, simple bread made of grain, of wheat; would that he had given us meat, the flesh of the steer, of the sheep, big, strong gobbets of meat. . . ."

"The meat they need for themselves," chimed in another voice. "Sacrifices to Jehovah; young goats, oxen, cattle—all for Jehovah."

"Only the fat is given to Jehovah; the meat is for Aaron, for Aaron the priest and his sons, for Moses and his little congregation. Hast thou marked that powerful neck of his, his massive body? Such things come not of laws and commandments; they come of gulping down good food, meat, marrowy bones, leeks, onions. . . . Us he crams on laws and commandments, and he and that precious brother of his, and their sons, stuff themselves with good things. Us he lets starve on this oozing manna; but for him and them there is meat without measure."

"And do you know what I say? Would that we had the leaders of the old time, of the Egyptian time, Korah and Dathan and Abiram. They would not let us starve. Rememberest thou how Korah stood up for us, and Dathan and Abiram with him, when Pharaoh's overseers wanted to do evil to us? They took the blame on themselves and shielded us. Would Moses do thus? Would he have endured the lash for us? Does he even know of our wretchedness? He chews on the meat of the sacrifices and lets us perish in hunger."

"And I have always said it: ever since Moses appeared among us he has brought only misery and suffering, from the time of Egypt on."

Joshua's hand burned on the hilt of his sword.

"Moses, our teacher! Shall I throw myself on them with the sword?" he muttered in his master's ear.

"Wherefore? Because I hear my shame? I do not feel their misery and know not their wretchedness! It is so! They speak the

320

truth. Korah, Dathan, and Abiram were more faithful leaders. They took upon themselves the lashes of Pharaoh's overseers. But did I ever interpose my own body between them and the Egyptian smiters? No! Moses, today thou hast listened to the truth. Come with me!"

And thus Moses went from tent to tent. No one heeded his coming and going; if they recognized him, they paid no attention to him. Everywhere he found men and women in a kind of trance, stripped of all impulse and emotion save the one overmastering desire—the desire for meat.

That desire had taken such possession of their hearts, had wrought so wildly on their spirits, that mirages of the longed-for dishes floated before them, endless rows of fleshpots; and their nostrils caught the tantalizing odor of roasting meat.

Finally Moses and Joshua came to the tents of the mixed multitude. Here another picture presented itself to them. Among the Bnai Israel the longing for the Egyptian fleshpots had been nothing more than longing, had expressed itself in nothing more than a dolorous plaint. Among the mixed multitude the lust poured itself out in an unrestrained orgy of gesture and mimicry.

"Dost thou remember the ducks which used to breed and multiply in the muddy pools about our mud huts? When I came home evenings I heard their quack-quack from afar. Oh, how sweet was the sound of their splashing and paddling! Dost thou remember? There the hut was, and there the pool. Thou hadst but to stretch out thy hand, and there it was—the thick, bursting white meat, cushioned with fat, right under the feathers. Thou hadst but to twist the neck, pluck the feathers, stick the spit in, and it was ready for the flames. Drip-drip—the fat started out, fell into the fire. The smell of roasting meat fills thy nostrils. Thou hast it now, thou holdest it, thy teeth sink into it, something to chew. Thus, thus—deep into the meat, the bones crack between thy teeth, thy tongue runs over with fat, thy mouth is full of fat, it flows over, thy lips are steeped in it, thy chin. . . . A warmth trickles into thy throat, and in an instant it is coated with fat. Thou feelest it pouring into thy inward parts. Thou art warmed through and through, thy bowels are strengthened, thy veins are swollen with blood and fat, and thou chewest, thou bitest deep into the unresisting meat —thus—thus—thus. . . ."

The man who was speaking, an Abyssinian, trembled throughout the length of his dark, bronzelike body, as he played out the pantomime before the crowd of Asiatics and Africans. A convulsion had taken hold of him. His belly writhed; its folds rose and fell in rhythm with the motions of his jaws and throat. He stuck his black, bony fingers into his mouth, mumbled and sucked them, smacked his lips, panted and grunted as though he lacked air, while the saliva trickled out of his lips.

The transport and ecstasy of the man infected the spectators. They began to imitate him. Their jaws were set in motion; they chewed; bodies were thrown into convulsions which became wilder and wilder. Here and there a man dropped to the earth, nosed the sand, and cried out in frenzied joy:

"And I am eating onions, sharp, biting, tasty onion leaves bursting with juice. A-ah, the juice fills my mouth, it crawls down my throat, it has a fiery bite. It fills my bowels with strength—my belly, my entrails—they become alive again—and I thought I no longer had entrails—entrails—entrails. . . ."

"And I am chewing on stinging garlic, bitter-tasting leek, spicy as horse-radish; it fills me with hot, peppery juices."

"Yes, yes, yes, garlic and onion, leek and carrot and radish and cabbage. . . . I am eating, my manly strength grows, my limbs are filled with desire toward woman. . . ."

"And I am drinking milk, delicate, white milk. It oozes from the fat teat right into my mouth. I feel the little one under my heart drinking the milk with me," cried a woman with naked, sacklike breasts, as she lifted up her mouth, from which sand ran out.

The word "milk" gave a new turn to their frenzy; it was as if their withered tongues had been loosened with a liquid.

"I am sucking the bones of a sweet young kid boiled in its mother's milk, prepared by the Egyptians on their festivals. Dost thou remember how the caldrons seethed in the temples—kids cooked in their mothers' milk? Delicious little bones, soaked and seethed in the mother's milk! The double taste of the mother and the kid—as if thou wert sleeping with mother and daughter at once, which Moses has forbidden us to do!" cried a man of huge build, while with contorted face and limbs, with bursting eyes, he accompanied the words with obscene gestures. Words and gestures produced their effect on those about him. They began to rub their gaunt bodies against each other, their flesh twitched, they emitted wild cries, as if the orgy of lust were driving out the pangs of their hunger.

Moses and Joshua stood in the midst of the mixed multitude of races and peoples: there were among them Negroes from Abyssinia, children of Arabian tribes, Edomites, Moabites, Midianites, white-skinned Canaanites, Assyrians, Libyans, and even inhabitants of the Greek islands—men and women from every land which Pharaoh's hosts had invaded to bring back slaves.

Moses had imagined that all these peoples had been fused with the Bnai Israel by the miracles and marvels they had shared, by the laws and commandments which he had given them in Jehovah's name. But nothing had changed. The yoke of the law had not brought a new soul into them, had not purified their heathenishness, had not remade their character. The first experience of hunger had obliterated from their hearts every sign of God's handwriting. The lust for meat had kindled in them the lust for idolatry and whoredom and vice. The tables of the covenant were shattered within them, and the fragments were being ground into dust by the iron teeth of their inherited and accumulated animalism. Everything was consumed by their lusts; it was as if no hope remained that the seed of God which he had planted in them should ever bring forth its harvest.

"Moses, our teacher, shall I destroy them with the edge of my sword?" cried the enraged Joshua.

"Them?" asked Moses. "Why them? It is we who have merited death, we and the elders of Israel, we, their leaders, not they. Who are they? Who was their father? The wild forest, which knows only the laws of the beasts. Who was their mother? The dumb, black night, which covers the face of earth with a thick veil and shuts out the light of God's heaven. To destroy them would be to admit that the heart of man is not fit for the seed of God. But if this be so, what purpose is there in creation? And if the seed of Abraham, Isaac, and Jacob sinks in the scum of lusts, how shall these be better? Listen to the lament which goes up from the tents of Jacob; hear the crying for meat, for onions, for garlic, which drowns out the words 'We will do, and we will obey.' Not they are guilty, but we who sowed badly, who failed in our task. We did not set a good example. Consider what the leaders did in the matter of the golden calf. My brother, the elders—they fled like mice and abandoned the people in their need. It is the shepherd's fault if the sheep are scattered and destroyed by wild beasts, as the Bnai Israel are destroyed by wild lusts. Come, let us return the flock to Him who entrusted it to us. Bad shepherds have we been."

And Moses returned and went into his tent. He let down the curtain at the entrance, stretched himself out on the ground, and wept into his hands.

"Merciful God, God of Abraham, Isaac, and Jacob, see my shame and my abasement. My weakness and my failure are uncovered before Thee like a running sore. Whom hast Thou chosen, into whose hands hast Thou entrusted the children of Thy friends, Abraham, Isaac, and Jacob? When Thou first camest to me, and tookest me from my sheep, that I might be the shepherd of Thy chosen people, I said unto Thee: 'Who am I, that I should go to Pharaoh, and that I should lead the children of Israel out of Egypt?' Not theirs is the fault, but mine. Thou hast placed Thy people in unworthy hands. See, Thou hast done but evil to Thy servant. Wherein have I sinned that Thou puttest upon my weak shoulders the burden of this vast people? Did I bear this people, that Thou biddest me carry it, as a nursing father carries his sucking child, into the land which Thou didst promise to the fathers? Who am I that I should give them meat? Where shall I take meat? No, mighty Jehovah, I can no longer carry this people alone. I cannot listen to its weeping, I cannot bear the pain of their hunger and thirst. And if Thou dealest thus with me, slay me, I pray Thee, out of hand. Let me not see my wretchedness, and bring not this evil upon me."

It seemed to Moses that God would descend upon him in a storm, in thunder and lightning, and crush him to the earth on which he lay, because he had rejected the mission which He had entrusted to him. This was what he awaited, and he was prepared to be destroyed; for in truth he could no longer endure the burden, could no longer look on the suffering of the Bnai Israel without being able to help them. But instead of thunder and destruction there descended on him a light cloud, which folded itself sweetly and warmly about him; and it was as he were enfolded by the wings of the cherubim on the ark. And he heard Jehovah's voice, mild and gentle and tender, like a mother's song. And like a father Jehovah comforted and strengthened him, and spoke to his heart; spoke with fatherly compassion and understanding:

"Go out, and gather Me seventy of the elders of Israel, whom

324

thou knowest to be elders and officers over the people; and bring them to the tent of the meeting, that they may stand there with thee. And I will come and speak with thee there. And I will take of the spirit which is upon thee, and will put it upon them; and they shall bear the burden of the people with thee, that thou bear it not thyself alone. And say thou unto the people: Sanctify yourselves against tomorrow. Ye shall eat flesh; for ye have wept in the ears of the Lord, saying: Would that we were given flesh to eat! For it was well with us in Egypt. Ye shall not eat one day, nor two days, but a whole month, until it come out at your nostrils, because ye have rejected the Lord, Who is among you, and have wept, saying: Why came we forth out of Egypt?"

In the blissful relief of God's mild words, in the ecstasy of his gratitude, Moses forgot himself, forgot Who spoke to him. It was as if an earthly father were comforting his son, as if an earthly father were taking council with him concerning the Bnai Israel; and it was like a son responding to the words of earthly father that Moses dared to answer:

"Where wilt Thou take flesh to feed six hundred thousand people? Wilt Thou slaughter the flocks and herds for them? Wilt Thou gather all the fish of the sea?"

And God's wrath was not kindled. Gently he reminded Moses to whom this question had been addressed:

"Is the Lord's hand waxed short? Now shalt thou see whether My word shall come to pass or not."

Whenever Moses came out of the ecstasy into which he was thrown by a visitation of God, he would ponder on the message he had received and weigh every word and hint contained in it. For each separate word was weighty with meaning, and to miss its purpose would be tantamount to sin. On this occasion, too, he brooded on what he had heard, regarding God's counsel as commands. The words had been: "Gather seventy of the elders of Israel, whom thou knowest to be elders and officers over the people." "Officers," He had said. This was to be the difference between the first seventy and the new seventy.

Since God had led the Bnai Israel out of Egypt, they had had no officers or overseers. They had had teachers, guides, bringers, and interpreters of Jehovah's law, but not overseers. Overseers had been set over them in Egypt, when they had been Pharaoh's slaves. Did it mean, then, that God was now directing him to place the children of Israel under a slave discipline? Were they to be driven by overseers to the service of Jehovah, as they had once been driven to labor in Egypt? God forbid! The children of Israel were sons of freedom. They had taken the ten commandments, the laws, and the statutes, upon themselves of their own will, like free men, when they had called out: "All that the Lord hath spoken we will do." How, then, could he place officers over them, officer overseers with whips in their hands? No, this had not been God's meaning.

What then had He meant by "officers?" Could it mean that He was taking away their freedom and making them into His own slaves?

By no means! Moses could not for a moment conceive that Jehovah sought to transform the Bnai Israel into slaves.

Long and in vain did Moses ponder the riddle, till God enlightened him through a vision of the far future.

And Moses beheld the children of Israel scattered among the nations of the world. He saw them living a separate life among the gentiles, islands in surrounding seas. He saw the long and bloody roads which the Bnai Israel would have to traverse, tortured and humiliated. He saw the age-long dedication of the Hebrew people; he heard its sons calling out with their last breath, from amidst the flames of the burning scaffold, "Hear, O Israel." He saw brutal hands laid on Hebrews, hands that pried their mouths open, tried to force the forbidden swine's flesh down their throats. He saw Hebrews submitting to the lash and the rod, twisting their faces away, clenching their teeth, refusing to swallow the abomination. He saw bodies smoldering amid flames, and from them came joyous songs, not lamentation and complaint. He beheld the happiness which was their reward. Ah, no, whipped and driven slaves did not serve their lord thus. Thus only sons of freedmen served, equals among equals, friends among friends. The yoke of the laws and commandments could be assumed only voluntarily. And now Moses understood that slavery to God liberated: the slave of Jehovah's commandments is a free man with a free will to serve God with all his heart, with all his soul, defiant of the hatred and cruelty of a whole world.

"I thank Thee, O God, because Thou hast made me see how Thy will makes Thy creatures free."

Moses left his tent and went in search of Dathan and Abiram, the old overseers of the Bnai Israel in Egypt. He did not seek out

Korah; for Korah, as a Levite, was exempt from all duties save those connected with the sanctuary service. Dathan and Abiram had served Pharaoh as overseers; they would now be overseers under Jehovah.

"Brothers Dathan and Abiram," said Moses, making obeisance to them, "I come before you with this request: that you help me with the guidance of the Bnai Israel. Be you the first among the elders which Jehovah has bidden me choose from among the children of Israel. The spirit of Jehovah shall rest upon you as upon me, and you shall be together with me in bringing God's mission to this people."

"We?" exclaimed Dathan and Abiram in astonishment. "We shall be with thee in bringing God's mission to the Bnai Israel?"

"You shall be given a share of my spirit."

"We who were overseers appointed by Pharaoh?" they still wondered.

"Have I not seen," answered Moses, "how you offered your naked bodies to the blows of Pharaoh's officers, when you refused to drive the Bnai Israel beyond their powers of endurance? My own flesh has not been privileged to feel upon it the lash, for the sake of Israel. God grant that my portion be with you, as your portion of the holy spirit will be with me. And as God was with you when you were overseers for Pharaoh, so He will be with you now that you are His overseers."

So Dathan and Abiram became part of the body of officer elders of the Bnai Israel, and as they had once served Pharaoh, so they now served Jehovah.

And God gave them meat, also, as He had promised Moses. In the morning the Bnai Israel saw the shadows of wings falling on the desert sands. Soon the sun was darkened by the multitude of birds. It was again the quail, which had come flying when they were by the Sea of Reeds, on the way to Mount Sinai—had come flying once, then had disappeared. They came again across the width of the desert from the shores of the sea, and again they fluttered down to the feet of the Bnai Israel. A tumult of jubilation went up from the encampment. Men, women, and children came running out of the tents; they threw themselves on the birds with eager hands and mouths, convulsive with excitement. Many of them did not even wait until the birds had been properly killed and decently cooked. They twisted the heads off the birds, plucked out a handful of feathers, sank their avid teeth into the raw flesh. Their stomachs, fallen into disuse with the long diet of weak manna, were no longer in condition to digest the hard, tough food which they stuffed into themselves. They stilled their lust for flesh, grinding the delicate bones between their teeth, swallowing everything down—but they could not still the hunger in their stomachs. Before the nourishing juices could reach their intestines, they fell on the sands in cramping fits. They choked on the undigested raw flesh, and many of them died. That place was thenceforth called Kibroth-Hattaavah, "the Graves of Lust."

And now Moses, provided with the new apparatus of enforcement which he had created by God's counsel, took up the task of fastening rigidly upon the people His laws and commandments. The officer overseers who had driven them to labor for Pharaoh drove them in the service of Jehovah. Dathan and Abiram, and even Eldad and Medad, appointed by Jehovah Himself, were to have power over the Bnai Israel: not by virtue of the lash, but by virtue of their exalted position, by virtue of the holy spirit which was in them. Moses raised them to the status of prophets, so that they should not be, in the eyes of Israel, slave drivers, but rather seers, as he himself was one. And he permitted them to prophesy.

Joshua, the pupil and aid, became jealous for his master's honor and could not bear to see how Eldad and Medad, or Dathan and Abiram, former instruments of Pharaoh's will, shared authority with Moses, and like him prophesied in the congregation. In his furious resentment he would have cut these men down, but Moses rebuked him:

"Art thou jealous for my sake? Would that all the Lord's people were prophets, that the Lord would put His spirit upon them."

Armed and empowered by God, the new officer overseers threw themselves into their task with the severity which they had shown under Pharaoh.

Before long they brought before Moses a man who had been caught gathering wood on the Sabbath, to make a fire and cook food. Cases in which the law had been broken or ignored had often occurred before, but no one had been empowered to interfere. Thus the elders were at a loss as to what course to follow. Were they to carry out the harsh sentence which Moses had pronounced against desecraters of the Sabbath, or were these laws to be suspended until the people had settled in its own land? The man was placed under guard, and the matter was referred to Moses. Moses, feeling secure now in his new officers, chosen by God's counsel, issued the command that the man be taken out of the camp, and stoned by the entire congregation. It was done. Outside the camp, the man was stoned to death, with the participation of the entire congregation, so that all might see, and know, and fear.

The new discipline of Jehovah had begun.

CHAPTER FOURTEEN

IN the midst of all this, Moses was a lonely man. He had not learned to know his family until he was a man, with a life and ways and surroundings of his own. Nearest to him was his sister Miriam, toward whom he felt as toward a mother; and indeed to some extent she had taken the place of the mother whose role in his life had been so brief and fleeting. Miriam had been his guardian spirit even in young days when he had not been aware of it.

Moses had no personal ambitions and no personal aspirations; his dreams and desires were focused on his people, its liberation, its transformation into God's elected. He could not find it in his heart to forgive his brother Aaron in the matter of the golden calf; and in spite of his own prayers to the Almighty, whereby he had obtained forgiveness for the Bnai Israel, he could not forget the ambitious strivings of his brother, which had driven him to betray Jehovah and to bring the people to the brink of the abyss.

Nor was there a true closeness between him and his Midianite family. This had been a refuge to him in the days of his wretchedness, when his brothers in Egypt had repudiated him and driven him off. There was warmth in his heart toward Zipporah and toward Jethro; but toward both of them he felt gratitude rather than love: toward Jethro because of the shelter of his home, because of protection, because of wisdom shared with him; toward Zipporah because of her faithfulness and devotion, because she had been willing to accompany him to Egypt, exposing herself and them to slavery. That he felt himself to be a stranger in the house of his father-in-law, Moses betrayed when he named his older son "Gershom"—"I was a stranger there." Nor did this feeling of remoteness from his own undergo a change later, when Zipporah and the children accompanied him into the desert after the exodus from Egypt.

It was not only that he neglected his family; it was rather that he felt no need for a personal life. His family was all of Israel; father and mother he found in the God of Israel, Jehovah. They had been aware of this in Jethro's household; it had awakened resentment, and even hatred: these feelings had spread from Jethro's household to the Midianites at large and transferred itself upon the Bnai Israel at large; and in the end the Midianites allied themselves with the enemies of the Israelites. The failure of Moses to found a dynasty after the manner of his brother Aaron infuriated both his father-in-law Jethro and his brother-in-law Hobab. The latter had curtly refused to guide the Bnai Israel through the wilderness, and had returned to his native land; both Jethro and Hobab had pleaded with Zipporah not to follow her husband into the dangers of the wilderness. She had turned a deaf ear to them; she had followed Moses again; and Moses put up a tent for her among the Bnai Israel—but he dwelt apart from her, in a tent of his own at the entrance of the sanctuary court; he dwelt there with Joshua, his minister, whom he never let out of his sight.

Moses, to whom God appeared and spoke face to face—often unexpectedly and with no warning sign—was always in a tenseness of expectation; at any moment a vision might appear, the voice might speak in his heart, through the holy spirit. He therefore kept himself in a state of sanctity and purity and did not approach a woman. He was stripped of all human desire, and his heart longed solely for the glory of the Presence. Now and again he visited Zipporah's tent and spent some time with his family; but since the incident of the golden calf, since God's offer to him to make him the father of a great people in the place of Abraham, Moses had withdrawn whatever little importance he had assigned to his family, had been more scrupulous than ever in withholding any sign of honor from his children. He set himself apart from them, and gradually they merged into the mass of the Bnai Israel.

All this Zipporah bore with love; she uttered no word of complaint but was like a quiet dove in her sorrow and neglect. Sometimes the wives of neighbors would speak of her reproach:

"It is the manner of the world that every husband shall cleave to his wife, and every father shall care for his children; and thy husband has abandoned thee, and he has taken a stranger to be his son."

Then she answered:

331

"But is Moses a man like all other men, and a father like every other father? Moses is the teacher of Israel, and whatever he does it is according to the word which comes to him. Who am I that I should lift myself up against Moses? Is it not enough that I am called by his name, and his shadow falls on me?"

Even Miriam—older than he, and the oldest in the family—took it upon herself to rebuke Moses for his neglect of wife and children. Moses, the man of humility, listened—and made no answer.

Of his earthly ties, the strongest was the one with his alien mother, the mother who had not borne him, but had found him and taken him to herself—Pharaoh's daughter, whom he had renamed Bathiya. He would remember, with a deep, far-off longing, her who had protected him from the jealousy of the priests; he would remember how she had intervened, at peril to herself, when he had been threatened with the wrath of Pharaoh.

More than once he asked himself what had become of her. Did she still worship the idols of the Egyptians? Did she still believe herself to be the incarnation of Isis, and himself to be the incarnation of her son Horus? He remembered how she inducted him into that faith when he had still been a child and had accompanied her to the temple: was she still given to that abomination? More than once he had implored God to open her eyes, so that she might understand that not the sun was God, whether as Aton or Ra, but He who had created sun and moon and stars—He alone! But if his prayers had been of effect, surely she was exposed to great danger in Pharaoh's court. Still, he was aware that God had taken her under His wing; and even if she clung to her folly, God would still be her protector when she needed it, because of the goodness of her heart. What the eyes had not perceived, the heart had felt —the single, compassionate God of Israel.

He had not seen her since his departure from Pharaoh's court. He had not kept his promise to come to her when God sent him to liberate Israel; he would not provide a pretext for evil and cynical tongues, both of his own time and of times to come, to hint that it was not God's mighty hand which had freed the Israelites, but that Moses had effected it through the intervention of his mother. Scrupulous for the glory of God, he had avoided her, as he had avoided anyone at court who might have been friendly to

332

him. He had not seen her, nor had word of her, since the far-off time of his first departure from Egypt.

Then it came about that he encountered, in the camp of the Bnai Israel, a face familiar to him from the days of Pharaoh's court.

Whenever Moses went through the camp with veiled features, the children of Israel stood in the doors of their tents, inclined their heads before him, and followed him with their eyes until he disappeared in the thickness of the cloud which covered the sanctuary field. And once it chanced that, as he passed by the area of the mixed multitude, which was outside the congregation, a woman came out of a tent; and instead of bowing her head when she spoke to him, as others did, she fell prostrate at his feet, as if before a king, buried her head in the sand, and called out:

"My lord! My master!"

Moses stopped.

"Before the Lord God of Israel, when thou comest into the sanctuary to pray to Him, and before Him alone, is it proper to kneel or lie prostrate; but not before one of flesh and blood. Rise, and stand before me, and say what thou hast to say."

When the woman obeyed, Moses looked at her, and recognized her.

"Art thou not Fiha, the servant of my mother, the Princess?"

"I am she," the woman answered, and inclined her proud head.

"What doest thou among the hosts of Israel?"

"I have come in order to cleave to the God of Israel. Didst thou not tell me that he that so desires, of whatever tribe or people he be, may become one with the God of Israel, because He is the father of all created things?"

"Those were my words. Knows my mother that thou art here in the wilderness, among the tribes of Israel?"

"It was at her command that I followed the Israelites into the desert."

"Then my mother, Pharaoh's daughter, lives!"

"She lives not. This was her command to me before she was taken to rest in peace in the shadow of the God of peace, who is the God of Israel."

"In the shadow of the God of peace, who is the God of Israel, sayest thou? And not in the shadow of the god of death, of Osiris, her husband, in the pyramid of her father, Rameses the Second?" asked Moses, starting.

"No! Those are her own words, which she spoke to her brother, Pharaoh Menephthah, and to the priests of the god Ra, as they stood about her at the moment of her death."

"Tell me all thou knowest concerning my mother; hide nothing from me, for my soul thirsts to hear what befell her."

"It was for this purpose that she sent me to thee. She bade me tell thee that she follows thee, to be with thy God."

"Why hast thou waited till now before bringing me the word of thy mistress?"

"Who am I that I should approach the holy tent where my lord has his habitation, in the shadow of God? I am an impure stranger."

"Those that cleave to the God of Israel are no longer strangers, and before Him all that believe in Him are pure. . . ." Moses turned to Joshua. "Bring this woman to my tent, that she may tell me of all that happened with my mother."

And Fiha stood before Moses in his tent. Her nakedness was covered with dark draperies, and she had covered her face and her hair; only her feet were bare; she was a naked column swathed in black. And she told Moses of the last days of his mother Bathiya.

"It was soon after Pharaoh left, at the head of his riders, to pursue you to the shores of the Sea of Weeds. For messengers had returned with the report that you were wandering in the wilderness. This was interpreted as meaning that the god Ra had cut off your retreat on the shore of the sea. And the priests said that this was the last battle of Aton, his last stand against Ra. For they believed that the God of Israel was Aton, and that thou thyself wert the reincarnation of the fourth Amenhotep, and thou hadst taken the name Moses even as Amenhotep had taken the name Tutankhamen. Therefore they set out in pursuit of thee.

"And on the advice of the priests the host took with it a great treasure. It was their purpose to overcome Aton not with the sword alone, but with their wealth, bringing with them proof that Pharaoh Menephthah was much richer than Tutankhamen, and had built for Ra temples mightier and more luxurious than those which Tutankhamen had built for Aton.

"But Pharaoh Menephthah led his horsemen only as far as the rim of the wilderness, and returned thence alone. The priests commanded all the faithful to assemble in the temples, and with prayer and sacrifice to help Ra in his battle with Jehovah-Aton. Thy mother, too, whom thou callest Bathiya, was commanded by Pharaoh Menephthah and the priests to conduct the service before her goddess. For the fear of the God of Israel had fallen on the Egyptians. After the death of their eldest born they believed more firmly than before that it was Aton who had returned not only to take vengeance for the destruction of his temples and the wiping out of his name from among the living, but to punish the Egyptians for the abomination which they had done in enslaving the Hebrews of Goshen. Therefore they trembled for the outcome of the battle on the seashore. More than all others the temples of Ra were crowded with worshipers. Pharaoh and his attendants and a great concourse of the people kneeled on the banks of the Nile and with outstretched arms sang hymns to the god Ra; they burned incense and offered up sacrifice. The same was done in the Temple of the Writing of Wisdom and Knowledge—in the temple of the god Thoth—and in all the other temples. Throughout the land there was solemn prayer and ceremonial. But one temple, the temple of the great goddess Isis, remained locked. Thy mother, the priestess, would not open it. She refused to open it, she refused to conduct service before the goddess—and she would not be moved by the threats of her brother and the priests. In the end they compelled her. I was there when Pharaoh and the first 'friend of Pharaoh,' his chief minister, burst into her apartment. She was weak and ailing, and I stood by her side; I held the lotus leaf to her nostrils, and I anointed her with oil. They took her out, they brought her before the goddess Nephthys, they purified her for the service, washed and anointed her; they clothed her in the priestly raiment and put upon her head the double-horned helmet of Isis; and they had her attendants lead her to the locked door of the temple.

"At first she did what she was bidden to do. She took down the wreath which hung on the temple door, and she uttered the formula of the priestess drawing near for the service: 'I come before thee with smoking incense. My purification is upon my hands. I am a priestess and daughter of a priestess. I have been with the goddess Nephthys. Nephthys purified me. I come before thee to do that which should be done, and not to do that which should not be done.'

"And all were content. They believed that now the priestess would conduct the service and pray for the defeat of her son. Thus they stood waiting, and she opened the door of the temple with these words:

335

" 'It is my right to cross this threshold. I have rejected all the evil that was in me.'

"She crossed the threshold, the priests and the people following. She took the smoking censer from the hands of a priestess and she approached the goddess Isis, who was veiled in the smoke of incense. Then she stationed herself on the steps before the goddess and stretched out her hands, not to the goddess, but to all the worshipers, who lay prostrate, with their faces to the earth. Her eyes, deep sunk in her head, suddenly began to burn with a great fire, her face took on life, and she began to speak with a high, clear voice.

"At first they thought she was inditing a hymn of praise for Isis, reciting the deeds of the goddess. Then they perceived that she was uttering prophecy:

" 'The god Ra became old, and water ran from his mouth. And like my mother Isis, I will take his saliva and brew a poison therefrom and let him drink of it. I will light a fire in him, I will torment him with manifold torments, until I will wring from him his secret, the secret of his name, with which I will bind him.'

"And the priests waited, thinking that now she would pass to a hymn imploring victory for Ra. But suddenly her voice rose higher, and rang more clearly:

" 'For Ra is no god, neither is Aton, with his many rays. Ra and Aton are but creations of the one God of Israel, who created all things. The sun does His will and obeys His commands; even so does every bird that flies and every worm that creeps. The sun rises every morning, sets in the evening, because this is the bidding of Jehovah. Slaves have seen this, lords have remained blind.' And her voice rose still higher: 'Come, let us fall upon our knees before the great God of Israel, creator of heaven and earth, father of poor and rich, of small and great, of slave and lord—the mighty God who has shown us His mighty hand and His outstretched arm.' Therewith she fell on her knees, and lifted her hands to heaven, crying: 'O God of Israel, have compassion with Thy creatures, and bring them to Thee. . . .'

"More she did not say; for the priests ran up to her, wrapped her in a black covering, and carried her to her apartment, where they laid her on her couch.

"Later her brother came to her, with the high priest Meneko, who held a drink in his hand. After them came embalmers, pre-

336

parers of mummies, with a sarcophagus and with baskets of linen wrappings.

"Then Pharaoh Menephthah took the beaker from the priest's hand and said:

" 'Take this, my sister, and drink. The time has come for thee to rest in the shadow of thy husband Osiris, the lord of death.'

" 'Not by the lord of death shall I rest, but by the Lord of eternal life, under the shadow of the wings of God of Israel, where eternal peace is,' she answered.

"Then she took the beaker in her hand, and she looked about her until she perceived me. And she beckoned to me to approach, and I bent down, and she whispered in my ear:

" 'Go out into the desert, where my son is leading the congregation of Israel to Mount Sinai. Turn thy spirit to the God of Israel; and tell my son all that thou hast seen and heard.'

"And when I stole out through the many embalmers and mummy preparers who filled thy mother's apartment, I heard the song of the blind keeners. They were singing the hymn of death:

> 'Today death stands before me,
> I am like the sick one who has seen his cure.
> Death stands before me,
> I am like one who comes home
> After many years of captivity.' "

Moses threw himself on his knees, raised his hands to heaven, and cried out:

"I thank Thee and praise Thee, God of compassion, for the mercy Thou hast shown to one of Thy creatures, who forever sought Thee in her heart. Thou didst open her eyes, to know Thee as the one living God of Israel, before Thou tookest her to Thee, to rest in Thy eternal peace. O God of justice and grace, may Thy glory rest upon all the earth, that all Thy creatures may see Thy power, that all may know Thee as their father, who lets the abundance of His goodness pour upon them, whether they call Thy name or call not Thy name. For even before they know Thy name they seek Thee."

Then he turned to the Negro woman and said:

"May God reward thee for the grace thou hast done with me and with my mother in bringing me her last message. And now thou art free, free to return to thy native land, whence thou wert snatched away into slavery."

The tall, dark woman swathed in black made obeisance before Moses, and wept:

"Wherein have I sinned against my God that thou, my lord, sendest me from His presence, and drivest me forth from the camp of Israel?"

"Camest thou to the God of Israel, and art thou in His congregation, because it was the command of thy mistress? or camest thou of thine own will?"

"Have I not seen God's righteousness? Was I not a witness of the hand which punished the mighty and defended the weak and wronged? I have no home but that which the God of Israel has given me in His congregation, and I have no native place other than my portion in the God of Israel, even as thou hast said. And if I am not worthy of being a daughter of Israel, because of my descent —as others have said to me—then let me be the handmaid of my lord, to serve him as I served his mother. But drive me not forth from before thee, lord Moses," and she stretched out her hands and took hold of his raiment.

"Who has dared to say this thing, and who has dared to make a distinction and division in God's camp?" asked Moses, in a lionlike voice.

"Many of the Bnai Israel say this of us, the strangers. They say it in the name of the officer overseers, of thy brother Aaron, and thy sister Miriam. We are strangers, and never shall we be a part of Israel."

"The Lord has said there shall be one law for the stranger as for the homeborn. Thy faith in the God of Israel has made thee a daughter of Israel, and Thy faith in Him has made thee free. Thou art likened to the daughters of the tribe of Judah. Go, my daughter, into the encampment, and rejoice in thy part in the inheritance of God. And if anyone offend thee, or seek to diminish thy portion in the inheritance because of thy descent, come to me. The door of my tent shall always be open to thee, as my ear shall be open to thy word. Go, my sister, in peace."

CHAPTER FIFTEEN

THE plaint of Fiha concerning the hard lot of the mixed multitude came to the ears of Moses from other sources.

The decision to take the alien throngs which had accompanied the Bnai Israel out of Egypt and to elevate them to equality as subjects of Jehovah was so revolutionary an innovation that it startled both the people and its leaders. The Bnai Israel were a people like all others, taking on the coloration of their environment; in Egypt they had acquired some of the outlook and attitudes of the Egyptians. In Egypt slaves were forbidden to have a god or to profess a faith. The Egyptians alone were privileged to serve Ra or to enter his temples. Slaves and aliens even had to keep a certain distance from temples. The breath of a slave was defilement. It was beneath the dignity of an Egyptian lord to lay his hand on a slave, even in the way of punishment.

A rivalry for relative position had already been evident among the tribes of Israel before the exodus. From of old there existed the distinction between the "true" wives of Jacob and the "maids," hence between their descendants, the tribes; and even among the "true" tribes there was competition. The tribe of Reuben was the eldest born in fact, but it lost this position spiritually to the Levites, whom it never forgave. But Judah finally rose to pre-eminence over both, while the children of Dan, from among the tribes of the maids, were degraded almost to the status of the mixed multitude. There was, however, the general bond of a common descent from Abraham, Isaac, and Jacob which held the Bnai Israel together and gave them a feeling of importance and superiority over the newcomers.

The proclamation by Moses, in the name of Jehovah, of "one law for the homeborn and the stranger," and his stern insistence on its fulfillment, was powerless to overcome the sense of privilege in the Bnai Israel. They regarded it as an impairment of their hereditary rights. It was incomprehensible and unacceptable to them that

339

aliens should have a portion in the God of Israel exactly like the children of Abraham, Isaac, and Jacob; and all of the exhortations and emphatic repetitions of Moses were unavailing. In this respect they regarded Jehovah as the Egyptians regarded Ra: Jehovah was the God of the descendants of Abraham, Isaac, and Jacob, with whom He had made His covenant; all others, children of other forefathers, though they might convert to the God of Israel, though they might accompany the Bnai Israel into the desert and accept the yoke of the commandments, were outsiders and could not aspire to equality of rights. They could not expect to share in the inheritance of the promised land; they were to be the hewers of wood and drawers of water—that is to say, they must expect a condition of slavery; and many of the Bnai Israel sought to reduce the strangers to this condition even in the desert. Nor was this true of the upper levels of the Israelites alone; the masses were, in this, at one with the leaders of the aristocratic tribes of Levi and Judah. And the same point of view was held by the family of Moses, namely, by Aaron and Miriam.

It was quite true that the new multitudes, alien to those laws and customs which Israel had inherited from the forefathers, were more apt than the others to slide back into idolatry and the practices of the Egyptians. The sodomitic vices and the deification of reptiles could not be eradicated from among them; the officers encountered enormous difficulties in combating the sexual unions of close members of the same family. For the mixed multitude looked upon the prohibition against a mother living with her own son as an attack on the family. They also regarded as normal the lying of man with man, or of man with beast. Nor could they refrain from seething a kid in its mother's milk, which was a symbol and expression of idolatry, although Moses exerted himself to eradicate this practice on humanitarian and religious grounds, and repeated the prohibition several times, always in the name of Jehovah.

And yet some evidence of a gradual assimilation was not wanting. The laws and commandments touched off the higher instincts which reside in every human spirit. The newcomers awakened to a partial awareness of the unworthiness of their practices, to a perception of the distinction between right and wrong and therefore to a partnership with God in the order of His creation.

Moses was less concerned with individual cases of defection and disobedience as they occurred among the Bnai Israel and newcomers

—more among the latter than the former—for he felt stronger with the institution of the system of officer overseers. He aimed at the large general principle of the all-embracing significance of the God of Israel, His all-human immanence; and this he was determined to establish against all obstacles. Thus it came about that he took on the character of protector of the alien or mixed multitudes against his own people and against his own family.

The opposition to the newcomers continued to gather force; they became, rightly or wrongly, the scapegoat for the sins and failings of all Israel. For the incident of the golden calf the Bnai Israel laid the chief blame on the mixed multitude, though it was quite clear that a larger share of the guilt fell on Aaron. It was thus also with the cases of rebellion against Moses which resulted from periods of hunger or thirst; and after Kibroth-Hattaavah—"the Graves of Lust"—and the furious longing for the fleshpots of Egypt, the resentment against the mixed multitude grew to a new intensity. It was true that many of the newcomers had led the meat rebellion; they had been particularly shameless and vociferous; but it was false to throw the entire blame on them, as the Bnai Israel did after the pestilence which followed.

"The Negroes, the Africans, the Abyssinians, the children of Cush—it was they who longed for the Egyptian fleshpots, not we!"

"The manna is good enough for us. It has every taste in the world—whatever taste I want I find in it," boasted one man.

"We suffer for the sins of the mixed multitude," went up a cry from the encampment.

"The mixed multitude longed for flesh—and we are punished for it; on us His wrath is poured out."

"Remove them from among us; they are a stumbling block to Israel."

"Let them not be reckoned among us! Let them be hewers of wood and drawers of water."

"Never, never will they share the inheritance of Israel. They are not among the children of Abraham, Isaac, and Jacob."

"Aliens are they, strangers, a running sore on the body of Israel. Let them be cut out, as an evil growth is cut from the body."

"Lepers are they in Israel, and as lepers they should be cast forth!"

Moses heard the cry of the Bnai Israel and considered what was to be done.

341

The women were the first to have discovered prayer. Excluded from participation in the sanctuary service, forbidden even to come close to the sanctuary, they found a shorter and more direct path to what they sought. When they went out at daybreak to collect the manna blossoming in the dew, they beheld the gilded pillars glittering in the first rays of the sun—for Moses always had the sanctuary erected on an elevation, whence it dominated and glorified the entire encampment—they fell on their knees before the great radiance, lifted up their hands, and sent up their prayers and supplications straight to God, without the mediation of the priest. Moses did not deter them. On the contrary, he let it be known to the women through Miriam—who was in some sort their leader, as he was the leader of the men—that this practice was pleasing to God; and that the outpourings of their hearts, as acceptable to him as the sacrifices of the priests in the tabernacle, would not fail to obtain an answer.

The women of the mixed multitude followed the example of the women of Israel. Accustomed to prostrating themselves before the rising sun in Egypt, they went out in the early morning toward the hill of the sanctuary, fell on their faces, and raised a hysterical cry, as they had been wont to do of old. Moses sent word through Miriam forbidding these wild, ecstatic demonstrations, which were an echo of their former idolatry; he issued instructions to have them taught the manner of quiet prayer: the body motionless, the lips murmuring. And thus the practice remained.

But all this was against the inclinations both of Miriam and the priests, who would not have the women of the mixed multitude pray even in the vicinity of the sanctuary, because these aliens were unclean. After Kibroth-Hattaavah Miriam, with the help of Aaron, had her way. Without saying a word on the matter to Moses, they sent out officers in the morning; and when the women of the mixed multitude approached the hill of the tabernacle, they were driven off:

"Begone from here!" was the cry. "Your bodies are unclean, and cannot approach the sanctuary, your lips are unclean, and cannot address themselves to the God of Israel."

That same day Joshua came in to Moses and reported that the Cushite woman who had brought him the last words of his mother was standing at a distance from the tent; not daring to approach, she had sent a messenger to beg audience for her of Moses.

Moses sent forth Joshua at once to inquire whether the woman was in a condition of purity; and if she was, to bring her into the tent.

When Fiha, face and body veiled, appeared before Moses, she fell to her knees and cried out:

"My lord Moses! Why have our lips been sealed when our hearts are filled with the glory of God? We, too, long to utter ourselves in prayer and praise. Hast thou not told me, lord Moses, that the God of Israel is the God of all creatures? Wherefore, then, are we forbidden to sing God's praise, as every bird and every leaf on the tree is permitted to do?"

"Who has held you back from pouring out your supplication to the God of Israel?"

"Thy sister Miriam has declared, in Jehovah's name, that our bodies are unclean and may not approach the hill of the tabernacle, our eyes are impure and may not see the glory of God resting upon it, our lips are unworthy to offer up prayer to Him."

"These are not the words of Jehovah, neither did He so command me. I have said but one thing: when you come before God, you shall not do so as you once did before your idols, with loud and unseemly voice. Jehovah is not deaf, as the idols are. Jehovah sees your hearts, and He knows all your needs even before you utter them; and he hears the quiet murmur on your lips even before you have opened them. Go, my daughter, and I will look into this matter which thou hast brought before me."

"My lord Moses, didst thou not say to me that my faith in Jehovah, and my obedience to the commandments, have made me pure?"

"As pure as my sister, as pure as every daughter in Israel."

"Why do they drive us from God's presence when He has opened our eyes to His glory and greatness?" The woman wept quietly. "We are as lepers in their eyes."

Moses was silent. As always when he was made aware of an injustice, he felt the shame of it like a brand on his flesh. He remained sunk in meditation; he called upon Jehovah to send a ray of illumination, to show him the way out of the unhappy pass to which he had been brought by his own flesh and blood. He felt guilty before this woman, who had come to Jehovah in all simplicity of heart, and, through her, guilty before all the generations of the aliens who would seek God. What was he to do? How was he to undo the injustice committed against the alien-born seekers of God? He was seized through and through with the desire to perform an act, a personal and individual act, which would bring restitution to this woman—an act peculiarly and specifically his own, because his was the guilt when his own flesh and blood had committed the wrong.

And then on the instant it was as if God had opened a passage for the light. He saw! He understood!

"Art thou betrothed to a man, or art thou free?" he suddenly asked the woman, whom, in his confusion and distress, he had forgotten to raise from her kneeling position.

The woman was smitten silent. She did not understand the question, and Moses had to repeat it. Then she began to tremble in all her body. The crimson of her face, the terror in her eyes, shone through her dark veil, and she answered in a tremulous voice:

"My lord and master, I was brought as a child to Pharaoh's court. My life in captivity was dedicated to your mother. I have not known a man. My life in freedom I have dedicated to the God of Israel."

"Rise!" said Moses. "Art thou willing to be betrothed to me, Moses, and to be my wife?"

The woman almost sank to the ground again. Her breath came thickly and hotly through her heavy veil.

"I—the wife of Moses?" she repeated in terror.

"I can give thee no more than my name, which will be called upon thee. My place is here, by the tent of the people, by the door of God; I must forever be in a state of preparation, for at any moment the voice of God may sound for me. Therefore I must be separated from woman. But my name shall be called upon thee, that thou art betrothed to Moses, in holiness and purity, according to the law of Israel. Art thou willing to have it so?"

"Oh, my lord and master, let me be the handmaid of my master, to wash his raiment and make his couch."

"Not a handmaid, but the wife of Moses! A portion shalt thou have in Moses, even like Zipporah. With this condition, which I ask of thee, that only my name shall be called upon thee. Give me thy answer in clear words."

"My lord Moses, I am willing to be thy wife with the condition which thou askest of me, that only thy name shall be called upon me."

"As we stand before God, so God be our witness this day," said Moses.

Then Moses approached Fiha, lifted the veil, and looked into her face. After a pause he covered her face again, and turned to Joshua, who had been standing throughout all this at the entrance of the tent, and had heard and seen what his teacher did.

"Thou art a witness this day that I, Moses ben Amram, have sanctified this woman unto me by the token of this ring, in purity and holiness, in the presence of God, according to the law of Israel." And Moses removed his ring and put it on the woman's finger.

And Joshua answered:

"I am a witness this day for this thing."

Then Moses spoke further to Joshua:

"Set aside a tent for this woman, and bring her to it, and see that she lack not food or raiment. And have it proclaimed in all the encampment of Israel that this woman has been sanctified to me according to the betrothal which is recognized in Israel, by the uncovering and the covering again of her face; let this be known in all Israel, so that no man sin through her."

And when the woman was gone from the tent Moses believed that in this woman he had betrothed to God all the peoples of all the generations who would come to seek Him; for Jehovah made it known to Moses that what he had done had found grace in His eyes.

Miriam, sister of Moses and Aaron, was looked upon as the mother of the tribes. She was ranked as a prophetess, together with her brothers; it was held that God had revealed Himself to her even though she had no title in the hierarchy. It was the people themselves who had lifted her to this eminence. They remembered how she had labored for them in Egypt, knowing all their needs and doing what she could to relieve them. It was also known that Moses and Aaron held her in high esteem. It was noted that Moses always rose when she approached him, as one rises in the presence of a mother; and the regard which Moses felt for her was deepened and strengthened when her husband was killed resisting the worship of the golden calf.

Various legends concerning Miriam were current among the people. It was believed that she was in direct contact with Jehovah, even as Moses was; that some of the miracles which had been wrought for the Bnai Israel had been wrought for her sake, and that she had herself prayed for them. Thus they said that the wells which appeared for the Israelites in the desert were God's response to her, for her sake, not for that of Moses. One well was, indeed, called "Miriam's Well," and it was even believed that this same well followed the Bnai Israel in all their wanderings, as long as Miriam was with them.

Her standing and repute were highest, of course, among the women. She was to them what Moses was to the men, the leader and guide and teacher. They were exalted in their own eyes because of her, and in her they saw their own portion and importance in the eyes of the God of Israel.

In the desert as in Egypt Miriam always knew what were the needs of the women of Israel. Her energies had not diminished with the years, and age had no power over her strength. Indeed, it seemed as though time strengthened her and charged her with new power. Her lofty figure had not shrunk. Her body was lean, even meager —a wrinkled, sunburned leathery skin drawn taut over her frame; her eyes flamed in her face like magical fires; and she moved like a wind among the tents of the Bnai Israel. As in Egypt, so here, she knew what went on in each tent. To this one she brought a few drops of distilled oil which she had obtained from the priests for some sick child; to that one she brought comforting words for a widow or orphan. She lifted up their spirits, she supported the weak, she spread hope among the exhausted and wearied mothers that the promised land would soon be reached.

Moreover the women confided in her whatever was in their hearts. She knew it when a Cushite woman had tempted a man in Israel and had taught him all the ways of whoredom, so that the man compelled his wife to perform the same abominations. . . . She knew it when a Moabite woman brought a clay figurine of Ashtoreth to her neighbor as a specific against barrenness. There were Hebrew men who assembled in the tents of the mixed multitude to practice idolatry in secret, to participate in orgiastic rites, to partake of dishes of kid's meat seethed in the mother's milk; of this she would know, too. And she also knew it when there were found little images of the Calf god, smuggled into the encampment by the mixed multitude in a secret ritual of fertility.

These individual cases of backsliding into idolatry Miriam charged to the mixed multitude as a whole; she did not share or even understand the view of Moses, that for the sake of the universal significance of the God of Israel, it was necessary and proper to endure these defects in the mixed multitude. To Moses the mixed

346

multitude in the camp of Israel was a symbol of all the gentiles, of all the peoples which in the last account would accept the one and single living God of Israel.

Like a sandstorm rising in the desert and darkening the sky— such was the murmur of protest, the cloud of malice and scurrility which rose against Moses when it was learned that he had taken to wife a woman of Cush.

"Very different is the law for us! We are told that if one of us should see, among a conquered people, a comely woman, we must make her cut off her hair; she must let her nails grow; she must sit like an adulteress in a corner of the tent, without silk or ornaments, so that she may become loathsome in our eyes. Tell me, someone, did Moses behave so with the Cushite woman whom he took to wife?" So spoke one mocker to a circle of listeners.

Another said: "To judge by the way he takes their part, he will soon exchange us for the mixed multitude. No doubt he is thinking of returning to Esau the birthright which mother Rebekah fooled out of Isaac for Jacob."

"Yes, he keeps telling us, day in, day out, that we shall love the stranger, only the stranger, that we shall see him well provided with raiment and food, because Jehovah loves the stranger. But if He loves the strangers, why did He not take them for His people— why did He load us with the burden of the commandments and prohibitions?"

"Instead of blasphemies, may worms creep from thy mouth. Against whom dost thou wag thy tongue? Against the Holy One of Israel? What? Wouldst thou bring pestilence upon us again?"

"God forbid that I should blaspheme against God! But if Moses dare do something, so may I; he has taken a woman of Cush—shall I not do the same?"

"But who forbids it? Moses never forbade us to take a wife from among the mixed multitude, if she but accept the God of Israel. He warned us only against strange women who are idolatrous, so that we may not be tempted to follow after their gods."

"But Miriam, his sister, has forbidden it, and Aaron, too."

"Let us see whether she will forbid her brother, whether she will dare to upbraid him, and talk to him as she does to us."

And all Israel saw Miriam and Aaron hastening with firm step in the direction of the tabernacle and the tent of Moses. They opened a path for the prophetess, and they bowed their heads as she passed.

"There will be hard words for him to hear," they whispered.

Hard words were indeed spoken in the tent of Moses.

"Moses ben Amram, is this the example thou settest thy people? Is it not enough for thee that thou didst take a Midianite woman to wife, must thou now take a woman of Cush and bring her into the tent of the assembly?"

"Jehovah has never forbidden the Bnai Israel to take to wife the daughters of Cush. He has made no distinction between the black and the white skin. All are his creatures. He knows only those that believe in Him," said Moses humbly, standing before his brother and sister.

"Knowest thou not that she is of the mixed multitude?"

"Many times has Jehovah told me that there shall be one law for the stranger and the homeborn, and that we must love the stranger, because we were strangers in Egypt," answered Moses.

"Knowest thou not that the mixed multitude is like a leprosy on the body of Israel? They are a temptation and a stumbling block. They cling to their idolatries and tempt Israel into them. I come from among the tents of Israel, and I know the evil that spreads from the strangers. Their women corrupt the husbands of the daughters of Israel and teach them all abominable practices. Theirs is the sin of the golden calf, and the sin of lusting after meat. All that is evil comes from them."

And Aaron supported her. "I have always said it: the mixed multitude is responsible for the golden calf, not the Bnai Israel. They sacrifice to the dead, not to God, even to this day. They turn the Bnai Israel to evil. A stumbling block, a temptation—they must be placed far off, like lepers."

"Concerning this that you bring to me, that the mixed multitude is a stumbling block to Israel: I know that many of them fall back into their idolatries; but much must be forgiven them. Strangers they were when they came to us. They are not of the seed of Abraham, and they have not inherited the virtues of our fathers. Therefore we must be patient and understanding, and we must lead them slowly into the ways of God. God will bring forth harvest in time, from the seed of the law which He has planted in their hearts; and He will cause the evil weeds among them to be uprooted. They are not lepers! And if God has warned us against taking away the mother bird from her little ones, when we find a nest in the fields; if He has forbidden us to muzzle the ox when it treads out the corn —shall He not be compassionate with man, and above all with the man that followed Him into the wilderness, counting on His grace? No, brother and sister; the mixed multitude is part of Israel. If there be sinners among them, let them be punished, as sinners in Israel are punished. But, 'a father shall not be slain for the sin of his children, nor the children for the sins of their fathers. Let every man bear his own sin,' so Jehovah has spoken to me."

"These are the words of thine own lips, not the words of Jehovah. Hear me, my brother, Moses ben Amram," said Miriam, harshly. "It is a great sin which thou takest on thyself. Because of thee all Israel will be made to stumble. All the men of Israel will follow thy example and will bring strange women into their tents; and they will pollute the tents of Israel with abominations. Moses ben Amram, make good this wrong in the eyes of all Israel; send away the woman whom thou hast taken from among the strangers; and let it be a law in Israel that none shall take to himself a wife of the strangers. Declare it before all that thou hast erred in doing this thing which is forbidden of God."

"Do so!" Aaron interposed. "Forget thy honor for the honor of God and the good of Israel. Send her away."

Moses was silent under the humiliation. He held back his anger, and was silent. And when he had mastered his agitation, he answered in a tranquil voice:

"No, my brother and my sister. With all the respect I bear you, I cannot do what you ask. It would be a sin against God. God did not bid me prohibit the Bnai Israel from taking wives from among the mixed multitude; nor did He command me to exclude the stranger who has acknowledged Him from the congregation, and turn him into a slave. To do thus would be to act on my own responsibility, and not according to God's will. And I cannot turn to the right or to the left, away from the will of God."

"Is it Jehovah that speaks, or is it thou, Moses?" asked Miriam, in anger. "We too know the will of God! What is this presumption of thine?"

"We too know the will of Jehovah," exclaimed Aaron. "To us too He speaks, and we know what is pleasing in His sight."

"The right to proclaim the word of God is ours, too, and not thine alone. And we shall let the people know this," said Miriam, furiously, and she left the tent together with Aaron.

Moses sat silent, like one petrified. The dreadful words still rang in his ears. His authority had been challenged by his own family. It was not that he jealously denied his brother and sister the right to share his authority, for to them too God spoke. Would that all the people could see God and hear His voice! But in the present division of authority he saw a threat to the unity of the people and the establishment of God's commandments. If Aaron and Miriam went out now to challenge his authority, to whom would the people listen? Whom would they believe?

He would not submit this perplexity to God; he would not supplicate in this matter, as he had done in other cases. For now it was his own person that was involved; *he* had been humiliated, *his* authority had been placed in doubt; and Moses had never prayed to God for himself. His prayers had been exclusively for the people.

He thought: "If it is the will of Jehovah that I shall share my mission with my sister and my brother, He will so tell me. And let it happen according to His will."

But though Moses would not bring his personal tribulations before Jehovah, Jehovah knew them and considered them. He was, as it were, the personal friend of Moses, as he had been the friend of Abraham. He was not only the God of the universe toward Moses, and not only the God of Israel, having regard only to the vast whole, without regarding the individual, leaving the individual to chance and fate. He was the God of each separate person, over whom He kept watch and whose footsteps He directed. He was not the sun god of Egypt, fixed in the heavens, but the God who shone in each man's heart. Moses felt the oneness not of God alone, but of each man.

Scarcely had Moses had time to reflect on the turn of events, scarcely had Aaron and Miriam left his presence, intending to hasten into the camp of Israel and there to proclaim their right to equal authority with Moses, than all three heard the voice of God in their hearts, bidding them appear before Him in the tent of the assembly, before the tabernacle, there where Moses was wont to receive the visitations of God.

God's help had come to Moses on the instant.

The blue-flickering cloud descended and veiled the sanctuary. From without, the Bnai Israel saw, and knew that God was now appearing to Moses, and to Aaron and Miriam, whom they had seen ascending the slope. Their hearts beat, and they threw themselves on their knees, in awe of Him who was descending with the cloud.

The voice of God was heard from the midst of the cloud. He bade Aaron and Miriam to stand aside, apart from Moses. And then the voice was filled with wrath: it sounded with the fury of the hurricane, with the crash of the thunder:

"Hear My words: If there be a prophet among you, then I, God, reveal Myself to him in a vision, and I speak to him in a dream. Not thus is it with My servant Moses. He is trusted in all My house. Face to face I speak unto him, in clear words and not in mysteries, and he beholds the likeness of God. And how have you not been afraid to speak against my servant Moses?"

Then the cloud lifted with an angry crack of thunder. But when the cloud had departed from the tent, they beheld Miriam covered with leprosy.

And Aaron, seeing the leprous woman, felt his knees yielding with fear. It seemed to him that his own body was burning with the disease, and he would be excluded from the priesthood, thrust forth from the congregation of Israel—and he threw himself at the feet of Moses.

"Oh, do not charge us with this sin which we have committed against thee! Oh, let her not be as one that is deadborn, whose flesh is withered from the mother's womb."

And Moses, too, gazing on his sister, was filled with fear. She who had called the mixed multitude lepers was a leper herself—she, his sister—she was covered with oozing sores, throat, mouth, and cheeks, even to the eyes. He forgot what had happened, the words she had spoken: this was his beloved sister Miriam, a mother in Israel, now an outcast, rejected, thrust forth from the congregation of Israel. He fell to the earth with a great cry:

"Heal her, I pray Thee, heal her!"

But he heard God's voice in his heart:

"If her own father had spit in her face, would she not be ashamed seven days?"

Soon the whole people, prostrate in the sand, waiting for Jehovah's command, saw a procession issuing from the tent; they saw a guard which kept at a distance from a figure which, though covered from head to foot, they knew to be Miriam's; and they heard the voices which called out:

"Approach not! Unclean! Unclean! Approach not!"

Their hearts stood still with that which their eyes beheld. Miriam, the mother of Israel, the sister of Moses, being led out of the encampment, unclean—a leper!

"It is because she slandered God's creatures," murmured one of the learned. "The punishment for slander is leprosy."

"It is so! She called the mixed multitude lepers, and now she is herself a leper."

And the people did not go out of the encampment until she was declared clean again.

CHAPTER SIXTEEN

IT was as though Jehovah were carrying them on the wings of eagles into their land. Barely three months had passed since they had left the Sinai mountains, and here, despite all delays and obstacles—the dismantling and reassembling of the tabernacle with every removal of the camp, the onsets of hunger and thirst, the loads and burdens, the old people, the newborn infants, the pregnant women—here they were on the rim of the wilderness of Paran, beyond which lay the wilderness of Zin; and Zin was already accounted a part of the promised land. Between these two wildernesses lay the ancient and sacred oasis of Kadesh-barnea, with its wells and its green places. This area the Bnai Israel now occupied.

On their right hand lay Edom. Edom was settled territory from of old. True, the Edomites were largely cave dwellers. Their land was covered with rocks and cliffs in which they hollowed out cities and temples; but they had long been occupants, and they were fiercely attached to their land and jealous of its frontiers. The cliffs were desolate and fit only for fortress towns, but after the rainy season their valleys were rich in pasture, and close-dotted with their flocks. The waters had worn deep channels from the hilltops to the lowlands, which blossomed with trees and grasses. The Bnai Israel, starved for the sight of green, smelled the freshness of the fields of Edom from a distance; it seemed to them that they smelled bread and the udders of cows; and their eyes started in their heads. There, for good pieces of silver, they would be able to get water, roasted ears of wheat, jars of honey and beer, cakes of barley. There were also good roads in Edom, and by these, through the plains and the fruitful valleys of Moab, the Bnai Israel could pass straight to the promised land. But the invasion of Edom had been forbidden them by Jehovah. Moreover, the rock fortresses of Edom were strong.

The people and its leaders were in a high mood of expectancy. Here they were at last near the borders of their land; the promise of Jehovah to their forefathers was in process of fulfillment. But how would the completion of it come about? Would it be wrought by a miracle, as the exodus from Egypt had been wrought; or were they, like every other people, to acquire their land with sword and bow?

They could not tell. One thing Moses knew: it was not God's intention to make the Bnai Israel a folk of angels, living in an unworldly order utterly different from the rest of His creation. It was God's intention to make of them a chosen people, distinguished for its conduct and bearing: a new order, but of this world; an example to all the peoples, not something beyond the natural law. Even as the Torah, which with its laws and commandments bodied forth a just order, had not been given to angels, and was not lodged in heaven, but had been given to men, and lodged on earth, even so the Bnai Israel, a congregation of flesh and blood, was to be sustained and was to fulfill itself through the natural ways of all peoples. It was God's will that the Jewish people should be His partners in the process of their own liberation; they were to acquire their rights by their own acts. It was one thing to intervene in the natural order when no other possibility remained, as in the exodus from Egypt, in the splitting of the sea, in the providing of water in the desert; but where other possibilities were offered, where the people could help itself, the matter was quite different.

Thus Moses had thoroughly prepared the Bnai Israel for the task of conquering the land by its own efforts. To this end he had organized it in its religious, civic, and military functions. The entire tribe of Levi, with the priesthood at its head, directed the people in the ritualistic laws and commandments of the Torah, in the service of the sanctuary; the seventy elders, the new officer overseers, were set over the moral conduct of the people; they were the judges and guardians in the laws and commandments touching the relations between man and man; the princes of Israel, the officers of thousands, the elders of the tribes, directed the youth in the military discipline, in the preparation for the conquest of the promised land—with the help of Jehovah, it was true, but with their own right hands.

Moses now trusted that the wonders and miracles which the Bnai Israel had witnessed in the last two years had at last given them the permanent assurance that Jehovah was in their midst and that there was no power or force capable of resisting Him. He felt that this people, equipped with the privileges of divine election and

354

inducted into the new moral discipline, was ready for the great enterprise. Immense had been the preparations. Had not Mount Sinai been the altar upon which Israel had offered up its life, like a purification offering to God? Had not Mount Sinai been the crucible in which God had melted the soul of the people, so that it might issue from slavery into freedom, from uncleanliness into purity? Slaves they had been when they left Egypt; as princes they would enter their land.

Now, on the borders of the wilderness of Zin, the entrance to the land, Moses began the preparations for the final stages of the struggle.

First, at God's command, he sent forth scouts to spy out the land and its peoples, to discover what strategic points were occupied, and by whom. The territory was unknown to Moses. He had acquired his military training in Africa, chiefly near the Nile source in Abyssinia. The land and climate were different there, so were the peoples—half-savage tribes with primitive weapons. Here, he knew, he would encounter skilled warrior peoples whom even the Pharaohs had learned to respect of late. Some, like the Philistines, had even dared to take the offensive against Egypt. It was the rise of the military power of the Asiatic peoples which had, in part, moved Rameses the Second to build his new capital, named after him. Moses also knew that the inhabitants of the promised land, the Canaanites, the Philistines, the Hittites, were of powerful physique. They had not been corrupted and spoiled by the fruitfulness of their land, as had happened with the Egyptians. For their land was meager and poor; they depended for water on rainfall and on the Jordan, from which they irrigated their fields; very different was their lot from that of the Egyptians, with their inexhaustible supply. They had to wring their bread from the soil by heavy labor which hardened their bodies. Moreover, the territory in which the fighting would take place was not the kind in which Moses had fought before; here were neither the free, sandy spaces of the desert, nor the dark African swamps, sparsely occupied by half-nomadic tribes. Here were strong cities, some of them walled, inhabited by long-settled nations which would defend tooth and nail their plowed fields, their gardens, and their inheritance. Some of the peoples dwelt on the hills; he would have to fight with hill peoples of Lebanon and Hermon accustomed to eternal snows and to the heights; and neither he nor the Bnai Israel had ever felt the touch of frost on their bodies. Whipped into hardness by the winds, firm as their native crags, these mountain dwellers would put up a desperate resistance. Yet this was the one land which Jehovah had promised to Abraham; and for the Bnai Israel there was no other. This was the inheritance set aside for them from of old, the eternal inheritance of Abraham's seed. It was now occupied by strangers who had come from beyond the hills, aliens not of Abraham's seed. They did not belong to this place; they would have to be conquered and driven out before the Bnai Israel would be able to inhabit the promised land.

Nor were the approaches easy. The land was ringed by settlements of peoples, some of which were descended from Abraham and had received their territories from Jehovah Himself. These peoples Moses was strictly forbidden to disturb.

On his right was Edom, the descendant of Esau. Edom had long since changed from a nomadic to a settled people, peasants deep rooted in their soil. Moses could not cross their borders without their permission. He believed implicitly that the Edomites, descendants of Abraham, would rejoice to hear that the Bnai Jacob, too, were now free at last and had left their Egyptian slavery behind them. Edom should be prepared to help them in the taking up of their inheritance.

Farther up, on the shores of the Dead Sea, dwelt Moab, likewise of the seed of Abraham, by his nephew, Lot. Moab had inherited the place of the cities of Sodom and Gomorrah, which God had desolated. Beyond Moab were the Amorites, who had become strong in the hills, were the "gatekeepers" of Canaan, and were descended, it was said, from giants. The Amorites were a military people; they would have to be conquered before the Jordan could be approached. On the same side of the Jordan were the Ammonites, sprung, like the Moabites, from Lot. Their land, too, Moses was forbidden to invade; he could pass through it only with their permission. And in the simplicity of his heart Moses believed that the blood kindred of the Bnai Israel would extend a helping hand.

There was a direct path to the promised land through the hill country of the wilderness of Zin, stretching from Kadesh-barnea to Beersheba and Hebron. The wilderness of Zin was a fiery oven in which there wandered various tribes and races, nomads, the raw material of still unformed peoples, fragments of the Amalekites, bands of Hittites, Jebusites, Amorites. The Canaanites and the Philistines, who had settled along the shore, would make sorties from Gaza and other cities, for they laid claim to the wilderness of Zin and were forever at war with its nomadic tribes.

Moses hoped that he would not have to lead the Bnai Israel through the wilderness of Zin. Not that he was afraid of the unorganized nomads, which were no match for the Israelites. But he knew that the Bnai Israel were weary of the desert, weary of hunger and thirst, and he did not want to put them again to the test; the less so since, resting at Kadesh-barnea, they had smelled the plowed fields and the gardens of Edom, which had put a new spirit into them. Their hearts overflowed with the hope of God's promise. They had ceased to complain; they accepted in silence the hardships which they had been wont to throw up to Moses on the least provocation. The near prospect of home and settlement only made them joyously impatient to press forward. They would assemble in the early morning outside the tent of Moses, pleading: "Send forth men to spy out the land, to find the places we must conquer, through which we must pass."

The eagerness of the Bnai Israel filled Moses with contentment. He picked out twelve distinguished men, one from each tribe, the nearest to him and the most trustworthy: among them were his minister, the youth Joshua ben Nun, and Caleb ben Yephunneh, an elder of the tribe of Judah, a bold and active spirit. Since it was not in his mind to invade the lands of the Bnai Esau and the Bnai Lot, he sent the men not by way of Edom, or of Ammon, but across the wilderness of Zin.

Forty days were allotted to the expedition, for Moses wanted a report covering the entire land. He bade the men go to the borders of the Lebanon and Hermon country, and eastward to the sea. Concerning the Canaanites and Philistines, on the shore, he knew that they were courageous and vigorous peoples. They went forth in their ships to far-off places and founded cities and colonies. They had mastered the Egyptian art of smelting copper, which they mined in Cyprus. They cultivated their fields, and they hewed down their forests and were shipwrights. They also had a slave system, like the Egyptians, for the working of the copper mines; and their slaves were recruited from the distant lands which they raided. They had also mastered the crafts of the builder and weaver, and they had erected magnificent temples to their god

Moloch, whom they worshiped with abominable rites, including the sacrifice of children. They were, moreover, given to the foulest sodomitic practices. All this Moses knew. What he needed now was an exact report concerning the strength of their cities and the extent of their armies. He also wanted evidence of the fruitfulness of the land, and he bade the scouts bring back exceptional samples of pomegranates, grapes, figs, dates, grain, vegetables, and other produce.

And the people waited for the return of the spies. Enviously they looked across at the cultivated fields of the Edomites and longed for the time when they would be working their own fields, pasturing in their own meadows, and living in their own cities. Not that they saw too much to envy in the land of the Edomites; for it did not compare with the thick, dark, oozing soil which the Nile deposited in their old home, Goshen. Here, in Edom, every patch of land had to be wrung with ceaseless labor from the sands of the desert. Very meager were the windblown harvests which they saw in the fields, when they went across the border to the habitations of the Edomites, to buy a handful of roasted ears of wheat, or a jar of water. For whatever they needed from the Edomites they purchased for silver, on the command of Moses. But they hoped that their own land, the land of promise, was very different from this of Edom's. And they had the word of Moses for it, too. Had he not told them that it was a land flowing with milk and honey?

Then, at last, the trumpets sounded for the return of the expedition. Messengers had run ahead to announce its arrival, and Moses stood near his tent, at the entrance to the tabernacle, in the company of Aaron and the elders. The open place which was always reserved for the assemblies before the tabernacle soon became packed with men, women, and children. They came pouring out of the tents. Fathers put their young ones on their shoulders, so that they might be witnesses of the marvelous hour; mothers bore their little ones in their arms. The place was dense with bodies, heads, beards—and Moses and Aaron in the midst.

The returning expedition approached and the mass divided. The spies came on, in single file, and in regular order. Each of them carried an extraordinary sample of the produce of the land, grain, fruit, and green things. Two of them bore on their shoulders a gigantic cluster of grapes. Each in turn deposited his load at the feet of Aaron and Moses, and the assembled stared in astonishment. Fathers pointed and bade their children look well: "See, these are the fruits which grow in our land"—and in the midst of all this the scouts began to deliver their report.

The first speaker was the elder of the expedition, the representative of the tribe of Reuben, a heavy, phlegmatic man, with a flattened face, not unlike an unbaked cake of dough. He spoke slowly and offhandedly, as though somehow the matter did not concern him at all:

"We came into the land to which thou didst send us. True, it is a land of milk and honey, and here are its fruits. But the peoples which dwell in the land are mighty, their cities are great fortresses. And we saw there the sons of the giants. Amalek dwells in the southland, in the Negeb; the Hittite, the Jebusite, the Amorite dwell in the hill country, and the Canaanite dwells along the shore and by the Jordan."

The assembly ceased its tumult and listened. A great silence, a fearful silence, fell upon it. All eyes were turned on Moses. And then a low murmur was heard, like the opening whisper of a storm.

Now Caleb ben Yephunneh intervened and tried to reassure the people, and to still the anger which was rising against Moses.

"Yet we shall go up into the land," he cried, "we shall go up and inherit, for we shall surely conquer it."

"How?" demanded the emissary of the tribe of Dan. He was a man with a huge face and a wide mouth, powerful of build, and hot of spirit. "Canst thou snatch its prey from the paws of the lion? Or canst thou pursue the eagle, when he ascends to the sky with his prey in his claws? Who are we, that we should go up against this people? It is mightier than we!"

These words of the emissary of Dan were like a signal to the other scouts; and they did not turn to Moses, but to the people.

"And what manner of land is it? Every footstep of it thou must tear out from between the clefts of crags. Thy water must come from the heavens, from Jehovah, not from the Nile. It is by no means like the land which we have left behind us. There thy feet sank everywhere in rich, slimy earth; thou hadst but to plant, and whatever thou didst plant grew of itself. Here thou must labor in the sweat of thy brow, here thou must plow and furrow and dig. With the blood of thy hands wilt thou force thy food from the earth. It is a land which makes its inhabitants old before their time, it eats up its inhabitants. And to approach it, you must pass through the mountains, where the giants live, true giants, the children of the Nephilim, who fell from heaven. They are the gatekeepers of Canaan. They dwell in fortified cities in the hills, and they let no one approach the Jordan."

"Like grasshoppers were we in our own eyes, and even thus we appeared in their eyes," added another spy: "So mighty are they."

All that night the camp was in tumult. There was no sleeping. Circles stood about the spies, and the latter poured out fantastic stories concerning the giants whom they had seen in the hill country. Fear had magnified their vision; and in their terror they exaggerated even their visions. "They are not men—they are mountains. As for their weapons, and their fortified cities, and the walls about them—they are even as the inhabitants, who tear out rocks with their teeth, and fling them into the deeps."

But these exaggerations would have been insufficient to uproot the faith of the people in the God Who had brought them out of Egypt and performed for them the miracles of the desert. The spies, however, began to undermine the belief in the promise itself; they spread an evil and slanderous report concerning the land, and the anger of God was kindled against them more than if they had spoken evil of Him.

"Do you understand now? Jehovah plans to keep us bound to Him, dependent on Him, as He has kept us bound and dependent in the desert. Without Him we are lost in the sands of the desert, as a ship is lost without a pilot in the midst of the sea. We must look to Him for every bite of bread and every mouthful of water; and so it will be in the land to which He brings us. Only when He sees fit to give us rain shall we eat bread. For the tiniest sin He can lock the heavens and withhold the rain; then we and our children will wither away in our own land."

"We cannot draw breath without Him. To make us ever mindful of Him He will keep us in everlasting terror of starvation, as we were in everlasting terror of the lash in Egypt."

"No, He does not bring us into a land where we shall perish of hunger and thirst; He brings us into a wilderness where we shall perish by the sword. He has ringed us with enemies. Thou hast heard! The Amalekite lies in ambush in the valley, the Amorite sharpens his sword in the hills, and the giants wait for us on the cliffs. Before we set foot in the land, we and our children will feed the hyenas and the wild fowl. Our corpses will roll in the sands, like the carcasses of fallen camels."

And a weeping went up from the congregation. From every corner of the camp, from every tent, the lamentation rose:

"Woe and misery and wretchedness! What has He made of our wives and children? Offal for birds of prey and for the hyenas of the wilderness!"

From his tent Moses heard the wailing of the people. He felt it pass through him, drenched in horror and fear, bitter with hope undone. This was no longer the weeping of the past; it was not the protest of men lusting for meat. That lamentation had been a kind of wild braying, a capricious, spoiled screaming, as of undisciplined children; it had not been uniform throughout the people: Moses had been able to distinguish, at that time, between the utterly self-abandoned and the more restrained. Here it was the entire people, from the highest levels down, which lifted its voice: not the mixed multitude led the weeping; it was the elders who were caught up first in the sweep of the mad panic. It was the ululation of a people which saw itself hopelessly trapped, deceived, and delivered to destruction.

Moses was no dreamer of fantasies, but a man of reality. From the first moment of contact with his brothers in Egypt he had understood that he was dealing with difficult human material, with men and women who had been degraded by slavery. Yet he had believed that somewhere within they had guarded an element of freedom, had never relinquished the tradition of faith in that Spirit which had made the covenant with their forefathers. In the long passage from Egypt to Kadesh-barnea, too, there had been evidence enough for the Bnai Israel that Jehovah was not an illusion or delusion, but a reality firmer than their lives and their very bodies; the presence of the sanctuary in their midst should have exalted and inspired them with ardor to follow and obey Jehovah blindly, even unto death, as their forefather Abraham had done. Were they not the children of Abraham? Did not the blood of the patriarchs flow in their veins? If not, wherein were they better than the other peoples? If God had performed for the Bnai Esau that which he had performed for the Bnai Israel, the former would assuredly have shown more faith in Him.

This being so, what had he to do with the Bnai Israel? It had been a mistake, a frightful mistake, to become one with them.

There was no Israel, there were no children of Abraham, Isaac, and Jacob. This rabble was as worthless as all the children of men. It was not a chosen people. Neither Sinai, nor the laws and commandments, nor the Torah had availed to make it one. Slaves they were, and slaves they would remain. It had been a dream of Jehovah's, or of his, that a chosen people could be fashioned from slaves.

Yes, he would flee from them, he would leave them in the wilderness, to the fangs of the wild beasts. Let them perish, let them become the prey of hyenas and vultures.

The mood passed as swiftly as it had come; anger darkened his spirit for a moment, then the inmost light shone clearly again, and its beams were thrown into the far-off future. He glimpsed again what he had glimpsed on Sinai, when God had opened a window for him into the end of days. Israel as it was at the moment, the Israel wailing in its tents, might be small and pitiful and afflicted with blindness: the Israel of eternity saw, and it was the eye with which mankind would see the light of God.

He lifted his voice suddenly in a cry of faith:

"If God is true and endures, then Israel is true and endures!"

Come what might, the seed of Abraham would not perish, but live: not for Israel's sake, but for the sake of Jehovah and of mankind and all the future. He would go out to them, he would plead with them, he would do all that lay in his power to awaken in them the Spirit of Abraham.

It was they who came to him in the early morning. They assembled before his tent, the princes and elders of the tribes in front, the masses behind them. They were not tumultuous, there was no raging. They wept with choked voices, and they stretched out their arms to Moses and Aaron.

"What have you done with us? Why did you take us out of Egypt, where we had a shelter for our heads and bread to eat? Why does Jehovah bring us to a land where we shall fall by the sword and our wives and children shall be the spoil of the enemy? Is it not better for us to return to Egypt?"

"Back to Egypt! To Egypt!" cried voices behind the elders.

"Let us set a captain over the host and return to Egypt!" The clamor was taken up by the mass.

Moses threw himself to the ground before the congregation, and Aaron did likewise. And Moses began to implore them:

"Remember what Jehovah has done for you. Why are you seized with fear? Jehovah will go before you and will do battle for you, as He did battle with Pharaoh. Have you not seen how Jehovah carried you through the desert, as a father carries his child, until He brought you to this place? Why are you afraid now?"

And when Joshua ben Nun and Caleb ben Yephunneh saw Moses lying in the dust before the people, and pleading with them for faith in Jehovah, they tore their garments in sign of mourning.

"Brothers in Israel," cried Joshua. "We have seen the land. It is a good land. If God desires us, He will bring us into this land, which flows with milk and honey. Fear not the inhabitants of the land. They are our bread. Their spirit has departed from them. They are abandoned! God is with us!"

And Caleb ben Yephunneh added his voice:

"What have you to fear? If Moses were to ask you to go up into heaven, would you not go? We would put up ladders and climb into heaven, because Jehovah is with us."

"Look at the traitors! Traitors! Deceivers! Away with them!" came back the shouts of the people.

"Stone them!"

Hands were lifted, with stones in them. But no sooner were they lifted than they froze in mid-air.

"Look!"

"Jehovah!"

"Jehovah!"

The people had perceived the cloud descending, vast, storm laden, shooting a thousand forked fires. Its folds billowed thickly, became heavier and darker from instant to instant. It was like a mountain settling on the heads of the congregation, a whirling mountain which threatened to carry all before it. Under its pressure the people flung themselves to the ground.

"Jehovah! Jehovah!" went up the terrified cry.

Lying with faces buried in the sand, they felt above them the tearing and pulling of the storm wind. The breath of God seared their bodies and threatened them with destruction. Momently they awaited a tongue of fire which would pass over them and would burn them to cinders, as the sons of Aaron had been burned. The pressure became intolerable, and the fury above them increased. Yet they were not destroyed. Slowly and fearfully they lifted their eyes and they beheld the arms of Moses uplifted in prayer: two

363

mighty arms, like pillars which held up the tremendous cloud of God's wrath and prevented it from annihilating them. The countenance of Moses, illumined with prayer, was between God and Israel, a barrier of faith and supplication. They beheld the cloud withdrawing toward the sanctuary, spreading away from them. Then they saw Moses rise from his knees and follow the cloud. They saw him, in the midst of its billows, enter the tent of the assembly.

They remained prostrate in the sand before the sanctuary; they waited with beating hearts for the sentence which Jehovah would pronounce over them through Moses.

Within, amidst the smoke which filled the tent, Moses fell on his face before the awful majesty of Jehovah:

"Mine is the guilt! I have been too hasty, I was impatient, I could not wait until they had wholly conquered the slavery in them, until they were fit for the freedom which Thou bringest them. Mine is the guilt, in that I did not understand their nature, and did not guide them into the spirit of Thee. Punish me, and have mercy on the children of Abraham, Isaac, and Jacob."

Once again, as in the time of the golden calf, Jehovah offered to raise a new chosen people from the descendants of Moses:

"How long will this people despise Me? How long will they not believe in Me? I will smite them with the pestilence and destroy them, and I will make of thee a nation greater and mightier than they."

But Moses answered:

"Lord, Thou canst not destroy the Bnai Israel, Thou canst not change them for another people. Thy name is called upon them, and they are Thy glory. What will the Egyptians say when they hear what Thou hast done with this people after Thou didst bring it forth from among them with a mighty arm? What will the inhabitants of this land say when they hear that Thou didst slay the Bnai Israel as one man? They will say: Because Jehovah, Who was in their midst, was not able to bring them into the land which He swore to them, He slew them in the wilderness. Thou hast bound Thyself to Israel for eternity; therefore let Thy power be great according to Thine own word when Thou didst say: The Lord is slow to anger, and great in mercy, forgiving iniquity and transgression; but He will by no means clear the guilty, visiting the iniquity of the fathers upon the children, to the third and fourth generation. Therefore, I pray Thee, punish this generation, but let Israel live. For Israel is Thine inheritance forever. Remember the generations which will follow, I pray Thee, and forgive the sins of this people, according to the greatness of Thy loving-kindness, as Thou hast forgiven it from Egypt even until now."

And Jehovah hearkened to the prayer of Moses and answered: "I have pardoned according to thy word."

He would not take vengeance of the second generation, nor of the third, nor of the fourth. Only he that had sinned would die— and the son was not to be slain for the sins of the father.

CHAPTER SEVENTEEN

IT was a long encounter, this time, between Moses and Jehovah, and throughout all of it the Bnai Israel did not dare to stir from before the cloud-enveloped sanctuary. Still prostrate in the sand, they waited for the word that Moses would bring them from Jehovah.

Moses came forth at length, and they marked the change that had come over him. Some of the darkness of the storm cloud of God was now on his face. He was no longer praying for them. Terrifying was his voice now as he uttered the sentence:

"Not for your sakes, but for the sake of your little ones, your children, whom you saw as the spoil of the enemy—the Lord will act. And He has said: Them will I bring into the land which you have despised. But as for you, your carcasses shall fall in this wilderness. And your children shall be wanderers in the wilderness forty years, until your carcasses be consumed. After the number of the days in which you spied out the land, shall you bear your iniquities, even forty years. So the Lord has spoken."

Then Moses called to his side Joshua ben Nun and Caleb ben Yephunneh, and proclaimed:

"Thus has the Lord commanded: Tomorrow you will turn and lead the congregation back into the wilderness by the way of the Sea of Reeds!"

"Back into the wilderness!"

When the people rose from where they had been lying, they left ten of the spies, those that had spread the evil report, dead in the sand. They had been smitten on the spot by God's pestilence. And the terror of God fell on the congregation.

The next morning a portion of the tribes rose early, and with shamed and mourning faces they appeared before Moses and Aaron, saying:

"We are ready to go forth and do battle with the enemy. We will go up to the mountain and fight there with the Canaanites and the Amalekites. We have sinned. Let us wipe out our sin with our blood."

"Go not up, and transgress not against the command of the Lord. You will fail, for the Lord is not among you. You will fall by the sword."

But they would not listen to the word of Moses, and they went up into the mountain. However, neither Moses nor the ark of God went forth from the camp. And it came to pass as Moses had foretold. The Amalekites and Canaanites came forth and smote the host of the Israelites, and scattered them, and pursued them as far as Hormah.

And now nothing remained for the Bnai Israel but to carry out God's command and turn back into the frightful desert from which they had just come, back to its trials and torments. The congregation mourned; groups sat weeping at the entrances of the tents:

"What will happen to us now? Is it for this that we left Egypt, that our bones shall bleach in the desert sands? Shall we truly never see real earth again? Shall we never again delight in the taste of green things, and of salt? Will our tongues never suck again at the sweetness of figs? And will we never feel again in our hands the good weight of a grape cluster? Shall we forever subsist on this oozing, slimy manna, while our palates long for a long draught of cool, springing water? Will it always be so, till we fall in the desert, like the ass or the camel, for our bones to roll in the sands and whiten in the sun?"

Moses listened to the moaning of the people. He could see the bitter, contorted faces, the yellow skins, the sunken eyes. The horror of God's judgment was stamped on their brows: sentence of death had been pronounced against every grown person. What could he do now but address himself once more in prayer to Jehovah?

He lay prostrate in a corner of his tent, and Joshua could hear his broken voice raised in supplication:

"I have implored and beseeched Thee to tell me, by what principle dost Thou direct the world, and Thou didst answer: By mercy and love. To these I turn my prayer, Thou gracious and compassionate God! Look down upon the children of Thy friends, see how they repent them of their sins. Remember the covenant with Abraham, and have mercy on them. They are confused by Thy awful might, and broken by Thy punishment. They are like threshed ears of wheat, crushed by Thy wrath. Restore them, O God of mercy, and bring the light back to mine eyes. Let me behold Thy justice, for Thy justice is the guide of my life. Tell me what I must do, and how I shall lead them. For we are affrighted by Thine anger and are like strayed sheep."

And God vouchsafed to Moses the light of His justice. And Moses said in his heart that he would not compel the Bnai Israel to leave Kadesh-barnea, he would not compel them to break up camp. Nor, indeed, did the cloud above the sanctuary rise in sign of departure. And even though God had bidden Moses to turn back into the wilderness on the morrow, Moses interpreted the word "morrow" to mean "after a time." Moreover, Moses himself wanted time for reflection, so that he might plan the new wandering. It was all too clear to him now that the generation of the exodus was lost. It would perish in the desert—so God had sworn. At last he himself, Moses, saw the fullness of the error into which he had stumbled. He had let himself believe that the Bnai Israel could pass from the spirit of slavery into the spirit of freedom without the intermediary nomadic stage, that they could be transformed as it were overnight into warriors and conquerors of a land. It was not so. Like every other people Israel would have to develop slowly, by degrees, into a free people. The odor of the fleshpots of Egypt would have to cease haunting their nostrils, their palates would have to forget the onions and the garlic and the leeks, their eyes the sight of the thick, rich ooze which the Nile spread over the earth. Their bodies, tempered by the fierce desert sun, would have to harden and become like beaten copper. Their eyes would have to become sharp, fiery, and direct, their nostrils responsive to the hidden presence of water and pasture for their flocks, responsive and sensitive as the nostrils of jackals snuffing the scent of their prey. For now their possessions would not be their bodies and the hours—sole possessions of the slave—but flocks and herds. Like their forefathers, they would be shepherds and herdsmen; they would follow their cattle, they would dig wells in the wilderness. And they would fight for the wells and for their pasture fields.

Many years would pass; forty, had been the word of God. The old generation, the generation of Egypt, would die; the second generation would be ready to conquer the land, as the Lord had sworn. And what would be his own fate? Was he not one of the grown persons who had come out of Egypt? Was he not himself of the first generation?

The thought made him tremble. He could not entrust the Bnai Israel to other hands. He must see them into their land. God would be merciful to him and let him live long enough to complete God's work. And perhaps God would relent and shorten the sentence of forty years, hasten the growth of the Bnai Israel, prepare them sooner for the conquest. He would not cease to pray. He had already observed a new spirit among the younger people—a stronger inclination to take care of their own flocks. The tribes of Reuben and Dan were foremost in this transformation. They showed a certain reluctance to slaughter a sheep, or a kid, even though they hankered after flesh. They were learning to guard their charges more closely than themselves, and they suffered more for the thirst of the cattle than with their own thirst. Jehovah was opening up in them the virtues of their forefathers, renewing in them the spirit of the shepherd.

He would exert himself to keep the Bnai Israel close to the borders of the promised land. He would not force them back into the horrible desert. Let the wind bring to them the odor of the cultivated fields of Moab. He would penetrate by degrees toward Ezion-geber in the south, so that the Bnai Israel might learn to conquer pasture fields for themselves and become like the nomadic tribes which wandered about in the vicinity of Edom. He would try to create bonds of amity with the kindred peoples, with the Bnai Esau and the Bnai Lot, with Moab and Ammon, dwelling on the borders of the land; and with God's help he would drive away the foreign invaders, the Amalekites and the Canaanites. So he would wander with the tribes between Ezion-geber and Kadesh-barnea, push his way through to the borders of the promised land. Perhaps God would take pity on His people and let it proceed to the conquest before all the forty years of its punishment had passed.

CHAPTER EIGHTEEN

THERE were others, besides Moses, who took note of the confusion and despair of the Bnai Israel; and these now felt the hour propitious for the long-planned revolt against the leadership of Moses and Aaron.

Korah had never relinquished his ambition for the high priesthood, the birthright of the tribe of Levi, of which he was the elder and leader. In the old days he had expected Moses to invest him with the dignity in spite of the hostility which had sprung up between them. Did not his family share the highest rank in the tribe of Levi with the sons of Amram? Korah was deceived in these calculations; but after the incident of the golden calf he was confident that his hour had come. And when he was deceived a second time, his resentment was boundless. Again he asked himself: Was not the high priest the representative of the interests of the people before the Godhead? Was it not the duty of the high priest to take upon himself the sins of the people and to plead their cause before God in a time of danger? And what had Aaron done? Not only had he failed to defend the people before God: he had himself been the chief cause of God's displeasure with Israel.

"How," argued Korah with the Israelites, "can Aaron plead for Israel when he himself made the golden calf and himself persuaded Israel to worship it?"

Likewise Dathan and Abiram, of the tribe of Reuben, and with them On, the son of Peleth, of the same tribe, had their reckoning to make with Moses. Their grounds were in part personal, for they felt themselves slighted as individuals; but more deeply they felt the slight to their tribe.

Now Korah was far too shrewd to lead a rebellion against Jehovah. His attack would be directed against Moses, and, precisely, in the name of Jehovah. For a long time, therefore, he, like the others, played the loyal supporter—and, like them, waited for the right moment. Now, with the catastrophe which followed the return of the spies, it had come. The leadership of Moses and Aaron had failed wretchedly; upon it rested the blame for the deferment of the promise. The spirit of Jehovah had departed from Moses; as for Aaron, he was forever stamped with the sin of the golden calf.

"There was a time," said Korah to the Bnai Levi, "when we had to defend Israel against a foreign ruler, and against alien slave drivers. Today we must defend Israel against a ruler from within, against slave drivers of their own blood."

"Whom meanest thou, Korah?"

"Whom can I mean other than the ruler Moses? See now what he does to us. To whom should we deliver the offerings and the tithes? Whose are the first-born of Israel? Do they belong to a single family, or to a whole tribe? Jehovah has chosen us, the Bnai Levi, as his first-born, ours are the tithes and the ransoms of the first-born, for Jehovah has given us no other inheritance in Israel. Now comes the man Moses, takes away that which belongs to us, and bestows it on his own family—a reward, no doubt, for the worship of the calf."

Someone from among the Bnai Levi said: "Moses bade Aaron to share the tithes with the Levites. The priests are supposed only to collect and control the tithes."

"The beast that stands at the trough does the eating. The others chew the cud. Slaves and ministers of the priests are we to the priests; and our children will be the slaves and ministers of the children of Aaron."

Korah went out among the people. He crawled into their tents. He visited them when they were with their little flocks. When he saw a mother carrying her newborn son in her arms he would ask her:

"Hast thou already paid the ransom to Aaron with thy last raiment, or with the last piece of silver which thou hadst hidden away for a time of need? In Egypt Pharaoh took away our children; here Moses and Aaron take away our last possessions for the ransom of our first-born."

"Was not this the command of Jehovah to Moses? Did not Jehovah say that this was the livelihood of the priests and the Levites?"

"The priests and the Levites? Thou meanest Moses and Aaron. For there is but a single family of priests. Dost thou truly believe that God commanded thee to take thy one kid, which He gave thee

371

for the beginning of a flock, and surrender it in payment for thy child? Ah, no, Jehovah is good, and knows thy needs. He would have thee keep the kid, and breed the flock from it. He asks not for thy last lamb as a sacrifice to Him. And surely He asks not for the tenth part of thy labor, to be given to the priest. It is an invention of Moses, for the enrichment of his family. It is as though we were still in Egypt. There the overseers said that such and such is the will of Pharaoh. But it was not the will of Pharaoh to torment us with impossible labors, and it is not the will of God to rob us of our last possessions. Here, as there, it is the will of the chief overseers. Thou rememberest me well from Egypt, thou knowest who I am. There I protected thee from Pharaoh's overseers—here I protect thee from the oppressors who speak in the name of Jehovah."

Moses was still wrestling with the darkness of spirit which had descended on him after God's sentence against Israel; he was still exerting himself to keep alive the spark of hope in the night of pain and despair: and in the midst of it Joshua entered with an overcast and embittered countenance to report that the princes of the congregation, the foremost men, with Korah, Dathan, and Abiram at their head, were at the entrance of the tent, demanding speech with him.

When Moses went out he beheld not only Korah and Dathan and Abiram and On ben Peleth, and not only the princes of the congregation, but an assembly of his own counselors and a great multitude of the people. The Bnai Levi stood behind the leaders, but it was clear from their bearing that this was a united mass.

Korah was, as ever, the spokesman. His shaved head shone pallid, his face was naked, without eyebrows, his gray eyes were deep set. Carrying his rod, the emblem of his office, he looked like an Egyptian high priest. He began:

"We have come to thee, ben Amram, to hear from thee what thy plans and intentions are. Whither wilt thou lead this terrified and confused people? We are its leaders and spokesmen, and we demand to know what thou wilt do, now that God has closed off thy path to the promised land."

Moses looked at him long and darkly before he answered. He was stricken by the new disaster which this visit portended, and his answer was quiet and pointed:

372

"Not I lead the people, ben Izhar, but Jehovah; whither His pillar goes, there we follow. And who are we to tell Jehovah whither He should lead us?"

"Jehovah indeed we will follow, but not thee and thy brother Aaron. Jehovah is not with the sons of Amram. You have sinned grievously against him."

"The judgment will be made by Jehovah, and not by one of flesh and blood. As for you, sons of Levi: is it not enough that the people have rebelled against Jehovah, and have received their punishment? Would you kindle Him to new anger by new revolts— you, the leaders of the congregation, and you, the Bnai Levi, whom God has chosen from among the house of Israel?"

"Not we rebel against Jehovah, and not for the sins of the people are we being punished. Jehovah's punishment is upon us because of the sins of Aaron. Thou hast made the priest of the idolatrous calf the priest of Jehovah. How can he, then, take our sins upon himself before Jehovah? His offering and his sacrifice are not acceptable to Jehovah. This it is that has kindled God's anger, and for this the whole people suffers. It is for the sin of the golden calf, not for the sins of the innocent scouts that God has barred our path to the land. Take away the priesthood from thy brother, and God will turn His countenance once more toward us."

"Why," said a voice, "did he not slay his brother? Three thousand of the innocent folk he slew, but was it not Aaron himself who made the golden calf?"

"No! Aaron he rewarded! And to the sons of Aaron he assigned the tithes of wheats and fruits, the first-born of the flocks and herds, the ransom of the first-born among the children of Israel. Did God likewise command thee, Moses, to reward thy brother for his sin?"

But Korah lifted his rod of office with a commanding gesture to silence the agitated multitude, and in his customary cold voice addressed himself to Moses:

"All of Israel is holy, and Jehovah is among the people. Why do you then exalt yourself above them? Thyself thou hast made a king over us, and thou takest counsel of none; thy brother thou hast made the high priest. Thou hast divided the inheritance among thine own. Didst thou not say once that this was a kingdom of priests, and each man may bring his own sacrifice before Jehovah?

Wherefore, then, hast thou made Aaron the high priest, and his sons priests, and bidden the people pay heavy tribute to them?"

When Moses heard all this he fell on his face and began to plead: "Children of Levi, chosen ones of the congregation, what is this you are doing? Bethink yourselves of the sin which you commit in making this rebellion. Not one thing have I done of my own accord, and I have not acted save as God directed me. He it was that commanded me to sanctify Aaron and his sons for the priesthood—only Aaron and those that are issued from him. And this thing will be made clear to you. Return to your tents. In the morning God himself will tell you whom He has appointed, and whom sanctified. Whomsoever He has chosen, Him he draws close to Himself. Now let this be done: tomorrow let Korah and his congregation take fire pans, and put fire on them, and offer up incense to God; and the man whom God will choose, he shall be sanctified. And let this be enough, children of Levi." Now he addressed himself to Korah and his group: "Is it not enough that God has chosen you from among His congregation of Israel, to serve Him in the sanctuary and to stand before the congregation and serve it, that thou, Korah, demandest the priesthood? I say that thou, and these that are with thee, are assembled against Jehovah. For what is Aaron that you murmur against him? Stir not up the congregation, and kindle not the anger of God. We have been punished enough, and tomorrow you shall see whether what I have done is from Jehovah or not."

And Moses withdrew into his tent, and left Korah and his people outside. But these did not disperse. On the contrary, they arose and addressed the whole assembly, and spoke bitterly against Moses and Aaron.

Moses was profoundly concerned to stifle the flames before they could spread further. This rebellion, coming so soon after the incident of the spies, terrified him, for now it wanted little that God should wholly abandon the Bnai Israel. He would therefore seek to turn the intended rebellion into a tribal dispute within the ranks of the Bnai Levi, detaching from it the other tribes. He had seen Dathan and Abiram among Korah's people; he considered them more honorable men than Korah, more genuinely afflicted by the sufferings of the people. They were, moreover, among the most respected elders, and he needed them now in order to win over the people. Now, as always, he ignored the promptings of pride, and sent messengers to Dathan and Abiram—Joshua ben Nun, Caleb ben Yephunneh, and others of his closest spirits—asking them to come to his tent, that he might take counsel with them. For he trusted them; they were acting thus not like Korah, out of ill will and envy, but because they did not know the true posture of affairs. This that had happened was the edict of Jehovah Himself; perhaps by prayer and supplication the harsh edict might be softened. But the anger of Jehovah was not to be mollified by murmuring and rebellion.

The delegation brought the words of Moses to Dathan and Abiram, and the latter answered loudly, so that all about them might hear:

"We shall not go up to the tent of Moses. Is it not enough that he has taken us out of a land flowing with milk and honey, to slay us in the wilderness, and has not brought us into a land flowing with milk and honey, nor given us an inheritance of fields and vineyards? Will he put out the eyes of these men? We will not come up to him."

And they took sand, and threw it in the air, and called to the people:

"See, see, how Moses has deceived us!"

The words of Dathan and Abiram stirred Moses more deeply than all the murmuring and slanderous speaking of Korah and his congregation. For these words were the words of the people; moreover, there was in them a great element of truth. Korah's reproaches had been easily answered: what he had done had been at God's bidding. But the words of Dathan and Abiram were an accusation against his leadership. He had not been able to perform God's bidding and carry out God's mission. The leader who cannot obey God's instructions in the face of all obstacles is no leader, but a deceiver and misleader. Such he must seem in the eyes of the people. The people wanted to know nothing about reasons; it judged only by the issue and acknowledged only the leader who succeeded.

He had brought the Bnai Israel to the gates of their land, as a midwife brings a woman to the birthstool. But there had been no birth. There had been thunder and lightning, but no rain.

And if he could not bring the Bnai Israel into the promised land, then not only was the promise false, but equally false in the eyes of the people was everything else he had said in the name of Jehovah. The Torah which he had taught them was false—the invention of his own mind. The shadow of doubt fell not on himself alone, but on Jehovah and Sinai. The rebels were undermining all that had been done until this moment to transform the Bnai Israel into the peculiar people which God sought to make of them: and with the loss of Israel all mankind, and the ascent of mankind to God, were lost.

No! This could not be permitted to happen.

"A sign must be given, a sign must appear to Israel, that all which I have taught them was by the word of God. Jehovah must intervene now, and demonstrate in the eyes of Israel that He commanded me to appoint and sanctify my brother Aaron in the priesthood. For I did not do this thing unbidden."

And Moses cried out to Jehovah:

"Demonstrate in the eyes of Israel that Thou art true and Thy Torah is true. For Thy people are in dire straits. Thou hast placed upon them the sign of death, and they are prepared to believe in Korah and his congregation. Turn not Thy countenance to his sacrifice. I have not taken one sheep of theirs, and I have done no evil to any one of them. I have only done that which Thou hast bidden me do."

The next morning Korah and his congregation came to the sanctuary, and they brought two hundred and fifty fire pans with them. They placed fire upon the pans, and added incense, and they stood at the entrance of the sanctuary. And the people assembled, to see with whom Jehovah would be. And Moses and Aaron also stood before the sanctuary.

Moses did not know what death Jehovah would visit on Korah and his congregation. He was inclined to believe that fire would come out of the altar to destroy them, as had happened with the sons of Aaron, Nadab and Abihu. But no flame came out of the sanctuary; and no flame came out of heaven; and the people saw how Korah and his congregation smoked incense on their fire pans, even as Aaron was wont to do, and nothing happened to them.

And while Moses and Aaron were still standing in wonderment and fear before the people, the glory of Jehovah appeared, and the voice of Jehovah was heard, speaking to Moses and Aaron:

"Separate yourselves from among this congregation, and stand not with them, for I will consume them in a moment."

Moses perceived that all the congregation, which had assembled to witness the sign from Jehovah, was in danger of destruction

376

with Korah and his followers; therefore he fell down before Jehovah and cried:

"O God, the God of the spirits of all flesh, shall one man sin and wilt Thou be wroth with all the congregation?"

Then God spoke to Moses, and instructed him. But neither Korah nor his congregation heard the warning and instruction which God now uttered in the ears of Moses; and they withdrew to their tents in triumph: for they had burned incense before Jehovah, and nothing had happened to them. The sign which Moses had sought for the congregation had not been vouchsafed him.

Although Korah was a Levite, his tent was placed by the tents of Dathan and Abiram. And now the three stood at the entrances of their tents; and their followers encircled them, and heard the meaning of what had happened: Jehovah had accepted the offering of Korah and his congregation, whence it was clear that He had punished the people only because Moses had taken it upon himself to exalt his brother to the high priesthood. And while Korah and Dathan and Abiram held forth in this wise, Moses and Aaron drew near, accompanied by as many of the elders of Israel as they had been able to assemble. Korah was throwing sand into the air, to show the people how Moses had blinded them, when Moses stationed himself opposite him and Dathan and Abiram and called out:

"Depart, I pray you, from the tents of these wicked men, and touch nothing of theirs, lest you be swept away in all their sins."

The people crowding about Korah, Dathan, and Abiram took fright at this warning, and withdrew from the tents. But Dathan and Abiram took their wives and their children, and assembled before Korah's tent, together with his people, to show that they were with him, and were not frightened by the words of Moses.

Then Moses called out: "Hereby shall you know that the Lord has sent me to do all these works, and I have not brought them forth from my own heart. If these men die the common death of all men, then God has not sent me. But if the Lord do a new thing, and the ground open its mouth and swallow them up, with all that belong to them, and they go down alive into the pit, then shall you know that these men have despised the Lord."

And it came to pass that as Moses made an end of speaking the earth opened and swallowed up all the men that belonged to Korah, with their households and their goods; and they went down alive into the pit, and the earth covered them. And all Israel fled at the cry, saying, "Lest the earth swallow us up."

CHAPTER NINETEEN

THE death of the leading blasphemers did not close the Korah incident. The poison spread by Korah, Dathan, and Abiram continued to work after the earth had swallowed them. It availed nothing that every one of Korah's followers who had dared to enter the sanctuary with blazing censers or who had assembled about him had been swallowed by the earth; and that the others, who had neither entered the sanctuary, nor had been assembled with Korah when the earth opened, had been destroyed separately by fire, according to the doom which awaits all who blaspheme against the Supreme Sanctity. Korah's followers had included some of the most distinguished leaders of the tribes. Among the Levites who had stood with him had been carriers of the sanctuary vessels, who were ranked with Aaron and the priests. And among the partisans of Dathan and Abiram there had been representatives of the overseers whom the Bnai Israel remembered from Egypt. Now the people began to murmur against Moses and Aaron, saying that not Jehovah had slain the "men of God," but Moses and Aaron, who had employed magical arts against them because they had been the friends of the people and their protectors.

In the access of blind despair which seized on the Bnai Israel when they learned their punishment, when they understood that they were to wander among the sandstorms of the deserts until they died, and that only their children would enter the promised land—in this blind despair and bitterness they were ready for any kind of mischief. Nothing terrified them now—not even the dreadful fate which had overtaken Korah and his congregation: if anything, that grim incident only inflamed the Bnai Israel the more against Moses and Aaron.

"What," they asked, "was it that Korah and Dathan and Abiram did, they and our other leaders of the Egyptian days, that such should be their end? Was it that they took our part, and demanded reckoning from Moses and Aaron for these, our wasted lives? A

378

land of milk and honey we were promised, and in the end we shall perish like beasts in the wilderness."

"Certainly Dathan and Abiram were right: Aaron and Moses deceived us, threw sand in our eyes."

"I fear nothing and no one. Let him thrust me down alive into the pit, as he did with Korah," shouted a Danite, a long, skeleton-like figure with a pair of fiery eyes. "Better a quick death, I say, than a long dying of hunger and thirst in the desert."

"Ah, it was not for nothing that Korah said, again and again, that this Moses was a calamity to us, from the first moment of his coming. How peaceful were our lives in Egypt! We labored there —true. But who must not labor? In the land which was promised us, would we not have to labor? If not for Pharaoh, then for another ruler—for the priests, that they may gorge on the flesh of our herds and flocks, while we hunger. What did we lack in Egypt? And what did Moses want of us? To bring us here into the desert, so that we might perish here?"

"But our children! Our children at least will come into the land. We shall die out, but our children will live for us."

"I, too, want to live!" insisted the Danite, and the foam of his vehemence came out on his lips. "I am I, and I want my portion and my inheritance, according to the promise. I want to see green grass, I want to eat human bread, and green things, and meat; I want to drink the juice of grapes and of pomegranates; I want to take my ease in the shadow of a palm tree, as I used to do in Egypt; I want to thresh my own corn, as I did in Egypt, and eat the fruit of my trees, the meat of my flocks; I want to wear raiment from the wool of my sheep. The promise was made to me, not to my children!"

"To our children! And who knows if *that* promise will be kept? What certainty have we that *they* will enter the promised land? For some little sin against Jehovah—for demanding water when they are thirsty, a bite of bread when they hunger—God will grow wroth with them, and they too will perish in the desert." So spoke one cunning son of Judah, a little man with a round face and two small eyes set in his face like two dried grapes.

"The man speaks truth!"

"Then woe to us, and woe to our children! And those that protected us have been slain. Who will take our part now?"

"From Moses we shall get only what we got in the past—laws

and commandments: 'This thou must, that thou mayest not.' And: 'This thou shalt do in the land of thine inheritance, and that thou shalt not do'—as if he were indeed leading us there, as though we stood upon its threshold. Bring us into that land first, and then tell us what to do!"

"And his brother Aaron? What has *he* done for us? If he is indeed the high priest, why does he not obtain forgiveness for us? Why did he not avert God's anger?"

"How could he—he, the maker of the golden calf?"

"Those were Korah's very words: How can Aaron do penance for us, being himself the chief sinner?"

"And for those words Moses made the earth open and swallow Korah!"

"Why do we stand here, then, why are we silent? Shall we let ourselves be led like sheep to the slaughter? Let us choose a captain and return to Egypt, and let us beg Pharaoh to take us back as slaves!"

Of all this that went on among the people, the murmuring and complaining, Moses was fully aware. He saw also the sunken faces, the lightless, hopeless eyes, the bowed shoulders, the stifled resentment not only against him, but against the sanctuary. The courts of the sanctuary were empty; the people did not come thither. The great organization which Moses had created was in danger of falling to pieces. The discipline had been shattered. Many of the officer overseers had been sympathizers with Korah, and they had perished with him. The others lost spirit; they were apathetic and confused in the face of the sentence which had gone out against the Bnai Israel. In like case were even the guardians of the sanctuary and its ministers, the Bnai Levi. It was as though the last vestiges of authority were dissolving and the tribes were becoming a flock without a shepherd.

Moses was haunted by an unnamable fear: that which God had intended to do with the Bnai Israel after the golden calf, and after the return of the spies, that which he had been able to avert, might yet come to pass. There might now come a burst of divine fury which he would not be able to arrest or mollify; in that fury not the one generation would be condemned, but all the generations to be: God would reject the Bnai Israel out of hand and look elsewhere for His chosen people.

He stood between two fires and tried to damp their flames alternately. On one side were the embittered tribes of Israel, which seemed ready to break all restraints, to withdraw from the covenant of the tables; on the other side was the wrath of Jehovah; and he was enveloped in the midst.

The dark rebelliousness of the Bnai Israel mounted steadily. Small agitated groups wandered about the camp, coalesced with others, became enraged multitudes, like clouds gathering in a stormy sky; until one day the entire camp was swept into the revolt, and the host poured toward the sanctuary entrance: gloomy faces, clenched fists, tensed bodies—they were prepared for anything and everything. This time it was not a murmuring and complaining which proceeded from them, but a fierce shouting and threatening against Moses and Aaron:

"You! You have slain the men of God!"

Moses and Aaron went out to encounter the wild multitude, and before it could reach the sanctuary entrance, the thick cloud with the fiery edges descended. Then Moses and Aaron turned back from the multitude, which even the cloud of Jehovah no longer seemed to frighten. They hastened into the sanctuary court, and in the midst of the cloud threw themselves upon their faces; and the voice of Jehovah came to them from amidst the cloud:

"Separate yourselves from this congregation, that I may consume them in a moment."

In that moment they heard, from the forecourt of the sanctuary, an inhuman screaming of thousands of voices, a choked, rattling screaming, as if hosts of invisible angels, cherubim, and seraphim, with invisible swords, had descended from heaven, and were mowing down the rebellious tribes. Moses understood at once: this was the ultimate threat of God's anger.

In that desperate moment, when the Bnai Israel stood between life and death, an inspiration burst open in the heart of Moses, as if Jehovah, even in the extremity of His wrath, had still left ajar the gates of His mercy. But it was not a moment for supplication. Words would achieve nothing now. An act of self-sacrificing devotion was called for, an offering up of the one for the many; and this act had to be performed not by Moses, but by Aaron. For Aaron bore the sin for the golden calf, and Aaron must expiate it now by a deed of his own. And Moses commanded Aaron:

"Take thy fire pan, and put fire thereon from the altar, and carry it quickly into the midst of the congregation, and lay incense thereon, and make atonement for them; for the anger of God has gone out among them."

Aaron paled. Terror danced in his eyes, and he reeled as he tried to stand on his feet. He stammered:

"My two sons were consumed with fire, Korah and his congregation were destroyed, because of their improper use of the altar flames. Wouldst thou have me share their fate? If I approach the altar with this intention, I shall surely be slain, for Jehovah is jealous for His fire."

"Show that thou art ordained for the high priesthood because thou art prepared to take upon thee the sin of the people, and to perish for it before God."

With knees that trembled Aaron approached the altar, placed fire upon the pan, and went out to the congregation.

Meanwhile death was at work in the congregation. Row after row of bodies fell, screaming, and flung themselves about in the last convulsions. The invisible avengers were cutting them down as the reaper cuts down the grain, and the bodies lay upon one another like sheaves of harvested ears.

With shaking hand Aaron threw incense on the fire pan, and a thin, blue smoke went up from it. He went out among the people, stationing himself between the dead and the living, and he lifted the censer above the heads of the living. The smoke spread over them like a thin veil.

And the invisible angels and cherubim and seraphim with the invisible swords withdrew, and the pestilence ceased.

Then all the people saw that Aaron had been designated by Jehovah to atone before him for their sin.

Now, to silence forever the murmuring of the Bnai Israel, and to add final proof that only Aaron, and not another, had been chosen from among the Bnai Levi to bear the priesthood, God commanded Moses to have the Bnai Israel bring the rods of the tribes into the sanctuary. Every tribe had its rod of office, the symbol of its authority; and the rods were always in the keeping of the princes of the tribes. The rod of the Bnai Levi was entrusted not to Moses, but to Aaron, as the prince of the tribe. And God commanded Moses to take the rod of Aaron and place it, with the eleven other rods—each rod with the name of the prince inscribed on it—in the tent of the assembly in the sanctuary. And God said to Moses: "And it will come to pass that the man whom I shall choose, his rod shall bud."

Moses did as he was commanded. He placed the twelve rods in the tent of the assembly in the sanctuary. And on the morrow, when he came into the tent, the rod of Aaron for the house of Levi had put forth blossoms and bore ripe almonds. And Moses carried out the rods, and the Bnai Israel looked, and every man took his rod.

Then, on God's command, Moses carried back Aaron's rod into the tent of the assembly, to be kept there as an eternal token and warning, that murmurings of the rebellious Bnai Israel might be ended, and that they might not die.

A great terror fell on the Bnai Israel, and they came weeping before Moses:

"We are undone, we shall perish, all of us. Everyone that approaches the tabernacle of the Lord dies. Shall all of us perish?"

But Moses calmed and reassured them; and in the name of Jehovah he proclaimed the laws of the ritual and the service of the sanctuary. Aaron and his sons were to bear the sin of Israel before the sanctuary; and only they were to bring the sacrifice of the sin offering and other sacrifices and perform the ritual of the sanctuary. The Bnai Levi were to assist the priests as carriers and servants, to purify the vessels, and to guard the sanctuary.

Moses also fixed the relations between the priests of Aaron's house and the rest of the tribe of Levi. He proclaimed, in the name of Jehovah, the nature and source of their income. For both the priests and the Levites had been consecrated to Jehovah, to do the service of the sanctuary, and they would have no inheritance or portion in the land. "For I am thy portion and thy inheritance among the children of Israel." To the priests He had assigned, in addition to their share of the sacrifices, which they were to eat in purity, and the heave offerings, "all the best of the oil, and all the best of the wine, and all the best of the corn, the first part of them which they give to the Lord, to thee have I given them. Everything that opens the womb, both of man and beast, shall be thine; but the first-born of man thou shalt redeem." "And to the children of Levi I have given all the tithe in Israel for an inheritance, in return for the service in the tent of the assembly."

CHAPTER TWENTY

BUT still Moses had not answered the crushing question of the next move. Whither was he to lead the Bnai Israel? A return into the dread desert was unthinkable. It had been frightful enough before: now there had been added to its other horrors the certainty of their death in it. He began to hope that with the acceptance of Aaron's atonement for the sins of Israel in the last rebellion, the hour might be at hand to soften with prayer and entreaty the grim decree of death for the older generation. His heart was wrung whenever he looked upon the Bnai Israel; they went about with bowed heads, shrouded in sadness. Until now they had had, in the midst of all their tribulations, an aim and purpose; they were going to their own land. Hunger for fresh, solid food, thirst, all discomfort, snakes, scorpions, sickness had been halfway endurable, because there was a term to their suffering. And was not Jehovah with them, in their midst? But now what prospect was there? For themselves, only death; and for their children, freedom. Very rare were the spirits among them which could rise to this challenge: to live out all their remaining years in privation and suffering for the sake of their children. They had been simple laborers for Pharaoh, accustomed to the laborer's reward of bread; bread had become the meaning of life, bread, and the mere fact of existence.

Moses lingered in Kadesh-barnea as long as he could. It was a good resting place for a large host. Yet there the command was to lead the Bnai Israel back into the wilderness, by way of the Red Sea. The nearest stretch of the Red Sea was the arm which reached to Ezion-geber, by the borders of Midian and the Paran wilderness. Here he faced, in addition to the familiar lack of water, new obstacles. Amorites had occupied the wilderness of Paran. He might also expect an attack on the part of the Canaanites, to whom it would become evident before long that the Bnai Israel were wandering about aimlessly in the desert and could not approach the promised land. Such an attack would assuredly be an invitation to others—the Amalekites, for instance. But at this time it was necessary at all costs to avoid a clash; in their present mood of embitterment and despair the Bnai Israel could not stand up to a foe. No! He simply would not lead the Bnai Israel back into the wilderness. There would be no backward step. He would see whether he could slip the host through the territories of Edom and Moab. He would beg them, kindred peoples that they were, for the right to pass through. He would pay for everything the Bnai Israel needed, every bite of bread, every mouthful of water; and they would keep to the king's highway until they came to the borders of their own land.

But what of Jehovah's command: "On the morrow thou shalt lead the Bnai Israel into the wilderness, by way of the Red Sea?" How would he dare to provoke the anger of God by transgression of such a strict prohibition?

Moses resolved to take upon himself, and upon himself alone, the entire guilt for the transgression. The Bnai Israel would be guiltless if he bade them march through Edom's territory. God's punishment would fall on him, not on the Bnai Israel. And what was he, Moses, that he should be spared? He that could not take upon himself the sin of all the people, and expiate it with his own life was not fit to be the leader of the Bnai Israel. For Israel's sake he was ready to go down into the pit; for Israel's sake he was prepared—dread thought!—even to rebel against God.

"Let a hundred like me perish before the hair on the head of one of the Bnai Israel shall suffer," he said to himself.

And Moses did that which he had never done before and would never do again. On his own responsibility, and without inquiring of Jehovah, he sent messengers to the king of Edom, with these words:

"Thus speaks thy brother Israel: thou knowest all the travail that has befallen us, how our fathers went down into Egypt, and we dwelt in Egypt a long time, and the Egyptians dealt ill with us and our fathers. And we cried unto the Lord and He heard our voice, and sent an angel and brought us forth out of Egypt. And now we are in Kadesh, a city on the limits of thy borders. Let us pass, I pray thee, through thy land. We will not pass through field or through vineyard, neither will we drink of the water of the wells; we will go along the king's highway, we will not turn aside to the right or to the left, until we have passed thy border."

And Edom sent back answer:

"Thou shalt not pass through me, lest I come out with the sword against thee."

The children of Israel replied:

"We will go up by the highway. If we drink of the water, we and our cattle, we will give the price thereof. There is no hurt. Let us pass through on our feet."

"Thou shalt not pass through."

And Edom came out against Israel with a large host, and with a strong hand. And the Bnai Israel turned away from him.

Jehovah did not say anything to Moses regarding his disobedience, and did not do anything to him. It was as though God pitied the simplicity of Moses, who had believed that "brother Edom" would reach out a helping hand.

And now Moses saw that nothing remained for him but to obey God's command and to move into the desert by way of the Red Sea, so as to encircle the land of Edom. And the heart of Moses was heavy within him.

About this time, when Moses, in the sadness of his spirit, was preparing himself to obey God's command, word was brought to him that his sister Miriam had fallen sick and was on the point of death. And Moses put everything aside and went to see his sister in her tent, before she was gathered to her fathers.

He found her already in the shadow of death; but her eyes, dark flashing and alert, still held the enemy at bay. Her grandson Bezalel stood by her bedside and behind him other members of the family. When she was told that Moses was coming, she put forth her last strength and sat up on her bed; and she stretched out her skeleton hands to the hands of Moses; and she fondled his hands, and the fiery glance of her eyes pierced into him. She began to speak, not concerning herself, not concerning her departure to her fathers before she had seen the promised land, but concerning Moses:

"Why do thy hands tremble so, my brother? Are these the hands that hold up the heavens above the head of Israel? Why is thy face so darkened? Has the light of God turned from thine eyes? Have they not bathed in the light of the splendor which is beneath the seat of glory? If thy heart is shaken, the foundations beneath Israel will be shattered. If thy hand is weak, the walls will tumble upon the head of Israel. Art thou sad because of the decree which God has issued against us?"

386

"Is it not enough, my sister, that I must lead a congregation which must die in the wilderness without sight of the promised land—is this not enough to close my eyes in eternal night? It is more than I can bear, to obey God's command and to lead away my people from the borders of the land into the shadow of death."

"Where is thy vision, which reaches as far as the arrow sent forth from his bow by the mighty man? Dost thou not see the urging of the young bodies, their bursting forth, like waters which break from their channels, and remove all markers, and pour over the fields? Hearest thou not the pealing of joyous voices echoing back to us from the generations yet unborn, to resound upon our graves? Believest thou not, my brother, the promises of Jehovah? Israel can fall like a kid, and rise again like a lion. Pierce with the vision the shadow of death which rests upon the generation of the exodus and behold the eternal life of Israel, shining like a sun beyond the night of death."

"I believe in Jehovah. His judgment is true and just, and His promise shall not fail. I believe that the seed of Abraham is eternal. It is only in myself that I do not believe, my sister. I am a shepherd who has let his flock wander away and fall into the clefts of the rocks."

"Brother! Son of Amram, son of two mothers, the stars watched over thee, and God Himself set thy destiny, even from the day of thy birth. Thy cradle was thy tomb, and I stood by both, and I saw the hand of God stretched over thee. Hear me now, son of Jochabed, son of Bathiya. Thy mother Jochabed placed thee in the ark on the waters of the Nile. I helped to carry thee to the bank. Thy face shone like the sun from the ark-tomb in which thy mother Jochabed prepared thy burial. With trembling hands she wrapped thy body in linens, yet thou were consecrated unto death. The hands which fondled thee when thou camest into the world, these same hands consecrated thee to the waves of the Nile. And thy mother Jochabed drew the black veil over thy eyes, that thou mightest not see thy death; and she fled with swift steps not to hear thy weeping and thy last cry. But I stood on the bank of the Nile and watched the waves playing with thy ark-tomb, lifting thee and carrying thee. Thy face shone out from the death ark; and radiant with the light of God it sang to God's heaven. Thine eyes shone with joy, though the waves were carrying thee to the gathering place of the waters, where the crocodiles waited. Swift as the arrow

387

flying from the bow the waters carried thee to the dens of the crocodiles. Wave beat behind wave, and each one tossed thee further toward thy death. Already the tender odor of thy flesh is in their nostrils, head behind head they raise themselves and wait the taste of thy body. My heart stood still, my hands were heavy as lead, and my eyes were fastened to thy body, which fled on the waters into the open jaws of the destroyer. And then a wave came suddenly, turned thee aside, lifted thee upon its heart, and carried thee with pious care away from destruction, away from the ravening teeth which awaited thee, away to the opposite bank, where the daughters of Pharaoh were bathing in clear and tranquil water. And behold, the hand of compassion and love, of everlasting motherly faithfulness, is stretched out over thee. I could see only the hand, the hand of help and light stretched over thee, the hand of Jehovah stretched over Israel. Whom fearest thou, my brother? Before whom tremblest thou, if Jehovah is with thee? Thine ark floats on secure waters, Jehovah's hand marks out its path." And Miriam bowed her head into the hands of Moses.

"Thou hast comforted me, O mother in Israel."

These were the last words which Miriam heard from her brother, Moses.

PART III

CHAPTER ONE

EIGHT and thirty years went by, eight and thirty years of God's punishment. An entire generation—the generation of the exodus —passed away. Their bones whitened under the hot sun till they crumbled into dust amid the desert sands. The entire region of the Negeb was sown with human remains. From Ezion-geber, by the shore of the Red Sea, as far as the foothills of Edom, the winds carried the withered fragments in waves. Who could have foreseen that these, the condemned and rejected, the abandoned of God, delivered up to the hyenas—these despised Egyptian slaves—would spread and swell like a flood, would cover the surface of the wilderness with flocks of goats and sheep, of camels and asses, which would, like the ox, clear all the fields of grass? Where had they all come from?

Year after year Moses continued the sojourn in Kadesh-barnea. He did not hasten, after the incident of the spies, to lead forth a despairing host which had just heard sentence of death pronounced against it, to consign once more to the howling wilderness a congregation demoralized by rebellion. He did not move the host either backward, toward Egypt, nor forward into the desert beyond Kadesh-barnea where it might become one of the nomadic peoples wandering homelessly about the Negeb. He remained in the lowlands, where a little water could still be found between seasons in the stony water channels. He set himself the task of reorganizing the overseer elders, the guides and directors of the tribes, seeking out new leaders to take the place of those who had been destroyed in the rebellion of Korah. He was waiting, too, for the new generation to grow up, the little ones who had come out of Egypt, and those who had been born in the first years of the wandering—a generation which would not remember the fleshpots of Egypt.

Nineteen years the host sojourned in Kadesh-barnea. Then Moses led them to the Red Sea, to Ezion-geber, and year after year he looked on the wastage and disappearance of the older generation. Where did he find the strength and patience to endure through these years? Two truths were his comfort and support in this period.

The first was the promise which God had made to Abraham that He would multiply his posterity like the sands on the seashore and like the stars in heaven. This promise, as Moses knew, was not to be taken as applying to single generations; it was the overall promise for the seed of Abraham throughout all time. And therefore he interpreted the promise in this wise: there would be times when the children of Israel would fall to low estate, would be as unimportant, as commonplace, as disregarded, as sand on seashores; and there would be times when the children of Israel would be exalted even as the stars in heaven. And yet the star was in every grain of sand; the grain of sand and the star were one. The generation of the sands must disappear the faster in order to make place for the generation of the stars. The second truth on which Moses leaned was the covenant; for by this covenant with Abraham God had chosen the Bnai Israel as His peculiar people. And therefore, no matter how great the sins of Israel, no matter how often Jehovah's anger was kindled, no matter how often He was tempted to destroy this people, to remove all trace and memory of it from the earth, there was the covenant, which could not be voided or evaded. Therefore the Bnai Israel were compelled forever to carry the yoke of election. They were to be whipped into the slavery of God, as the ox is whipped into his yoke. Israel's was not the right of free choice, as was the case with other peoples. By Abraham's covenant he had been sold and delivered into the service of Jehovah, to be the chosen people for all eternity.

Moses saw with ever-increasing clarity how true and just was the sentence which God had pronounced against the generation of the exodus. There was no way out of it: the generation of the sands had to be transformed into the generation of the stars; the generation of slavery would have to die out in order that the generation of freedom might live and become the Chosen People of God's purpose. And in this, as in all things which Jehovah did or commanded to be done, there was an eternal truth; here as everywhere else He pursued the ultimate objective of that perfection which had always been the end of creation. Toward this objective, too, foreordained at the very beginning, he impelled the Bnai Israel. In that final goal, in that fulfillment of perfection which the last days were to witness, every phase of creation, no matter how defective, had its share and portion. The generation of the exodus, too, had its portion in the chosen people; the generation of slavery had its role in the vast process, and its contribution would be remembered forever: in it, too, the process had worked. For the generation of slaves had become the generation of the liberation; that generation—the last in slavery—had been found worthy of redemption. It was the generation of the splitting of the Red Sea, the generation of Sinai. It had launched into eternity the great cry of "We will do and we will obey," which was to peal throughout all the generations. Blindly, like dumb cattle, this generation had followed its shepherd into the desert. It had endured the long martyrdom of the wilderness; and with all its failings and defections it, and not another generation, had been chosen to initiate the great road to the election. Its bones, indeed, might whiten the sandy wastes of the desert, like the bones of asses and camels; but its deeds would live and with the freshness of the dew bring faith and trust to the generations which were to follow.

And Moses saw in these—the Dead of the Wilderness—the vision which his sister Miriam had called up before him: the little ark which his mother had trusted to the waves of the Nile. He saw himself, an infant, lying in the floating bed. The waves carried him, passed him on as it were from hand to hand, guiding the ark in the direction of the destroying horror, the basin where the crocodiles were already distending their hideous jaws. But suddenly a new and irregular wave, born of a mysterious purpose, individual, designed, came rushing forward, snatched the ark from the regular procession of waves, and carried it to a side, toward the basin where Pharaoh's daughter stretched out her hand to him.

The generation of the Dead of the Wilderness was the great wave to which was entrusted the mission of rescuing the ark: to this generation God had assigned the task of redirecting the movement of the chosen people, away from destruction toward salvation and perfection.

Slowly and heavily the ranks dragged themselves forward through the thick sand. It was as though massive chains were fastened to the weary feet which trod the ascent leading back from the Red Sea and Ezion-geber to Kadesh-barnea. They had made an immense detour in order to avoid the territory of Edom, which they were forbidden to cross. The caravans pushed on laboriously, in endless file. The closing section of the procession consisted mostly of flocks and herds, driven by shepherds, and guarded by warriors. The dust which rose from under the feet of men and beast hung over them like a dense cloud, concealing the rear of the hosts. Here no one knew what was happening in the van; there only rolled back a dull, confused sound of motion, a thrusting forward against obstacles, a flat echo of bursting waters carried across the curtain of dust. Perpetual twilight reigned under the curtain, which remained suspended for many hours after the host had passed, leaving behind them the naked skeletons scattered among the slopes. Singly and groups they lay there, castoffs, refuse of the hosts, skeletons—but not all of them dead; for while some were already buried in the sea of sand, itself in perpetual motion, others still tried to struggle forward, lifting their heads and even their entire bodies out of the engulfing sands. Like drowning men rising convulsively to the surface of a sea for a gulp of air before they go down forever, so these, in their mortal agony, quivered with the last attempt to move their limbs, to regain their footing. But the sand waves whipped furiously against their feeble bodies, which fell back and were drowned. There were some who accepted death willingly, surrendering themselves to the desert soil with childlike trust, laying their heads against the sand as if it were a breast, and closing their eyes; others sent out a moaning from their sand-filled mouths, a guttural lamentation and protest against their fate, before they yielded to this wild death in the desert wind. Nor did all die alone, abandoned. Here and there a brother or sister sat by the doomed one, sat and waited till the last signs of life had faded. Here a son held up the head of his dying father, comforted him, held a cruse of water to his faltering lips.

"To what end, my son? Keep this water for thy children. Why waste it to quench the thirst of the dying?"

"Leave me, leave, follow the host before you lose it," pleaded another with his kin, who would not abandon him in the wild desert.

And there were some who rebelled furiously against their fate.

"This is mine inheritance, which Moses promised me, my field and my vineyard: the grave in the wilderness," an old man screamed with his last strength; and he managed to lift his skeleton shoulders out of the sand, managed to rear his shock of white hair, and to glare about him with his bloodshot eyes which were like living wounds in a dead face.

"Moses did not promise thee eternal life! Hadst thou even received thine inheritance, thou wouldst still have had to die, for thou art old." So spoke his neighbor, one likewise doomed, whom his children had left with a cruse of water, to lie there till death came to him. "As for me, I implored my eldest son to leave me here. I will not be a burden to him. For in any case all we of the old generation must die in the wilderness, one sooner, another later. Wherefore, then, torture ourselves on the long road?" And a smile that was all goodness broke out on the wrinkled face of the speaker.

"It is not this dying that I question, but my life!" groaned another from his couch of death. "Why have we lived, I ask. What was our life?"

"What? Thou thinkest still of the fleshpots? Consider, man, that in any case thou wouldst no longer have been enjoying them. For in Egypt thou wouldst long ago have been dead from the bitter labor. Why thou hast lived? That thy son may be free! Sin not in the moment of death; die rather in God's faith. The privilege has not been granted thee, but to thy children it will be granted to enter the land and to inherit the portion which was prepared for thee."

And as these dying ancients discoursed thus, a voice near them rose suddenly in a singing cry:

"I see him. . . . I see him. . . ."

The ancients turned their heads toward him who was uttering these words.

The man that lay near them was wholly immersed in the sand. It was a long time since he had moved, and they had thought him dead. But now he had pushed his head up, and the sand poured down from his eyes, his mouth, his long white beard; he lifted a bony arm, stretched it out tremulously, and pointed, while the withered lips continued to cry:

"I see him. . . . I see him. . . ."

"Whom seest thou?"

"Him, Moses . . ." the doomed man cried, still pointing.

As many as lay in that place, and had not yet been overwhelmed by death, summoned enough strength to turn their heads, to open their eyes, to look. And they beheld Moses, a mighty figure robed in white, a column of whiteness, and by his side Joshua ben Nun.

"Moses . . . Moses . . . Moses . . ." went up the dying whisper.

From all sides the living skeletons began to crawl toward the pillar of light. They brushed aside the sand, they propelled themselves on their bony elbows, they pulled agonizingly toward him, they stretched toward him their white, withered faces, and they called to him in a last, lamenting supplication:

"Moses, our teacher. . . ."

"Moses has come to see the Dead of the Wilderness."

It was the chorus of the doomed.

"Moses! Hast thou come to look upon the Dead of the Wilderness?"

"No! Not the generation of the Dead of the Wilderness shall you be called! I have come to see the generation of the exodus, the generation which went forth from slavery to freedom. Where shall another people be found like unto Israel? One of its kind is this people in the world. Till the end of all the generations shall your deeds be told. You are the generation which Jehovah loved, and He chose you for His peculiar people. It is well with thee, Israel, and may my portion be with thee. Be gathered in peace to your fathers. Your children come after you. You will be in your children, and your children will be in you, until the last generation, until the end of the world."

"Moses, our teacher, has come to comfort us. Moses . . ." they whispered. And here and there a head sank peacefully into the sand.

"I see. . . . I see. . . ." a voice called.

"What seest thou?"

"I see our land, and I see the house of my inheritance. It stands among the tents of Israel; the tree blossoms, and the song of children goes up from the banks of the stream where they pasture the sheep."

"The banks of the stream where they pasture the sheep," voices repeated softly, sinking into the sleep of death.

CHAPTER TWO

AT last they came once more to Kadesh-barnea, which they had left so many years before to go into their desert exile. For now the end of the exile was nigh. The old generation which had been sentenced to death was no more; it had died with the fire of hope in its eyes, had gone down in the midst of a shining light into the graves of sand. And now Moses was leading a new generation out of the merciless desert, a generation which had been hardened in the heat of its crucible. Other men these were; their limbs were as of molten steel, their bodies molded by storm, their faces brown, like polished bronze: their thick-curled locks and beards had been combed by the iron combs of the desert wind. This new generation Moses was now leading into that old, familiar, friendly place, Kadesh-barnea, on the road to the promised land.

Great was the grace which Jehovah had vouchsafed the new generation. To the enemies of Israel, the surrounding peoples, the Amalekites, the Canaanites, the Edomites, which kept watch on Israel from the clefts of the rocks, like hungry hyenas—to them He had shown only the skeletal remains of the Dead of the Wilderness, fallen in the sands. But he did not let them see what the dead had left behind—the ten living souls sprung from every grave, the flocks of sheep, the herds of cattle, born from the carcass of every fallen goat and ox.

But it was a new Kadesh-barnea that Israel returned to. The older ones remembered, the younger had heard tell, that Kadesh-barnea had been blessed from of old with many springs. On the way from Ezion-geber they quenched their thirst with the anticipation of the springing waters which they would find in Kadesh-barnea. For Kadesh-barnea, which was sometimes called Ein-mishpat, the Well of Judgment, was famous among all the wandering tribes as a place of benediction in the desert. The Bnai Israel had a claim on the place because of their long sojourn in it; and even though they had been absent a long time, Moses had never broken the connection with it. He had maintained there for years a small standing garrison, as a protection against Edom and Moab and to discourage other wandering tribes. Meanwhile the people itself, the Bnai Israel, had been kept in that part of the Negeb which stretched from Kadesh-barnea to Ezion-geber, so that the young generation might grow hardy in the desert. But when Moses returned with the Bnai Israel to the long-awaited Kadesh-barnea, he found the place a desolation. That had happened with Kadesh-barnea which often happened with oases in the desert. The springs had wandered underground to appear as new wells in distant places. The drifting sands had moved over it, as the waves of the sea move over and swallow little islands. The green pastures were covered, the roots of the palm trees were withered, the wells were stopped up : everything was sealed with the seal of death.

In vain did the Bnai Israel seek, like thirsty hinds, a channel, a split, a flow of water. In their fantasy they heard the plash and gurgle of streams; but the earth was covered with a mantle of brittle stone, on which lay the sandy pall of death. The ancient channels were lines of dry stones, corpses of wells buried in the desert sand.

The well has been likened to a woman; very deep is the grace of woman, and out of her womb comes life; just as deep is the grace of the well, and from its womb comes living water. The stopped-up well is called "dead water." The Bnai Israel recalled the time when they had drunk from the wells which were now water graves. They remembered Miriam, the sister of Moses and Aaron, and they ascribed the stopping up of the wells to her death : for, as long as she had been alive and in their midst, the wells had overflowed with water for her sake; now that she was dead, the springs had died. Nor did the Bnai Israel hope that the springs would ever come to life again, so that a great lamentation went up from their midst. For thirst held tight the throats of man and beast and sucked the life out of the little children.

Just as their parents had done before them, they held Moses and Aaron responsible for their trials in the wilderness. Again there rose a murmuring against Moses in the host. They came in multitudes to the place of assembly before the sanctuary which Moses had caused to be put up in Kadesh-barnea, and they stormed the tent of Moses. They clenched their fists and lifted up their voices and shrieked:

"Would that we had died even when our brothers died before God! And wherefore have you brought the congregation of God into this wilderness—is it in order that we and our herds might perish?"

And once again there was heard the terrible utterance of the Dead of the Wilderness:

"Wherefore did you bring us out of Egypt and into this evil place, where no seed can take root, and where neither the fig nor vine grows, nor pomegranates, and where there is no water to drink?"

Moses listened and shuddered. His giant's body shook like a reed, his long white beard rose and fell with the rise and fall of his breast, his arms stiffened, his hands became clenched, his eyes darkened. What was this he heard? What was it he saw? Were these the Dead of the Wilderness risen from their graves and standing before his tent with uplifted fists, with stones in their hands, with embittered faces and eyes that darted fire, screaming: "Deceiver! Misleader! What didst thou want of us? Let us choose ourselves a leader and return to Egypt!"

They too, then, who had no Egypt to remember, who had not eaten the shameful bread of slavery; they too, who were born, for the most part, of the wilderness itself; they whom the sun had baked into hardness, whom the winds had formed; these, the children of freedom born in freedom, they too longed for the bread of slavery? If this was so, what purpose had there been in the long martyr road of the desert? To what end had they triumphed over all obstacles? What had it all been for, if at the end of it the sun of liberation did not shine for them, but instead they stood in the shadow of the night of slavery? Ah, they had been born in slavery, enslaved blood ran in their veins, the curse of their fathers was like a rope round their necks, pulling them back to the pit whence God had redeemed them. Would he be able to perform with this people, whose eyes were still turned toward Egypt, the wonders which God proposed—to overcome peoples stronger and mightier than they?

Heavyhearted, with eyes eclipsed by doubt, with a spirit of darkened belief, Moses went before Jehovah, to pray for a people in which his faith was not complete. And he took with him one to help him, his brother Aaron, and the two of them fell on their faces before the tent of assembly.

399

Moses could not find words to utter before Jehovah. For the first time he was terrified by the thought that if Jehovah came with storm and fury to destroy the Bnai Israel, he would not have the strength to arrest His wrath, to move Him to forgiveness, as he had done in times past. For the strength of Moses consisted not only of faith in God, but likewise of faith in Israel. When his faith in the Bnai Israel became weak and shadowy, his position of privilege before Jehovah also failed. And Moses lay there with a trembling heart, his face on the threshold of the tent of assembly, and his lips were locked. Yet Jehovah came before him swiftly; not swathed in the gloomy cloud of wrath, as he had awaited, but in the radiance of grace. And He spoke to him not out of the storm of vengeance, but out of the kindness of compassion:

"Take thy rod, and assemble the congregation, thou and thy brother Aaron; and speak to the rock, in their presence, that it yield up its waters. And thou shalt draw forth water from the rock, so that the congregation and its herds may drink."

And now Moses and Aaron stood before a mighty rock. About them were assembled the Bnai Israel, men, and women, and children, to hear and see the wonder which God would perform for them. They stood with tensed hearts and faces, awaiting the miracle. Moses lifted in his mighty arm the rod which had cloven the sea, the rod of wonders, the rod which was guarded in the sanctuary as a memorial of the love and grace which Jehovah had shown to Israel.

Moses, who from of old had been cautious in carrying out Jehovah's commandments in every detail as he had been bidden; Moses, whose sensitive heart responded to every hint of God's wish; Moses, who had always sought to understand not only the command, but the purpose behind the command, as if God's mind and his were one; Moses, at this instant of doubt in the Bnai Israel, was confused and divided within. Anger had stretched a curtain between his soul and God's desire; and for the first time he carried out the command of God in the midst of inner darkness and uncertainty of spirit.

To begin with, he turned to the Bnai Israel with words which God had not bidden him or intended him to utter:

"Hear me, ye rebellious ones, shall we draw water forth from this rock that ye may drink?"

400

Then he lifted his rod, and, instead of speaking to the rock, he smote it.

The rock was but one of the many which protruded from the stony plateau about Kadesh-barnea: its front was shattered by storm and polished by many winds; on its summit, as it were sunk into its shoulders, rested a head, cone shaped. And now it seemed that the head took on a human aspect, acquired a face, the face of an ancient who had been stationed there in the desert since the six days of the creation, waiting, waiting for the moment when he would be called on to fulfill the commandment which Jehovah had reserved for him since the creation of the world: the commandment to change the nature of the rock, so that from its stony heart springs of water might pour. From the beginning of time it had squatted here, this guardian of the promise, here on the rim of the wilderness, at the close of the long travail of the Bnai Israel, waiting with frightened and consecrated heart to respond to God's foreordained purpose. And there stood Moses before it, in his hand the rod of assurance which God had entrusted to him: and Moses did not fulfill God's command, as it had been delivered to him: he smote the rock with his rod.

The face of the stony ancient took on eyes, deep, dark, gigantic holes, which stared at Moses: a Moses of stone confronting a Moses of flesh and blood. And from the eyes of the rock tears started and ran down the wrinkles of the stone face.

The assembled masses stood there with beating hearts and cowardly eyes, their gaze fixed. They saw the drops of water, they did not understand that these were tears, tears of humiliation and pain: to them the tears were merely drops of water, to be measured only as quenchers of thirst.

A shadow passed over them; their faces reflected despair.

"What? Shall we fill our troughs and water our herds with these drops? Will they suffice to quench the thirst of our children?" The murmur ran through the multitude.

And Moses, too, did not see tears. He saw drops of water, and he measured them with the same measure as the multitude. He lost the remnant of his patience, he lifted up his rod, and he smote the rock a second time.

Then the ancient tore open his heart of rock, and the springs burst forth with violence—those springs which God had prepared in the six days of creation to quench the thirst of the Bnai Israel.

The air was still ringing with the joyous voices which mingled with the music of the streaming water; the song of praise still rose into the air, and its echoes were carried across the vast spaces of the wilderness; and in the heart of Moses an ominous voice resounded, the voice of Jehovah. It was not laden, as it had been so recently, with grace and kindness: it was heavy with wrath.

"Why hast thou shamed My creature?"

And Moses lay, in a cramp of speechlessness, with his face buried in the earth.

"Thinkest thou that My other creatures are as rebellious against Me as My creatures of flesh and blood, so that thou wert compelled to use violence? My will was poured into this My creature. My will grows in the heart of My creature as the fruit grows on the tree; and when the hour of ripening comes, it gives forth its benediction with joy and praise, not with rebelliousness and murmuring. I commanded thee to speak to the rock, and not to smite it."

The cramp of speechlessness was lifted from Moses. In the deep perception of his guilt he whispered:

"I have sinned against Thee, Father of mercies."

"And why didst thou shame My people? Rebellious ones thou didst call them. What have they done? They were thirsty and they cried for water. I made thee a shepherd of My flock; it was for thee to feel the pain of those that I entrusted to thee, and thou shouldst have cried for water to Me. But thou didst smite them with the lash of shame and humiliation. It was not thy prayer, and not thy weeping, but theirs, that I heard, and I hastened to their help."

"I have sinned against Thee, Father of mercies."

"And I looked into the crevices of thy heart, and I searched out thy thoughts concerning My people. A generation of the wilderness thou didst call them, and thou didst condemn them as the Dead of the Wilderness. No, not they, but thou and thy brother Aaron belong to the generation of the Dead of the Wilderness; for ye have not had faith in Me, nor sanctified Me in the eyes of the children of Israel. And therefore ye shall not bring this congregation into the land which I have prepared for them."

"Thou art just, and Thy judgment is just, Father of mercies." And Moses buried his face deeper in the sand before the majesty of Jehovah.

CHAPTER THREE

THE vast moving cloud, as it approached at first, was impenetrable, and only by the sounds which issued from it was its content made manifest: a concealed and manifold tumult as of multitudes of waters. The tumult hinted at the vastness and denseness of the marching people; there was a drumbeat of countless footsteps, an infinite agitation and turmoil. Then, approaching, the cloud would split, and the dust-covered marchers were revealed to the view. A confused pealing of trumpets and of rams' horns hung perpetually over them; but the march of the multitude was not confused; it was ordered and firm, a massive advance across the dust-covered hills of Moab.

First came the leader of the fighting host: a lofty figure of a man in the pride of his best years, rocking on a camel. A mass of black hair streaked with gray fell heavily over his broad shoulders; the eyebrows, thickly sprinkled with sand, stood out grimly; the beard was thick and widespread. Who would have guessed that this mighty, sun-scorched body towering on the camel, these stern lineaments with the grim eyebrows, this shock of hair tumbling over the powerful neck were those of the sensitive lad, Joshua ben Nun, who used to sit like a shadow in the corner of the tent of Moses?

Behind him, mounted like him, rode the leader of the first subdivision of the hosts, Caleb ben Yephunneh. He too was gray, but he too was filled to bursting with manly strength and valor. He rode under the banner of the host of Judah.

The two leaders of the hosts were in the ripeness of their years, but those whom they led, who came after them like floods of fresh waters bursting from the earth, were in that first flush of youth which radiates into the surrounding air the strength of the blossoming body. Not one old face there, not a glimmer of gray. Their thick locks and beards were darkly lustrous under the dust which settled on them. Their broad, naked breasts were browned by the hot desert sun, interpenetrated by fiery sandstorms; their teeth flashed white, and their naked feet, with skin and muscles hardened to steel, ground into dust the lava pebbles on which they walked. Thus they advanced, rank after rank of half-naked bodies, with swords hung on their thighs—every rank under the banner of its proper tribe. And regular as the squadrons of the warriors advanced the Levites, the carriers of the sanctuary: young men led the oxen which pulled the wagons laden with the boards and coverings of the sanctuary; young hands carried with the assurance of strength the vessels of the sanctuary, young shoulders bore the burden of the instruments of service.

Behind the dismantled sanctuary came the wagons with the children of the priests—the blossoms of the priesthood—all of them desert born. These were followed, in turn, by the last squadrons of the warriors, the guards of the sanctuary and its vessels, of the Holy of Holies and the Book of the Covenant—the ten commandments resting in the golden ark, itself wrapped in the purple cloths and covers of rams' skins.

After the fighting men of the tribes came the immense congregation itself, stretching back mile after mile and covering, like a swarm of locusts, the hills of Moab's Sodom country. As far as the eye could reach this vast forest of bodies was in motion, dark shocks of hair, heavyladen sacks, folded tents on the backs of countless asses and camels—a flood which poured over the heights of Moab's borders. And even as among the warriors, so here too, no aged people, only the young, with fresh, lively, vigorous bodies. The men were laden even like the asses and camels which they drove or led: laden either with bundles of their household goods, or with the more precious burden of their children. The women too, full-breasted, carried their young ones: on their hands, or their shoulders, or, still unborn, within: an overflowing benediction of children, thick clusters of human grapes. Countless were the herds and flocks which the shepherd boys drove, one division after another spaced between tribe and tribe.

Nomads of the Moabite clans stared with stupefaction and terror at these advancing hordes and pulled back to the isolated water holes in the hills. Whence came they, these innumerable hosts, advancing from the wilderness of Edom? Who were they? And why had their tribal leaders permitted them to cross the frontier of their land? Where they passed the field was left bare around the water holes; and like a giant ox they licked up the waters and left the wells in their path empty and dry.

Messengers on fleet-footed camels rode from village to village, from town to town, by bridle path and byroad, to spread the dread news: "They are coming! They close up the wells, they stop them up with stones, place covers on them that we may not find them: for they will drink up the water to the last drop and leave nothing for us. Put out guards, assemble the young, prepare weapons, and let a watch be kept on this robber host, that it shall not leave the road and spill over into the fruitful valleys, to feed their countless herds and leave them bare and bleak."

After the incident of the Waters of Meribah—the Waters of Strife (so they called the place where Moses had smitten the rock) —the children of Israel had left Kadesh-barnea. Moses would remain there no longer, though he knew well enough the difficulties and obstacles which he would encounter in the lands of Edom and Moab, lands which he could not avoid in approaching the Jordan. With Edom he had finally broken; he had marched only along the Edomite frontier which ran through the Arabian corridor. But with Moab he had reached an agreement.

Hard and strewn with obstacles was the passage through the Arabian corridor. To the trials of hunger and thirst were added clashes with small tribes of Canaanitish blood, nomads of the Negeb, which tried to impede the advance of the Bnai Israel. But like an irresistible flood they poured forward, sweeping aside all those who attempted to stand in their way. Hungry and thirsty, plagued by the snakes and scorpions which infested the sandy hollows and glided into the tents, to bite the children, or to wrap themselves about the throats of the cattle; tormented by fiery-blood-sucking insects, they went forward obstinately, overcame all difficulties, and at last reached the waters of Zared, in the valley which divided Edom from Moab.

Zared was the frontier line between the two peoples; it was therefore considered a no-man's land, an unclaimed area. There was perpetual war between Edom and Moab for the springs of Zared. Moses took advantage of this circumstance and occupied the valley, so that the Bnai Israel might rest and recover from the toils of their journey through the wilderness of the Arabian corridor. For he bethought himself that inasmuch as the springs of Zared belonged neither to Edom nor to Moab, he might possess himself of them without transgressing against God's command to respect the borders of these two peoples and not to cross them without their permission.

From the valley of Zared he negotiated long and patiently with Moab for that permission. Balak ben Zippor, king of Moab, threatened to come out with the sword against the Bnai Israel and drive them from Zared. But Moses succeeded in his negotiations with certain of the frontier tribes of Moab and Edom and received permission to cross their land, which lay by the edge of Moab's Sodom country: but they were to turn neither to the right nor the left into the fruitful valleys which lined the highway. Beyond this, the wayfarers had to pay fifty sheep and ten young steers for every well at which they paused.

Thus they advanced now, the tribes of Israel, along the mountain road of Moab, with sheep and cattle, with sanctuary and household goods; and they were parched with thirst, sick for a green resting place. They looked across into the valleys, into the fresh, tempting, blossoming fields. How easy it would be to turn aside, to pour downward like a flood breaking through a dam! But they were forbidden to turn either to the right or the left, for Moses had commanded them in the name of Jehovah: "Ye shall not bear enmity to Moab, nor shall ye attack him, for I will not give you his land as an inheritance—it is the inheritance of the children of Lot."

But they did not desire to possess the land; they were not tempted by the stony soil of Sodom. They were weary of the desert. It was another kind of soil they sought. Born though they were for the most part in the desert, grown though all of them had in its wastes, they had never become accustomed to its sandy floods, and their mouths had never reconciled themselves to the taste of the sandy dust; the desert winds had blown through their bodies a thousand times—but it was another kind of earth they longed for. Their eyes hankered for the green meadows of the promised land concerning which they had heard so much and for pastures for their flocks and herds. Throat and palate were constricted with the thought of the juice of grapes, the fatness of pomegranates, the sweetness of honey, the refreshing coolness of milk, with which the promised land, they were told, flowed freely. If only they could have water enough to still their burning thirst, to abate the suffering of their

406

children, to restore their fainting sheep and cattle! Would there never be an end to this desert road?

At the center of the squadrons which surrounded, like a powerful chain, the carriers of the sanctuary, in the heart of the mass of the people, were the heads of the congregation, with Moses in their midst. At the side of Moses, on a richly caparisoned camel with purple hangings and a purple saddle, rode the new high priest, Eleazar. He was covered by a mantle and a long white veil, which fell from the headgear over his shoulders. Only the long, black-gray beard protruded from the covering. His face was hidden, even like his body, in folds of white. About him were his sons and grandsons. His younger brother, Ithamar, was an overseer among the carriers of the sanctuary. All the members of the family of Aaron were robed in white, whether they rode on camels behind the high priest, or whether they followed on foot, or whether they attended him to minister to him. The princes of the tribes accompanied Moses and Eleazar, and every tribe had its representative in the group about Moses. With him, too, were most of his closest counselors, from among the seventy elders; also a number of message carriers and emissaries, scouts or spies, as they were variously called, who maintained continuous contact between Moses and all parts of the advancing host.

All the men of importance about Moses rode on camels; he alone went on foot. He, the foremost representative of the Bnai Israel, would not be otherwise than a simple ben Israel, a son of Israel. Yet it seemed that as he strode among them, his head covered like that of the high priest with a white veil, he towered above the riders about him. It seemed that the older he grew the mightier became his presence, the more powerful his hands, the more hardened his muscles. Not a man strode here, but a giant who had fallen from heaven. His crown of hair, under the headgear and the veil, poured down in thick white locks and burst forth from beneath the veil; his massive beard, of immense length and width, lay with a more dazzling whiteness on his white mantle. Everything about him was mighty, stature, limbs, and presence; everything about him was cut more sharply, with keener and straighter lines. Not body and limbs alone, but the lineaments of his face, too, seemed to be fashioned of something other than flesh and blood, seemed to have been carved by a master hand from a single block of granite. The sharp aquiline nose, the great circles of his eyes resting on their cushions and sending forth a commanding, heavenly light, the modeled features—these were dominant; and yet a deeply moving melancholy rested like a faint shadow on the glory of that face; the furrows of the mighty brow, the deep folds about the eyes, and the lines about his mouth were tremulous with human weakness. They were filled with a human pain and sorrow which softened the granite lines of their form, and transformed a more than human remoteness into an utterly human humility, for "the man Moses was very meek, above all the men that were on the face of the earth."

In that majestic figure, hewn as from the rock, there was a heart which was filled—even as a sponge fills with water—with the sufferings and sorrows of his people. He knew that his time was running out, that he must share the fate of the generation of the exodus. Yes, he was one of them: Jehovah Himself had said so. And when he had conducted his brother Aaron up into the mountain, had stripped him of his priestly robes and put them on Eleazar, when he had left his brother, naked, in the cave where an angel waited for him—when he had done these things he had said: "Go, my brother Aaron, into the kingdom of peace, whither this angel of the Lord will lead thee. I shall follow straightway; I have but to end the day's labor which Jehovah entrusted to me." For Moses considered himself a day laborer in the hire of Jehovah; he had to complete his day's work, that is, bring the Bnai Israel to the promised land, to the place of rest. And his heart still shook and trembled for the trials which confronted Israel. He knew their needs. This last passage through the desert was the hardest; he knew that the children were faint with thirst, that sheep and cattle sprawled in the sand and refused to move, what with weariness and thirst. Very bitter was the march along the desert frontiers of Edom, bitterer still was the road through Moab. These were the last energies which the tribes were expending; every instant their patience could give out; they could rebel again, again raise the slave cry: "Why didst thou bring us forth out of Egypt?" And again Jehovah's anger could be kindled, again he could sentence them to the desert. Who would plead for them when he was gone? Who would restrain the anger of Jehovah?

He was obsessed now by the need for haste. If God had revealed his fate to him, the time must be close at hand. Faster! he thought. No pause in the wilderness of Moab! They must reach without delay the springs of Arnon. Arnon lay between the boundaries of Moab and the Amorite and was an eternal bone of contention between them. Latterly the Amorites had taken Arnon from Moab. Therefore it now lay outside the boundaries of Moab, and Israel could occupy it, for the Amorites had no claim to it. The wells of Arnon gave water in abundance: what a refreshment they would be to the parched and exhausted wanderers, who had not known the taste of fresh water since leaving Zared! But would the Bnai Israel be able to occupy the place? Or would Sihon, king of the Amorites, be waiting with his army when the Bnai Israel left Moab, even as Moab had waited for them when they left the wilderness of Edom? Might it not be, then, that the Israelites would find in Arnon not water, but the sword? Would Jehovah let him occupy the wells of Arnon? Would he not do well to send emissaries to Sihon, offering payment for the right to pass through his country? Or should he wait till he came to Arnon, and perchance find it possible to occupy the place?

While Moses marched along, sunk in these reflections, a messenger came riding from the tribe of Gad. Because of its great herds and flocks Gad brought up the rear of the hosts of Israel, at a riding distance of several hours from the center. And this was the report: the men of Gad had been unable any more to endure the sufferings of their flocks, and they had therefore turned aside with their sheep into the forbidden territory of Moab; they had descended into a valley and had occupied it, with its wells. The inhabitants of the place had come out to do battle; for they had demanded payment in sheep for their water, according to the covenant which Moses had made with Balak, and the children of Gad had refused to honor the covenant.

"Prince of the tribe of Gad!" called Moses. "Go to thy tribe, and command it in the name of Jehovah to pay the Bnai Moab the sheep and cattle due them for every well of water, according to the covenant we made with them."

The prince of the tribe of Gad answered: "They have already taken away a great part of our flocks and herds. Hear me, Moses, our teacher! If we continue to pay thus for every drink in the land of Moab we shall have no sheep and cattle to bring into our land."

"This was God's command to me: 'Ye shall buy your food from them; and even water shall ye buy for money, that ye may drink.' Go and carry out God's command."

"Moses, our teacher! We can easily overcome them, for we are stronger than they. We can drive them off even as we drove off the Canaanites who attacked us."

"We do not wish to attack anyone and overcome anyone. We only defend ourselves against those who attack us and wish to overcome us. Nor do we occupy lands which Jehovah has already given as an inheritance to other peoples. We want only to take possession of that portion which God set aside for us."

"Where is it, this portion of ours?" asked a voice. "Why does it ever recede from us? Every span of earth through which we pass has already been set aside for someone. Will there never be an end to this frightful wilderness? Shall we forever have to buy each drink of water from strangers? Shall we too have to perish in the wilderness, leaving our children to dream the vain dream which we and our fathers have dreamt? We do not get even a glimpse of the fields that flow with milk and honey, according to the promise. We see nothing but the wilderness, nothing but the eternal chain of enemies about us."

"Go, prince, and carry out God's command. Why should you fall into mortal sin against Jehovah, as your fathers did, when you have all but reached the term of your wanderings? A little while more, the time is close at hand, and Jehovah is faithful to His promises."

Not once during the long trek through Moab had Moses permitted the setting up of the sanctuary. Arnon was the next resting place, and thither he pressed with all urgency. He had even issued the command that no tents should be unfolded for the night's rest: the tribes were to be on the march with the first ray of the morning star. Surrounded by the warrior hosts, the people—men, women, and children—slept the night through under the open sky, in the midst of their sheep and cattle and folded tents. Only three tents were erected. The first of these, surrounded by a strong guard of Levites, and attended by a group of messengers and signalers whose fires and trumpet calls would give the command for departure, sheltered the ark with the tables, likewise the vessels, the pillars, the curtains, and the coverings of the sanctuary. The second was for the high priest: the laws of his high calling made it necessary for him to take shelter in the night. He had to be guarded from creeping things, from all manner of uncleanliness, lest he become unfit for the service. The third was for Moses, because of his continuous contact with the Divinity. At any moment Jehovah might appear to him, or call to him, and he therefore needed a place of retreat where, unseen of mortal eye, he could commune with the Spirit. When with the approach of night the hosts rested in the open field, Moses sat at the entrance of his tent surrounded by the princes of the tribes and the elders. There he received all the reports brought to him by mounted heralds from every corner of the far-flung host, reports concerning the warriors, or concerning the people. With the same heralds he sent back instructions and commands in the name of Jehovah.

He sat now at the entrance of his tent, under the starry sky, surrounded by the elders and counselors. The reports which poured in made his heart heavy: "Since the Bnai Israel set foot on the heights of Moab their eyes are ever fixed on the west, filled with longing for a glimpse of their promised land." So one herald reported from an outpost of the host. "But what unfolds before their eyes? Nothing but desolate mountains, stony wastes heaped one upon the other, the Salt Sea shining like an eye deepset in the valley: but not one tree, not one blade of green. The bald hilltops stretch away into the farthest distance. They have been told that the waters of the great lake are salt and bitter, not to be tasted by man or beast. And the soil which they now tread do we not know that it is the soil of Sodom, which God destroyed with fire because of the sins of its inhabitants? The Bnai Israel are afraid that their promised land consists of nothing but desert and rock, and they have been utterly deceived. Do thou, Moses, send a deputation of the Levites to the Bnai Israel to enlighten them, so that they may know that it was because of the sins of Sodom that the land was destroyed with fire and brimstone—and let the spirit of the Bnai Israel be strengthened."

Thereupon Moses commanded one of the priests, an overseer of the Levites, to send a group of them into the congregation. Swiftly the Levites proceeded into the host, declaring and explaining on every hand who the Bnai Lot were and why God had given them the land as an inheritance. Furthermore, they spoke to the people concerning Abraham, and they pointed out in the distance the place called Beersheba, where Abraham had lived. Abraham had dug a well there, and the servants of the king of the Philistines had taken it away from him by violence; thereupon Abraham had made a covenant with Abimelech, king of the Philistines, and bought the well from him for seven sheep. And various other stories concerning Father Abraham were told by the Levites, to restore and strengthen the spirit of the Bnai Israel. They told the Bnai Israel that the boundaries of their land began even there, at Beersheba, and that the Jordan, which they would soon reach, poured into the Salt Sea which they beheld. Soon, soon they would cross the Jordan and occupy the land on the farther side, their portion and inheritance forever.

But the Bnai Israel would not be comforted. A great sadness had fallen on the congregation, and they said bitterly that if their inheritance was as desolate as the inheritance which God had apportioned to the other descendants of Abraham—the Bnai Esau and the Bnai Lot—they would rather not possess it. They were weary and sick of wilderness. Their forefathers had not been men of the wilderness, neither were they. Their forefathers had dwelt in fat fields by the river Nile, where they had not been dependent on rain from heaven, where the earth herself had supplied them with water, and with the fatness of dew.

And here and there a weeping was heard in the congregation: "Our souls are withered and parched by the wilderness, even as our throats are withered and parched by thirst. And Moses took us out of a land of milk and honey, and he leads us into a land which brings forth thorns and thistles." These were the words which messengers brought back from other parts of the camp.

Moses listened, brooding, to the reports of the Levite overseers. Yes, he knew now that the people, exhausted by the wilderness, had lost faith in the land of promise: yet God had promised, and God was faithful to His promises. And though he himself had never set eyes on the land to which he was leading the Bnai Israel, he bade the Levites return to the people and speak again:

"Say this to the Bnai Israel: in vain do ye fear, and in vain do your hearts melt in you because of the sight of this land. Thus speaks Jehovah: 'I will make the thorns and thistles drip milk and honey for you. And if ye will hearken to My commandments, and obey them, then the place that ye tread on, the land of Sodom, shall be turned into a garden of Eden for you.' Tell them further," continued Moses, "that no son of Esau is Israel unto the Lord God, and no son of Lot. Israel is His son, whom He has taken to Himself, His people, which He has chosen from among all peoples. And

soon, soon, a day or two more, and ye will see, as on the palm of
your hand, the land which shall be yours."

Yet not all the reports brought to him were of the same sad
tenor. The reports from the fighting host, sent to him by Joshua,
filled his heart with joy and hope, as the honey fills the ripe pome-
granate.

"Israel is like a ravening lion, who looks out fiercely for his prey;
his eye is sharp and his paw powerful. Like a young hart he sharpens his horns for the coming battle, and he carries his burden like
an ass which is not rebellious."

That night Moses knelt in his tent and cried out to Jehovah:
"Jehovah, God of mercy and grace, behold. Thy people is weary,
and Thy servant is weary. Our souls are withered and we are filled
with vain longing for the land which Thou hast promised our
fathers. We can carry the burden no further. Behold, thy people
has paid the full price, do Thou now fulfill Thy promise. Open for
us the founts of Thy grace, give us of Thy water to drink, for
we are thirsty, thirsty, thirsty."

And Moses stretched himself out in his tent, with his face to the
earth, and a deep sleep fell on him. And in his sleep he saw himself,
the shepherd of Jethro's sheep. He was wandering in the wilderness
of Sinai with his sheep, on the coppery heights and through the
clayey lowlands. The earth was stony and sealed, and the sheep
were tormented by thirst and weary of the eternal climbing. And
suddenly he saw water bursting mightily from a cleft and descending with a great tumult. In an instant the dry channels were filled
with fresh, living water pouring toward the feet of his flock.

He heard the voice of Jehovah:

"Assemble the people, and I will give them water."

In the dimmest dawn, when the morning star had just begun
to dart its fiery rays through the heavens, the hosts of Israel were
already assembled in their ranks, awaiting the signals to set out
on their daily march. Suddenly a tumult broke out in the vanguard
of the leader tribe of Judah. With astounded and unbelieving eyes
the Bnai Judah, in the forefront, gazed before them. Yesterday,
gazing in the same direction, they had seen nothing but scorched
lava soil and craggy heights; boundless the desert had stretched
before them. Now the earth had opened before them. It was as if
a mirage had suddenly unfolded, a phenomenon with which they

413

were not unacquainted: and yet it was too vivid for a mirage. At their feet the slope descended precipitously, as if half the hill had been sliced away, and below, at the foot, was another world, a new world which was disclosed to their view for the first time. Fat, green meadows extended far and wide. Under the luminous blue sky, in which silver-edged clouds swam about playfully, modest groves of cypress swayed in the wind, overshadowing townlets and villages—little white huts peeping out through the branches. And everywhere, beds of vegetables, furrows of grain, sheep nibbling the pasture. At the very foot of the hill, springing water—water bubbling out of a well and flowing over, gathering, moving forward with a singing sound, filling the channels and cracks, rushing forward and being ever and again renewed. It seemed to them that they were looking at the fountains of life playing before their eyes.

The Bnai Israel, of whom by far the largest part had been born in the wilderness, had not seen the like; even those that had been born in Egypt no longer remembered the abundance of the waters of the Nile, of which their fathers had been wont to tell with such mournful yearning. In the fiery desert their eyes had known as little as their throats of the benediction of free-flowing water. Their bodies baked by the sun and sands, their bones dried up by the heat, they had never before heard the song of water, never inhaled the earthy smell which is wafted from springing water; they had never before known the deep comfort which it brings to the soul, the hope with which it fills the heart of man. For this was not the water of a miracle, the water which Moses drew for them from the rock. That water had filled them, not with comfort and hope, but rather with the terrifying thought that soon, soon it would cease to flow; but this water was of the earth, constant and abiding, the water which God had entrusted to earth, the water which till now had been withheld from them.

The benediction of that sound came to the first ranks, and the word of benediction was passed through the host: water of the earth, water springing from a well, water which flows and fills the channels, and still flows, and never ceases; water that sings with its own freshness.

The word, as it flew backward through the ranks, filled them with heavenly bliss. They felt themselves being lifted; it was as if they had sprouted wings.

All faces were turned to Moses.

"Water! Is it open to us, or closed to us? Water! Is it Edom's? Is it Moab's? Can we have it only against payment?—that is, if brother Esau is willing to sell."

"Water! Has Jehovah given it to us, or to the stranger?"

And the exhausted leaders of the tribes of Israel, at the last gasp of endurance, awaited the word of Moses. They stood about him in their mantles, their rods of office in their hands. About him stood also the elders. The high priest was there, Eleazar, pale with anxiety, and with him the heads of the Levites. All stared at Moses, an agony of hope and fear in their fluttering hearts.

And Moses spoke:

"This is the well of which God said to me: 'Assemble the people, and I will give them water.' It is the well which our father Abraham dug, the well which our forefathers, the princes, dug."

And now, with a tumultuous freedom which ignored all order, the Bnai Israel broke ranks. Mothers carried their children, men led forward the parched flocks. . . . In a flash men and cattle were streaming downhill, themselves like a torrent, and they clustered along the water channels and the pools.

And suddenly girls and young women had made a ring, arm woven into arm, bodies swaying together, about the well. The song of their joy went up in shrill, nasal tones:

> "Our well, our well!
> The well which our forefathers dug!
> Kings they were, great lords,
> Princes of the people.
> With their scepters they dug it,
> With their staves they deepened it.
> Spring up, O well, burst forth, O water,
> Slake us with thy freshness.
> Our fathers, the princes,
> Did dig thee for their children."

It was as if the well knew that these who had come to it now were the children of the princes, so mightily did it renew its waters: it was as if it had discovered new and secret founts within itself, founts kept in reserve from ancient days for this occasion. It was as if the song of the maidens and young women were conjuring up the waters of the well, and the deep answered joyously, pouring out waters into the channels until they overflowed. Men and cattle fastened themselves to the streaming water as a hungry infant fastens itself to its mother's breast.

And now, exalted and intoxicated by the new hope which the living waters had awakened in them, the men sang against the women:

> "Drink the benedictions of our fathers!
> Drink the promises of Jehovah!
> Drink faith, drink trust,
> Drink strength, drink valor—
> For our land and our people,
> For Jehovah and His law!
> Our fathers dug this well,
> With their scepters they dug it."

With the waters of the well the men of Israel imbibed a new spirit, a spirit out of which flowed renewed powers of endurance and hope, and they said to one another:

"Surely it is the spirit of our forefathers which has entered into us with the waters of the well which they dug for us!"

CHAPTER FOUR

AND yet, after all, Moses did not give the command for the putting up of the sanctuary at Arnon, and naturally all the tents of the Bnai Israel remained folded. He issued instead the command for an immediate advance into the land of the Amorites.

And when the princes of the people turned astonished faces on him, he said:

"We must hasten ceaselessly; for before we will reach the Jordan opposite Jericho we shall cross the lands of many peoples."

And when the prince of the tribe of Reuben was bold enough to object that the wells of the valley of Arnon gave abundant water for the flocks and herds, Moses answered:

"Jehovah possesses many lands with deep wells of abundant waters, and the earth belongs to Jehovah, not to mortal man. And Jehovah has apportioned its inheritance to each people, and we dare not take what has not been apportioned to us."

"But it is not thus with the Amorite," insisted the prince of the tribe of Reuben. "The Amorites are not of the seed of Abraham; the land which they inhabit they have taken from Moab by violence, booty of the sword. Why, then, may we not take it likewise by the sword? The land has pasture for our sheep, and wells which our forefathers dug."

"They are alien intruders," spoke up other princes. "They are not of the seed of Abraham. Sihon took the city of Heshbon from Moab; he fought with Moab, and took away all the land as far as Arnon."

"It is true," said Moses, "that even the Bnai Esau and the Bnai Lot took their lands with the edge of the sword from peoples that dwelt there before. But it was thus that Jehovah confirmed their possession, and we dare not lay hands on it. For I have His command not to attack the Ammonites, who are the children of Lot."

"But the Amorite," they contended, "is no son of Lot. He is no

417

Ammonite. He is an intruder and usurper. And God has not given him a portion here; he is a stranger."

"That we shall see," answered Moses. "Meanwhile we must obey Jehovah's command and take only that which He promised our forefathers, the land beyond the Jordan as far as the Great Sea. We cannot attack anyone; we can only defend ourselves when we are attacked."

Then Moses assembled messengers from the tribes and sent them in the name of Israel to Sihon, king of Heshbon, with the following words:

"Let us pass through thy land. We will go only along the highway, and we will turn neither to the right nor the left. We shall buy of thee with silver, food to eat and water to drink. Let us only pass through on foot, as we did through the land of the sons of Esau, who live in Seir, and through the land of the Moabites, whose city is Ar; let us pass through until we cross the Jordan to the land which Jehovah has given us."

Hearing this message, one of the priests, in charge of the stores of silver and gold in the sanctuary, asked of Moses: "Where shall we take the silver for payment? We have spent our store buying bread and water from the Edomites and the Moabites."

"We shall pay with sheep and cattle to the value of the silver. Set a price with him for every well which we shall use up," said Moses to the messengers.

All the bitterness which had been sweetened by the prospect of the waters of Arnon, all the mournfulness of the desert which had been dispelled by the springing well, returned now. The people had believed that with their approach to the borders of their land everything would be theirs. And now once again they were strangers and wanderers. The curse of the wilderness was pursuing them to the very threshold of the land—perhaps beyond!

"But our flocks and herds are shrinking!" they cried. "First the wilderness took its toll by thirst, then of the remainder we gave away much for bread and water. We believed that at least the wells of Arnon would be ours, and that from Arnon onward we should know no want."

But it availed them nothing. Moses repeated the command for the resumption of the march. Trumpets and rams' horns resounded through the host, the foremost ranks were set in motion, and by degrees the congregation advanced into the new, unknown country.

They marched without spirit, longing always for the springs they were leaving behind. A considerable number of the Bnai Israel, mostly of the tribes of Reuben and Gad which, because of their numerous flocks, brought up the rear of the host, remained about the springs of Arnon. Dusk had fallen before the immense host was all in motion, and by that time the rearward section had decided to stay on at Arnon. Only the older ones went forward slowly, to maintain contact with the main body, but the young men and women remained behind with the flocks and herds. They believed that God had given them this land, and they would not leave it.

The vanguard of the host was still on Moabite land, and no one had yet set foot in an Amorite field or village, when the scouts came hastening back to Joshua with this report: "Sihon, king of the Amorites, has gathered his people together, and is coming out armed to do battle with the Bnai Israel. He is already close at hand."

Joshua himself rode back with the messengers to deliver the report to Moses. And Moses listened, and his face brightened:

"Surely God has hardened the heart of Sihon, so that he and his people may be delivered into our hands." The eyes of Moses flashed. "They shall be ours this very day. Sihon and his people must be destroyed at once before the other tribes, Yaazer, and Og, king of Bashan, will have time to gather their hosts and come to the help of Sihon. Let us destroy him utterly, so that the terror of Jehovah may fall on the others, and they will not dare to attack us."

After a pause he asked of the messengers who accompanied Joshua: "How big is his host, and what is its strength? How is it armed?"

"Host? It is a multitude of men and women, young and old. He called all the people to march out against us. Surely they believe that the very name of Sihon would terrify us, and we would flee before them. They believe also that we are but a handful, a remnant of the Dead of the Wilderness; for they heard tell that Jehovah had abandoned the Bnai Israel to perish in the desert."

"It is well," said Moses. "Let the best of our fighters, three thousand from each tribe, be mustered and armed with swords. Joshua, thou wilt lead one host of a thousand from each tribe against Sihon. Thou, Caleb ben Yephunneh, wilt lead another host of a thousand from each tribe around Sihon to beleaguer Heshbon. The third host will be needed as a guard against Moab, for it may well be that hearing of Sihon's attack upon us, Moab will attack us in the rear."

"Balak ben Zippor of Moab and Sihon of the Amorites are deadly enemies, since Sihon took away from Moab its best land, and the wells of Arnon."

"We cannot count on the enmities of the enemies of Israel. The hope of doing evil to Israel makes them friends."

An elder of the tribe of Reuben spoke up daringly:

"Moses, our teacher! Against Moab the young men of our tribe will make a stand. We have left our sons by the springs of Arnon; they have made a ring of iron about it, and no one will pass through."

"Then let the third host move forward and attack the Amorites on the left. Remember! Do not destroy the cities and villages, as ye did with the Canaanite tribes which attacked you. Spare the cities and villages, for we shall take possession of them. Jehovah has heard our weeping, He knows the justice of our cause, He knows likewise the evil which the enemy planned against us. And this is the word of Jehovah: 'See! I have delivered Sihon into thy hand. Go forward to battle and begin the conquest.' Take, then, what Jehovah has given you: swiftly, and with strength, before our other enemies have time to gather against us."

Rams' horns and silver trumpets sounded. Phineas, son of Eleazar, the young priest, went forward with Joshua ben Nun and Caleb ben Yephunneh. Like a swollen mountain lake bursting into the valleys the tide of warriors split into three streams and poured forward against the raw and insolent multitude which Sihon had called out against Israel. Long had the warriors of Israel been sharpening their horns; like a young steer fierce with hunger and pride Israel thrust right and left against the Amorites, and the terror of Jehovah which had fallen upon them did the rest.

In a few days the victorious warriors returned to the encampment. A vast cloud of dust accompanied them, sent up from the countless flocks and herds which they drove before them. They entered the encampment with a song of triumph on their lips:

> "Woe to thee, Moab!
> Thou art undone, O people of Chemosh!
> His sons have become fugitives,
> His daughters have become captives

420

Unto Sihon, king of the Amorites.
And we have shot at them!
Heshbon is perished even unto Dibon.
We have laid them waste even unto Nophah,
Which reaches unto Medeba."

And Moses said: "Heshbon is not perished—only Sihon and the Amorites are perished. Go forward, take the land of the Amorites, and occupy it. Jehovah has given it to you as an eternal inheritance."

It was a light matter for the Bnai Israel to occupy the towns and cities of the Amorites, for Heshbon and the surrounding settlements had been emptied of their inhabitants.

Moses confirmed part of the tribe of Reuben and part of the tribe of Dan in the possession of Arnon and of Heshbon with the villages surrounding; and with the rest of the host of Israel he moved forward toward the Jordan. He was compelled to take a roundabout path and followed the external line of the flinty mountains which rose like gigantic walls from the shore of the Dead Sea. Nor could he descend into the valley, which was occupied by the Bnai Ammon. And so the Bnai Israel walked as it were on a narrow ledge, and balanced their way delicately; and it seemed to them that once more, after having been given a glimpse of the settled life, they would have to turn to the wilderness before they could reach the Jordan, opposite Jericho.

And even this difficult and tortuous path through the heights was beset with obstacles. Among the clefts and crags of the heights, hidden from view, lived a tribe which was famous in the neighborhood for its warlike qualities. Their strongholds were hewn out of the rock, and even unopposed approach was difficult in the extreme. They were the "gatekeepers" of the land Canaan, a warrior people barring the road from the desert to the Jordan. The men were huge, and of enormous strength; and all manner of legends circulated concerning their king, or leader, Og, of Bashan. It was said, for instance, that he was the last of the giants who had fallen from heaven, and his bed was nine ells long and four ells wide. Now this king giant and his warrior people did not wait until the Bnai Israel had drawn near to their cities, but came pouring out in fierce attack.

When word came to Moses that Og, king of Bashan, had left

his strongholds and was coming out to encounter the Bnai Israel at Edrei, he fell on his knees and lifted his arms to heaven, saying:

"This Thou hast done, O Jehovah! Thou hast lured him out of his strongholds, him and his people, so that Thou mightest deliver them into our hands." And he prayed: "Break, O God, the rings of iron which Thou hast drawn about the land of our forefathers. Open the gates of Thy promise, for a mighty people has risen against us and stands on the path between us and our inheritance."

And Moses heard the voice of Jehovah calling to him:

"Fear him not! For indeed I have this day delivered him and his people into thy hand, so that thou shalt do with him as thou didst with Sihon, king of the Amorites, who dwelt in Heshbon."

Then Moses turned to Joshua and said:

"Thou goest out this day against a mighty enemy, the gate-keepers of Canaan against all that come up from the desert. This is the people which broke the spirit of the spies which I sent into Canaan, so that they brought back a false and frightened report. Their hearts melted in them when they beheld the inhabitants of the land, who were as giants in their eyes. But thou shalt not fear them, and thy heart shall not be shaken, for Jehovah has delivered them into our hand.

"And now hear me, and do according to my word: Jehovah has lured them out of their strongholds. He has blinded them, and they see not that we are mighty in strength and numbers. They think we are weak and small in numbers. Therefore they do not wait for us to reach their strongholds, nor do they lie in ambush in the clefts; but they have come out against us to destroy us on the road. Therefore thou shalt do thus: take the choice young men of the army, and divide them into two hosts. One host shall be given to Caleb ben Yephunneh, and he shall lead it by a roundabout path to close the return of the enemy to its strongholds. And thou with the other host shalt go forward in the open. And smite the enemy in the open, with all thy might, and keep the battle in the open. Thou in front, and Caleb ben Yephunneh behind. And Phineas ben Eleazar the priest shall be with thee to strengthen thee. Gird thy loins now, and deal with Og, king of Bashan, as thou didst deal with Sihon, king of the Amorites. Tread down the serpent which lies in our path, and open the gate to the land which God has given us. Be strong and of good spirit, for Jehovah is with thee."

It was as if the Bnai Israel were destined to learn every manner of warfare—the warfare of the hills and the warfare of the valleys. Even at the gates of their land Jehovah proved them. He placed obstacles in their way, enemies on the heights and enemies in the lowlands, so that Israel might be tested through and through in the fires of battle. And now the young fighters of Israel climbed and crawled up the flint crags, their swords between their teeth : brown bodies clinging to the black rocks. With powerful hands they gripped the ledges, swinging themselves from height to height. They leaped like hinds from foothold to foothold, across deep chasms. On the rude slopes their oiled skins glistered and shone, giving back the sunlight. Singly at times, and at times turning themselves into ladders, they ascended to the summit and then—giants or no giants —they poured down with a wild war cry which pealed among the summits: "Jehovah fights with us!" and flung themselves on the ranks of Bashan. Bodies began to tumble down the slopes, like the carcasses of sheep which a storm lifts and flings into the abyss.

Within a few days the cities and strongholds of Bashan were taken and cleared for possession by the Bnai Israel; and the warriors returned, some riding on camels, others on asses, driving before them great flocks and herds.

The victory of the Bnai Israel over the hosts of Og, king of Bashan, spread terror among the little kingdoms and tribes which occupied the remaining approaches to the Jordan, and their hearts melted in them with fear. They began to see now that a mighty Spirit fought with the Israelites—the Spirit of their forefathers. And they bethought themselves of what their priests had taught them—that their forefathers and the forefathers of the Israelites were the same. They remembered, and they trembled. And thus the road was opened for the Bnai Israel to the Jordan by Jericho, and all the land east of the Jordan was likewise open to them, northward to the hills of Gilead and beyond; for there was no people that dared oppose those who had conquered the giants.

Bashan had been from of old the barrier against the nomad desert tribes which had gazed with longing at the pasture fields along the Jordan. Even Pharaoh, conqueror of the Asiatic peoples, had not dared to attack the strongholds of Og. And here an obscure people had come up from the wilderness, a people of whom it had been vaguely told that their God Jehovah had given them as a prey to the desert, had come up and had burst open the barred gate guarded by the giants. Who could stand against them?

For all this, Moses took precautions against an attack on his rear by Moab and Ammon. He strengthened the position of the tribes of Reuben and Gad in the land of the Amorites, from Arnon and its springs to Bashan and beyond up the heights of Gilead. And now, with the road open before him, Moses ordered the Levites to put up the sanctuary. It was no longer the waste wilderness; it was sown land, and their own land, too; and a great humming went up, like the humming of a giant hive, from the Bnai Israel in the fruitful valley of Shittim. The Levites found a green hillock for the tabernacle; they cleared it of weeds and thorns and thistles; they measured out the court under the direction of Ittamar, the younger brother of the high priest, and they fixed the place of entrance, where Moses would assemble the people.

The silver thresholds of the sanctuary, and its gold-covered pillars, were already worn by the desert years; they did not fit as perfectly as on the day when they issued from under the master hand of Bezalel. The purple hangings and curtains were somewhat faded from long use amidst the sandstorms. But the gold and silver still sparkled and shone contrastingly, and the devotion of an entire tribe had been directed at the upkeep of the sanctuary. After these many years it was still a glorious sight on the hill—like an ancient banner rich with the memory of many battles.

Around the sanctuary, as far as the eye could reach, and beyond, sprang up, like gourds in the night, the tents of Israel. Men, women, and children plashed about in the waters tumbling into the valley: a great washing of bodies and of garments, for Moses had declared a great festival, a festival of praise and thanksgiving to Jehovah.

And when the preparations were ended the Bnai Israel assembled before the entrance to the sanctuary. They shone with cleanliness; their black hair fell lustrous on their shoulders, their earlocks —the distinguishing sign of the Bnai Israel—hung down to the ends of their strong, curled beards. Black shocks of hair, everywhere; hardly a touch of gray. They had covered their nakedness with mantles and veils of glittering stuffs set with spangles and semiprecious stones; they had adorned their ears and fingers with rings. Some wore gold chains on their throats, others had set helmets of steel and copper on their heads; the princes had decked themselves in breastplates of copper and silver, the trophies of recent victories, and they carried the weapons of their slain enemies. The women, too, had put on their finery. Nose rings, earrings, bracelets, and chains, the spoils of the Amorite women, sparkled throughout the host. Later Moses was to take all this gold and silver, this copper and iron, and place it in the treasury of the sanctuary, in the keeping of the priests; but now the adornments were worn by the assembly grouped about the sanctuary. From within, from the place of sacrifice, where a multitude of priests attended the altar, rose a column of smoke. There were among the priests sons and grandsons and even great-grandsons of Aaron, blossoms of the priesthood, children. And at a given signal, as a new burst of smoke went up from the altar, the people fell prostrate, faces to the earth, hands stretched out to the sanctuary.

And Moses lay, face to earth, at the entrance to the court. His white robe covered him from head to foot, only his arms were thrust forth, stretched toward the sanctuary. His voice was heard, calling mightily:

"O God of all spirits! Thou true God, Jehovah, our God, God of our forefathers, Abraham, Isaac, and Jacob! Thou hast fulfilled Thy promise, Thou hast sent a pillar of fire before us, Thou hast burned with fire all the snakes and scorpions which were gathered in our path. The breath of Thy nostrils has destroyed them. True God of Israel, all faith to Thee and all faith to Thy word."

CHAPTER FIVE

A LITTLE caravan was winding its way through the green pasture fields of the valley in which nestled the river town of Pethor: a curious procession, such as was rarely seen in these parts. The laborers in the fields suspended the watering of the vegetable beds, straightened their backs, stared at the unusual caravan, and said to each other:

"That is the seer, Balaam, with the great ones of Moab and Midian. . . . He is going up to King Balak."

An exotic spectacle it was in the glorious sunlight, advancing slowly through the fields and vineyards of Moab's fruitful valley. An outrider or herald preceded it, his long naked legs dangling almost to the ground on either side of the donkey. His body was covered with layers of motley rags, and he waved a large staff in the air as he called out in a high-pitched singsong voice:

"Make way, make a path, for Balaam, great among the seers. He goes up from Pethor with the king's men, he goes up to Balak, the mighty king of Moab."

Immediately behind the herald rode the messengers of Moab and Midian, their camels adorned with silken reins and bridles of silver, embroidered trappings and multicolored saddles and saddlebags. Themselves wearing the king's raiment, with heavy golden chains on their necks, the messengers carried, for all to see, the gifts which the monarchs of Moab and Midian had sent to the illustrious seer: cruses of water from secret wells which dated from the far-off days of the city of Sodom—a water whose virtues renewed the virility of old men and removed the curse from barren women; roots of secret plants with irreplaceable magic powers; tablets of stone and clay with mystic inscriptions which unlocked the future like the Urim and Thummim; mantles and miters embroidered with potent designs; ringlets and locks from the heads of ancient witches.

The royal messengers were followed by swarms of cripples of

426

both sexes, deformed creatures with twisted limbs and enormous, withered heads, monstrosities with the faces of apes and domestic animals, leading on strings animal monstrosities like themselves. Behind these came, in all dignity, the two sons of Balaam, the renowned magicians established since the days of Pharaoh, Yanes and Yambres.

They were men of immense stature, with long, pointed gray beards, their heads surmounted by tall, conical helmets, their bodies swathed in blue-striped white mantles, on which the beads and spangles flashed in the sunlight. In their hands they carried the magical emblems of their great father, the seer Balaam.

One of the emblems was Balaam's magic rod, an enormous olive root one end of which was a twisted mass of roots which looked like a welter of interwoven snakes. The other emblem was Balaam's tiara, which rose into a lofty helm with double horns, between which—as on the helm of Isis—the moon was held captive by a mystic inscription in an unknown tongue.

Finally, at a distance, as though guarding his meditative solitude, came Balaam himself, riding on an ass with a face that looked human.

Balaam had not aged since the days when he sought the corruption of Israel at Sinai. He stood outside time; he was eternal. He had come into the world old, with a lame foot and a blind eye. He had been born in the house of Laban, the Aramean, a son of Laban's brother, even as Jacob was a son of Laban's sister. He had known Jacob from the days when the son of Isaac, sent by his mother Rebekah to Laban, had paused by the well and encountered Rachel when she came to water her father's sheep. It was by Balaam's advice that Laban had exchanged Leah for Rachel on the wedding night, thereby forcing on Jacob another seven years of labor. It had been Balaam's hope and dream to win Rachel for himself. Gifted even in early years with insight into the mists of the future, Balaam had known that Rachel stood under the sign of grace, and Leah under the sign of justice. It had been his wish that Jacob's children should be subject to the rod of justice, and his own illumined by the light of grace. But Rachel hated Balaam and loved Jacob; and by persuading Laban to substitute Leah for Rachel on the wedding night, Balaam lost even Leah, who had been destined for him: thus he was excluded from God's grace and equally from God's justice. He therefore delivered himself to the

427

great demon of impurity, turning from God to every kind of idolatry. Thus he became a prophet to the heathen peoples and was for ever the enemy and accuser of Jacob and his children. Jacob had sought to reconcile him, and had given him, half present and half bribe, an ass. This was the ass on which Balaam still rode. The only pious soul in all of Balaam's household, she could foresee things even before Balaam; for which reason Balaam hated her and never ceased from tormenting her. Reared in Jacob's house, obedient and God-fearing, the ass endured her ass destiny in all humility, bore with love the blows which Balaam rained on her, and swallowed her sufferings in silence.

Now, riding in a space of solitude in the midst of the procession, clad in his magic mantle with its signs and conjurations, adorned with all sorts of images—worms, midget calves, serpents, turtles—so riding, Balaam spoke to his ass as one speaks to an old friend, to an old enemy, cursing and scolding: for Balaam held the ass responsible for all the deeds of the Bnai Israel, and upon her he poured out all the bitterness of his heart:

"Well then, what hast thou to say now, pious she-ass of mine? Thinkest thou truly that God is with them and will help them? Never, I say. And I say further that what they have achieved till now they owe to the teraphim which Rachel stole from her father, and which she hid under her saddle on the ass, at the time when Jacob robbed Laban, his benefactor—robbed him, and rode away with his two daughters. With the power of those teraphim, which Rachel's children took with them into Egypt, Moses performed all his miracles. A thief, a liar, and a deceiver was thy master Jacob always; theft and deception are the sources of his children's livelihood even today. First he stole the birthright from his brother Esau for a mess of pottage; then with his mother's help he stole the blessing from his father Isaac—that blessing which belonged to Esau. And no sooner did thy master Jacob appear—naked, unshod, empty handed—at the house of Laban, than he stole the heart of Rachel with his little pieties and modest glances, not to mention the kisses and caresses which he practiced on her in secret. And even so, with his peeled and speckled wands, he stole from Laban his best sheep. Now his children follow in his thievish footsteps: by guile and violence they take the lands which God gave the Bnai Esau and the Bnai Lot: all by means of the teraphim which Rachel stole in the first place from her father. Like father, like sons—theft and treachery through and through. All, of course, in the name of Jehovah, nothing but piety. And I say that Jehovah has nothing to do with it. Jehovah is a God of justice. I have always proclaimed that. Jehovah is not a man, that He should repent of His word. Not with the power of God does Moses perform miracles, but with the power of the images. Hearest thou, pious one? With the power of stolen images, of theft and deception, in the true spirit of his forefather, Jacob."

His white locks fell over his face and covered him as with a drift of snow. His white, blue-striped mantle, with its designs and spangles and beads, hung loosely about him. He wore a white cloth over his mouth, as he was wont to do in the desert, though he did not need it now. His seeing eye glittered out from the ash-gray flesh, wrinkled and pitted like the flesh of the turtle. Ceaselessly the words tumbled from his toothless mouth; half he spoke to the ass, half to himself:

"But who would have thought it? Who could have foreseen this of the sons of Jacob? Yes, I could have sworn that they were done for at the time of the golden calf: I was sure then that Jehovah would destroy them with His thunderbolts, would grind their bones into dust, and blow it over the desert. Then when they were turned back, went wandering in the desert, year after year, forty years, and no one heard about them any more—who would have thought they would ever be seen again? And here they are, suddenly, like a powerful young ox which licks up the green grass of the land— as Balak said when he sent his messengers to me. Noble messengers, messengers of high rank. 'Go, curse me this people.' Balak has no power over them now with his sword, therefore he would use my mouth. He knows, he says, that he whom I bless is blessed, and he whom I curse is cursed. 'Go, curse me this people; perhaps I will then be able to war against them, and scatter them.' Yes, Balak knows who Balaam is. Balak is himself not without magic, wherefore he knows the extent of my powers. But what avails all this if Jehovah bids me not to curse, and I cannot turn aside to the right or left? So I have sent word to Balak that though he were to fill my house with silver and gold I could not transgress against Jehovah's command, neither in a big thing nor a small. So I sent word to him: 'Not for all thy wealth . . . Balaam is not to be bought.' And what, when all is said and done, did the mighty Balak send me with his noble messengers? A mouthful of magic water which he drew from the hidden wells of ancient Sodom, a handful of moldy old magic-making roots, a string of locks from some old beldame witches. Potions and images I have a-plenty; no need to draw on Balak's stores. A shrewd head has Balak on his shoulders; not for nothing is he descended from Lot, who begot on his own daughters. I told him in the clearest words that I would not transgress against Jehovah's command. Do I not know who Jehovah is? I have always been a follower of Jehovah. I was one of the first to make known His name among the peoples; among the peoples, I say, not among slaves. And I have always reasoned with Him: 'To what end needest Thou, for Thy chosen people, a race of slaves; endless will be Thy trouble with them, and for their sake Thou wilt be endlessly at war with countless peoples, beginning with mighty Egypt. Take me for Thy prophet, in the place of Moses, and I will bring all the peoples of the world and lay them at Thy feet: peoples with larger flocks and herds than the Bnai Israel, peoples which will multiply their altars before Thee. Bethink Thee, likewise, who is this Moses on whom Thou pourest suddenly Thy love? A runaway Egyptian slave, and a stammerer to boot. If Thou but gavest me the powers Thou hast given Moses, if I but had in my hand his rod of wonders, I would bring all mankind to the foot of Thy hill, and in every corner of earth the altars would smoke for Thee. All, all would serve Thee. And we would hymn Thee far more gloriously than do the Bnai Israel. We would outsing even the Egyptians in their worship of their gods, for who is like to Thee, Jehovah, great and mighty Father of gods and men, who merits praise like Thee? Lord, Lord, what songs we would sing to Thee, and what praises we would raise to Thee!"

So meditating, Balaam broke inwardly into a song of praise, imitating the manner of an Egyptian hymn of love to Ra:

"The whole land does Thy work.
The cattle rejoice in the pastures;
The green things blossom;
The birds quiver in their nests,
Their wings praise Thee.
The lambs gambol on their legs,
The birds—all that flutters and flies,
All that lives;
Because Thou hast arisen in the sky.

The ships go back and forth on the stream,
All the roads are open
Because Thou illuminest the day.
The fish in the river spring up before Thee,
Because Thy beams penetrate the waters,
Thou lettest the glory unfold in the body of woman,
Thou createst the son in the belly of the mother,
The nourishment in the mother-body."

From this mingled absorption in the beauty of the landscape and the music of the hymn Balaam suddenly came to in a spasm of rage, and with the staff in his hand began to belabor the ass.

"Pious and saintly she-ass! Was it thieving Jacob thy master who taught thee to break through fences into other men's fields? Not from me didst thou learn it. . . . Surely Jacob's pretty son, Joseph, rode on thee, and from him thou caughtest the habit of dreaming when thy master rides thee."

The beast swung her head round and gazed at her owner out of such gently supplicating eyes that Balaam thought she had addressed him with human words: and indeed, her look had something of speech in it.

"Wherefore starest thou? Art thou displeased with my mission? Fearest thou that I will curse Jacob's whelps? Is it for this that thou strayest from the path? All these years thou hast been with me, and still thou art faithful to Jacob and his brood. What haddest thou with him that thou lackest with me? With what magic did he bewitch thee? Back to the road, thou, whither thy master leads thee." And Balaam smote the ass, so that she turned away from the field, back into the road.

"And thus or thus I can do naught without Jehovah," Balaam went on muttering to himself. "And Jehovah is a great God, a mighty one, an El-Elyon, supreme. Ah, if He were only not so jealous of the others gods! Why should it irk Thee, Jehovah, that there are other gods? So I argue with Him endlessly. The heavens are big enough for all. Let Ra be Thy overseer of the sun, and Ashdod Thy overseer of fruitfulness, Baal of abundance, while Thou art King over all. They will be Thy heralds and messengers, all obedient to Thy will. So I plead with Him, year in, year out. Jehovah, Jehovah, why must Thou fall out with a whole world of gods, making man's life a burden with so many laws and commandments? Let them be, I say, and Thou wilt see how all the nations will acknowledge Thee and serve Thee. Not only the slave race, which Thou hast brought forth from Egypt. Much pleasure hast Thou had of them! I tell Thee, Jehovah, hadst Thou wrought with the Bnai Esau the wonders Thou hast wrought with the Bnai Jacob, they would have been more faithful to Thee. And when all is said and done, we are descended from one father, Thy friend Abraham. O Jehovah, make me Thy messenger in the place of the speechless Moses. I can curse better than he, I can bless better than he. All the magicians of Egypt come to me to be taught, and my name is known far and wide among the peoples and nations. And if Thou takest me not, Jehovah, and still preferest Moses, then see: the great Balak, himself no neophyte in magic, having both the privileges of Abraham and of the gods, and even of Ashtoreth herself, because of his descent from Lot's younger daughter—the great Balak himself has been forced to sue for my help. He knows what power resides in my conjurations, what might is in my tongue. Ah, Jehovah, if Thou wouldst but take me in the place of Moses, Thou wouldst see what I could achieve for Thee."

And out of the midst of this sweet dream of greatness he started suddenly with an agonized cry:

"My leg! My miserable, lame leg! Oh, my leg! She has utterly crushed it against the wall!"

His two sons, riding ahead, hastened back to him. "What is it, father?"

"This wretched beast, Jacob's ass—it is she. For the second time now she has strayed from the path. She almost hung me on the hedge of a vineyard. She seems not to like it that I go to Balak, to curse the children of her former master. She serves me faithfully —and she remains Jacob's!" And Balaam brought down his stick furiously on the ass's hide.

Again the beast turned her head and looked at him with her mournful human eyes, laying back her ears, while her lips trembled as though she sought to speak and could not frame the words.

"Why starest thou at me? What wouldst thou say? Perchance thou seest something that I cannot see. In Jacob's household even the dumb beasts were moved by the Spirit, were they not? Seeing things that Balaam cannot see. Wouldst thou tell me that thou art greater than Balaam? Wouldst thou make me, the mighty Balaam, less than one of Jacob's beasts?"

And Balaam poured out his anger in a rain of blows.

The ass accepted the blows with the submissiveness of her kind. Balaam's sons helped their father out of the narrow trap into which the ass had thrust him, then seated him again on the ass and led her back into the wider road.

But scarcely had the sons withdrawn, scarcely had Balaam returned to his colloquoy with himself, muttering aloud as was his wont, than the ass ran him again into a narrow trap, but this time it was between two stone hedges, so that, having advanced, she could not turn right or left. And suddenly she sank on her hindquarters, as if utterly determined not to move from the spot.

"What is it now?" screamed Balaam. "Why has thou lain down? Wilt thou of a truth not carry me to Balak, so that I may curse Jacob's children? Then I will show thee who is master, thou or I."

Therewith Balaam broke off a sharp twig from an overhanging branch and, foaming at the lips with rage, lashed his mount mercilessly.

And a third time the ass turned her head and looked at Balaam out of her human eyes. Again her lips quivered—thick, gray, leathery lips; and this time words actually issued from them, human words: not the braying of a donkey, but human speech, in the language which was Balaam's:

"What have I done to thee, that thou hast smitten me these three times?" she asked her master.

Balaam was not at all astonished to hear human speech on the lips of his ass. He had himself, more than once, transformed a man into a beast, a beast into a man. Moreover, this ass was not a plain beast, being of the household of Jacob. That she understood all that was said to her had long been known to Balaam; now it did not astonish him to learn that she could speak, too.

"What thou hast done?" he returned, angrily. "Three times hast thou mocked me. Thou hast hinted that a beast of the household of Jacob has more of the holy Spirit than I; can see things that I cannot see. If I had a sword in my hand I would slay thee."

"But am I not thine ass?" returned the beast, and her eyes were humble and pious, with the humility and piety she had learned in Jacob's house. "Am I not thine ass, upon which thou hast ridden all thy life unto this day? Was I ever wont to do thus unto thee, my master?"

And Balaam answered: "I must say, No. Thou hast behaved becomingly until now. But what is it with thee today?"

Then suddenly Balaam perceived something, and it was through his blind eye that he first perceived it. Here, in the narrow pass, between the almost touching stone hedges, an angel stood, with gigantic wings, with drawn sword, blocking the way.

"Ah! It is thou! Forgive me, forgive me, I knew it not," he said in a frightened, deprecatory voice, and bowed himself to the earth.

"Why hast thou smitten thine ass three times?" said the angel, sternly. "I went out to withstand thee, because thy way is against me. Thine ass saw me, and turned away from me three times. Had she not turned away from me I would surely have slain thee, and left her alive."

"I have sinned, I have sinned, my dear lord; I knew not that thou stoodest in the way. And now, if the way I go please thee not, I will return at once," pleaded Balaam, bowing low again.

"No. Go with these men, but speak only the word which I shall speak with thee."

"Assuredly, my lord, assuredly. How otherwise?"

The angel vanished. Balaam crawled back upon the ass, bestowing on her a reluctant caress. She snorted contentedly through her wide nostrils and willingly dropped the dispute, in the spirit of peace which she had learned in the house of her former master. With asslike patience she backed away from the narrow place, turned with her burden to the straight road, and thenceforth carried him without further incident.

The reception which Balak had prepared for Balaam was by no means as rich and imposing as Balaam had been led to expect. In truth, Balak was furious with Balaam for having waited to be asked several times. Balak came forth alone to meet him, without his entourage—a solitary figure at the foot of the hill outside the city. Balak, whose gifts as a minor magician had descended to him from the destroyed children of Sodom, had put on, above his royal robes, the high conical helm which was the emblem of the craft of magicians, so that he looked as tall as one of the giant sons of Anak.

There was more than a touch of professional jealousy between these two magicians. It was rumored that Balak had access to the secrets of the ancient magicians of Sodom and that by means of magic waters he could infect men with certain types of sin. Balaam was envious of the Sodomic wells, just as Balak envied Balaam his blind eye, which was able to peer into the future. At this moment, however, they made partnership in their common hatred of Moses and the Bnai Israel; and they did their best—not a successful best—to conceal their mutual hatred.

After the proper formal greetings, in which each one rehearsed the long list of his ancestors, the importance of his name, and the evidences of his magical powers, and after the proper reverences and obeisances, which were accompanied by exclamations of joy and appreciation, they opened the conversations, which at once revealed the depth of their loathing and contempt for each other.

"Did I not send for thee? Why didst thou not come to me? Can I not receive thee becomingly, and do thee honor?" asked Balak.

"But see, have I not come to thee? But this thou shalt know: I can but speak the word which God will put in my mouth," answered Balaam, and turned his blind eye toward Balak.

"Assuredly so," said Balak. "Who is against God? Jehovah is the God of our ancestors, too, is he not? Did not our tribal father, Lot, worship him even as Abraham did? And was he not hospitable to all wayfarers, even as Abraham was? Dost thou remember what the sons of Sodom would have done to him when he brought home from the market place the angels whom he took for ordinary travelers? His own daughters he would have delivered up to the sons of Sodom rather than that evil should be done to those whom he sheltered."

"Oh, assuredly Jehovah remembers, and He counts it to thee for a virtue, for Jehovah loves those that are hospitable. But forget not thy ancestry, Balak—there are things that Jehovah loves not, and among them is, that daughters shall make their father drunk in order that he may beget on them."

"My rights and privileges are double in number, therefore my strength is without bounds. I am protected by Jehovah and guarded by Ashdod and Baal. In me are united the father and the daughter. I am the kid seethed in the mother's milk, mixture of father and daughter."

"And for all that thou fearest the Bnai Israel and hast sent for Balaam, saying: 'Come and curse me Israel.' But I have seen no sin in Israel. Not thy land have they taken, but that which thine enemy held. Thou refused to let them pass through thy land and threatened them with thy mighty sword. For the passage across thy

435

barren mountains thy tribes demanded their life's blood. They respected thy borders, and did not trespass upon them, even as Jehovah commanded them. What hast thou against them?"

"Didst thou come here to curse Israel or to bless him?"

"Is it thy desire that I shall curse them, that I shall crush them beneath the burden of my utterances? Show me their weakness. Show me that in them whereon I can hang my imprecations. Awaken mine anger, provoke my enmity, so that I may overcome in myself their rights. What evil have they done to thee, son of Lot, that I may demand restitution from them?"

"Come, and I will show thee where they have pitched their tents. They have come up like the locust from the desert, and they have settled in all the valley, from the springs of Arnon to the banks of the Jordan. They have come like a young ox, which licks up the green of the land. Countless are their flocks and herds, they have occupied all the wells, saying, 'Our fathers dug these wells, with their scepters they dug them.' Tomorrow they will spill over into our valleys, climb our mountains, like a fire spread by the wind. They will slaughter our young men like sheep, and our daughters will become their booty, even like our cattle. And thou askest me what they have done to me. I am weak before them. Is not that reason enough to fear them? Their bodies throw off the arrows sent against them, as if their flesh were bronze; the edge of the sword is turned when it touches them. Jehovah has wrapped them in a cloud. What man can war against them? The gods tremble in our temples, our priests flee and hide themselves in the clefts of the hills, for the fear of the God of Israel. Iron and bronze are unavailing against them, but it is not so with the power of thy hatred and the fire of thy curse. Recall, therefore, their sins of the past; pierce the future with thine eye, and conjure up out of it their failings and deficiencies. Call forth the shadows which sleep upon their path, and wrap them in darkness. Strip them of their privileges, make them naked in the eye of their God. Call the gods to thy help; exert the magic of thy word, for thou hast the power, seer."

"From the sons of Sodom thou hast inherited the scent for sin. Now find me the place whence I can attack their shadowy side, Balak."

Balak looked north, south, east, and west, to every corner of the earth. His nostrils quivered, he breathed heavily, his body trembled.

Then suddenly he became motionless and stood stock-still, his eyes closed, his spirit wrapped in ecstasy. From this condition he emerged as abruptly as he had fallen into it, and pointed to one of the heights:

"Go up upon that hill, where stands an altar of Baal; thence wilt thou see them as thou shouldst. Thou wilt see not all the people, but a portion of them. Their privileges will be concealed; Baal will enfold them in sin."

"Erect for me seven altars, and prepare for me seven oxen and seven rams. And bring me thither with the dawn tomorrow. It may be that God will appear to me and will open my mouth, which He has closed even as He opened that of my ass; and it may be that He will return to me the power of my word."

CHAPTER SIX

THEY stood on the hill overlooking the springs of the Arnon valley, by the ancient and neglected altar of the god Baal. There was an image of Baal, too: the likeness of a warrior holding a bundle of lightning in his clenched fist, ready to hurl it in defiance against an enemy. Baal, the god of possessions, who sent rain when he was obeyed, and the thunderbolt when he was disobeyed, who made fruitful the belly of beast and woman, or closed the womb according to his will—Baal stood here forlorn, forgotten, and shamed. But now Balaam and Balak and the lords of Moab and Midian were here, the latter in their conical copper helms, in multicolored robes, with golden chains on their throats, plates of bronze on their shoulders, their staves of office in their hands: they were gathered about the seven new altars which Balak had hastily erected at the bidding of Balaam. The smoke went up from the oxen and rams, the incense from the fire pans.

And Balaam, in the tiara of the high priest, in his embroidered mantle, held his hands above his head, and sent his voice toward heaven:

"Seven altars have we raised to thee, Jehovah, and on each of the altars smokes Thy sacrifice. Give us Thy sign."

But no sign came from heaven.

"Stand by thy burnt offering, Balak, I will mount still further. Perhaps Jehovah will encounter me there; if it be so, I will return and tell thee what He has shown me."

Balaam withdrew in his priestly robe and made his way toward the summit. When he had put a distance between himself and the lords of Moab he threw himself to the ground, lifted his trembling hands to heaven, and cried:

"Jehovah, Jehovah! Thou that art not a respecter of persons, and before Whom all are equal, I, the prophet of the gentiles, as Moses is the prophet of Israel, lie before Thee. Thou canst not lift out a single people and make it Thy chosen one. Thou art a God

438

of justice. All the peoples are Thy children. See, seven altars have I prepared for Thee: one against the merit of Adam, the second against the merit of Cain, the third against the merit of Noah, the fourth against the merit of Abraham, the fifth against the merit of Isaac, the sixth against the merit of Jacob, the seventh against the merit of Moses. And now all the gentiles are made equal with Israel. They have their merits and rights, even like Israel. Come, reveal Thyself to me, and give me Thy word to the nations of the world."

A spirit came over Balaam, and a change came over his body. It was as though he were growing, becoming taller; as though he were crawling out from beneath his age like a turtle crawling out from under its carapace; his ashen-gray leathery face discarded its dusty, embittered mask of generations, and took on youth. The folds vanished, and the flesh was irradiated. Even the white decay which covered his dead eye melted; and it was as if the eye had become a seeing eye, a living eye, with more sight and life than the other. The curse was lifted from his stooping and uneven shoulders; they were raised, thrown back, made even. And Balaam stood in the sun, a chosen seer of the Lord.

The voice in his heart said:

"Return, and speak to Balak the words which I will put in thy mouth!"

When Balaam drew near to Balak and the lords of Moab and Midian who awaited him in trembling by the seven altars, they did not recognize him; a blind old man had left them, a mighty seer returned to them, and they were filled with dread by the glory which rested on him. For Balaam was in a trance of the spirit, and he came toward them like a man possessed, his face lifted to the sky, his eyes wide open against its dazzling light, and he spoke as though he were reading from blazing tablets suspended above him. His face was pale, and the spirit spoke from his mouth:

> "From Aram Balak led me forth,
> From the eastern borders, the king of Moab.
> Come, curse me Jacob,
> And defy me Israel.
> How shall I curse
> Whom God has not cursed?
> How shall I defy

439

Whom God has not defied?
From the top of the rocks I see him,
And from the hills I behold him:
Behold, a people that dwells alone,
And shall not be reckoned among the nations.
Who can count the dust of Jacob
And reckon the seed of Israel?
Let me die the death of the righteous,
And let my last end be like his."

Balak and the lords of Moab and Midian turned white with fear and anger. They saw clearly that before them stood a man possessed by a spirit which compelled him to say what he would not. They saw the convulsions which accompanied the utterances, and they exerted themselves to awaken him from his trance. They laid hands on him, they shook him, shouting:

"Balaam, Balaam, what doest thou? We have brought thee here to curse our enemies, and thou blessest them!"

Slowly Balaam came to. The ecstasy was replaced by shame, and he said:

"What can I do? That which the spirit of God puts in my mouth, that I must speak."

Balak looked about the landscape. Below him was the encampment of the Bnai Israel, stretching from Arnon toward the bank of the Jordan. From the hill on which he stood he could see only a part of the flocks which the Bnai Reuben were watering at the springs, the greater part of the flocks and the people, even like the sanctuary in its midst, were hidden from him. He sniffed the air in all directions, he sent out a feeler of sin: in peoples, as in men, he could smell out the shadow side, the side inclined to evil and corruption—this was his inheritance from the sons of Sodom, this, and the gift of bringing out the inclination to evil. He was seeking out a place, a vantage point, from which Balaam could see the Bnai Israel in a light—or shadow—which would call forth in him his hatred and jealousy. Northward, closer to the main body of the Bnai Israel, rose the steep slopes of Pisgah. In the midst of the radiance which the morning sun threw on the tumbling hills, Balak perceived a single deep shadow, toward Pisgah. His prophetic intuition told him that there, on Pisgah, some calamity awaited Israel. He could not discern the nature of the calamity, but he knew that from the summit of Pisgah he would be able to see the main body of Israel, the gold-covered pillars of the sanctuary, and even Moses in his white robe. And the sight of Moses, he knew, would send such a shaft of hatred through Balaam that he would be able to master the contrary spirit, and recover the strength with which to curse Israel.

"Come with me, I pray thee, to another place, whence thou wilt see more of the people, but still only a part of it; and curse it for me from thence."

And Balak and the lords of Moab and of Median conducted Balaam up the slope of Pisgah, by the field of Zophim. There they hastily put up seven new altars of stone, and offered on them the appropriate sacrifices.

Then Balak said to Balaam:

"I see a shadow which has fallen on the tents of Israel. Pierce by the power of thy magic the concealed places of the future of Israel, penetrate their destiny, call forth their sins of the old time and their sins of the time to come, and throw them, like serpents, into the midst of the Bnai Israel and their privileges. Let those serpents eat away the roots which bind the Bnai Israel to their forefathers. Throw thyself against Moses with all thy powers. Thou art stronger than Moses. Thou art the prophet of many peoples. And Jehovah will repent Him of what he has done, and he will utterly reject the Bnai Israel as He often intended."

The mention of Moses stung Balaam to renewed hatred. He mounted the slope of Pisgah and turned his blind eye on the valley. But a mist rose between his blind eye and the encampment—and Balaam was unable to speak.

In vain did he exert himself to break through the mist, so that he might perceive the weaknesses of his enemies. And when at last he succeeded in calling forth the spirit of Jehovah, he was at once taken captive and all that he could utter before Balak and the lords was what Jehovah put in his mouth:

> "Arise, Balak, and hear,
> Hearken to me, thou son of Zippor.
> God is not a man, that He should lie,
> Nor a son of man, that He should repent.
> What He has said, that He will do.
> Behold, I have been filled with benedictions,

And I cannot withhold from blessing.
There is no iniquity seen in Jacob,
No perverseness in Israel.
The Lord is with him,
The graciousness of the king shines over him.
God brought them forth out of Egypt,
He is to him as the horn of the unicorn.
There is no enchantment against Jacob,
There is no divination against Israel.
Of Jacob and Israel it is said:
What hath God wrought!
The people shall rise up like a lioness,
Shall lift himself up like a young lion.
He shall not lie down till he has eaten of the prey,
And drunk the blood of the slain."

And Balak screamed in his anger: "Why dost thou bless them? Neither bless them nor curse them!"

"What shall I do if the Hand is placed on my mouth? Have I not told thee that only as God bids me can I speak?"

"Come, I will lead thee to still another place, the summit of Peor. My spirit tells me that Israel will be tempted and will fall at Baal Peor. There, perchance, thou wilt find the chink of weakness, and Jehovah will not be displeased, and thou wilt curse me this people from thence."

So Balak led Balaam to the summit of Mount Peor. Thence one could see not only the place of the sanctuary and the Jordan, but the road leading back from the valley into the desert. The whole encampment of Israel lay stretched out beneath them; and here it was as if God had again opened Balaam's blind eye.

For he beheld the tribes of Israel as they were poured out about the sanctuary; poured out in strict order, and filling the land as far as sight could reach. Countless were the Bnai Israel, and in their midst flickered the gold-covered pillars of the sanctuary, its red outer covering, and the blue curtains of its entrance. Like the four streams which take their source in the garden of Eden, even so were the four divisions of the host of Israel poured out about the sun-drenched sanctuary.

Balaam felt and saw the tumult of motion, the coming and going about the place of meeting, where the tent of Moses stood. He saw

Moses, in his white raiment, a giant, surrounded by the princes of the tribes. But he saw more, for God permitted him to penetrate to the mystery of the privileges of Israel. He looked back upon the desert, and he saw the long road which Israel had traversed from Sinai. Sinai he saw, too, glittering in the distance. And it seemed to him that he saw Moses on the mountain, holding aloft the tables of the ten commandments, black flame inscribed on white flame. And it was not a noise of drunken rioting round the golden calf that came up from the valley; he heard only the cry, "We will do and we will obey," echoing up and carried by the wind. He saw the Dead of the Wilderness, he saw their bones rolled about in the sand waves of the desert; and from the dead bones, too, came the cry: "We will do and we will obey." In that same instant there emerged upon the vision of his spirit the figure of Father Abraham. Taller than the sons of men, of the stature of the giants, the mighty ancient strode forward leading a boy by the hand. The ass, laden with a bundle of firewood, trotted by his side. He was marching at the head of the Dead of the Wilderness: for the bones had risen into life as he passed, and bone clove to bone, and the dead came out of their rolling graves to follow the giant who led the young boy, to follow Abraham as he led his son to the sacrifice. These were the Dead of the Wilderness; they and the living tribes now swarming about the sanctuary were the issue of Isaac. The Dead of the Wilderness had been with Isaac at the sacrifice, and after Isaac they were themselves the sacrifice, one long sacrifice, which was expressed in the words: "We will do and we will obey."

No: he no longer envied Moses. It was another hunger that consumed him: to be one of them—one of the Dead of the Wilderness, one of the resurrected which moved about invisibly in the midst of the living encampment.

The Spirit suddenly unveiled Itself to Balaam, and for a brief interval he was cleansed of all impurities; the idolatries of the countless years were washed out of him, his blind eye was cleansed, so that it could penetrate to the inmost mysteries of Israel. Balaam saw in the instant the price which men paid for redemption, and the reason why they paid it. He saw the merits which Israel had accumulated in the past, and the destiny which awaited him. Past, present, and future were one, embracing the entire vista of the days of Israel from beginning to end.

Balaam stationed himself opposite Balak and the lords of Moab, and in the commanding voice of a prophet he told of the generations to come. A prophet was Balaam in that instant, a prophet of Israel with a mission to the nations:

> "Thus speaks Balaam, the son of Beor,
> The words of the man whose eye is open:
> Thus speaks he who has heard God's word,
> Who sees the vision of the Almighty,
> Falling into a trance but having his eyes open:
> How goodly are thy tents, O Jacob,
> Thy tabernacles, O Israel.
> Like the date palms are they spread forth,
> Like gardens by the river,
> Like the olive trees which God has planted
> Like cedars by the waters."

Then Balak in his rage clapped his hands together and cried: "I called thee to curse mine enemies and thou hast blessed them three times. I would have done thee honor without end, but God Himself has kept thee back from honor."

The transformation and visitation in Balaam did not last more than an instant. The tide of uncleanliness, the spirit of idolatry and magic washed back over him, and there was a momentary struggle between two forces. Foam appeared on his lips, his body was shaken by convulsions. He fought to release himself from the compulsion of God, which had made him utter words that he had not willed of himself; and emerging at last, he said to Balak in a weeping voice:

"Did I not tell thy messengers that though Balak were to give me his house filled with silver and gold I cannot speak save as God bids me? I must see that which He forces me to see, hear the voices which He bids speak, and utter the words he puts into my mouth."

Suddenly he ceased speaking, and became petrified, like an ancient, withered tree in the wilderness. His face was rigid, a mask of death. Only his eyes began to start from their deep sockets, so that it seemed that they would fall out. The sick eye and the good eye alike started forth, and were fixed on the distance, like the eyes of a wanderer who perceives a mirage.

His voice was lifted again, but in a twittering rather than a speaking:

"I see! I see!"

444

"What seest thou?" cried Balak and the lords, terrified.

"I see, I see"—and the twittering changed to a singing.

"Tell us what thou seest."

> "I see him, but not as now,
> I behold him, but not from near.
> A star arises in Jacob,
> And a scepter will be lifted up from Israel."

"Stop up his mouth! Let me not hear! Stop up his mouth and take him home," screamed Balak at the two sons of Balaam.

CHAPTER SEVEN

WHEN Balaam came out of the trance in which God's spirit had held him captive, he fell once more under the spell of uncleanness and sorcery. He found himself on his ass, riding homeward. The ass trotted cheerfully, as though she were prepared at any moment to open her jaws again in human speech, and to sing the praises of God in her master's name, because He had not let him yield to the temptation of Balak. Balaam himself, however, felt far otherwise. He was still muttering to himself: "Though Balak were to give me his house filled with gold and silver . . ." but his heart was not in the words. He looked about him. He was on the way home, riding his ass—and he was utterly alone. Balak had sent him forth without a single companion; gone were the honorable messengers and attendants, gone was the horde of monstrosities, gone was all the pomp with which Balak had surrounded the prophet of the gentiles when he had sent for him. Gone, too, was the tiara of the high priesthood, his mantle with its magic embroidery: he had been robbed even of the insignia of his rank. His two sons, the carriers of the high vessels of his craft, were gone, too. What was this? Were they ashamed of him? Whether or not—they had remained with Balak. No doubt they would crown him chief seer of the gentiles, betray to him all the signs and secrets, all the devices and deceptions, which they had learned from their father, who in his day had learned them from the magicians of Egypt: and he, Balaam, was now left stripped, a servant of Jacob's, a humble follower, a hewer of wood and drawer of water.

Bitter remorse took hold of him. He saw in a new light that which he had done in the trances. The ancient, long-nurtured curse which he had guarded for generations in his embittered heart had been turned into a glowing benediction; it had gone forth from him, transformed, and he himself was left without content, like a serpent emptied of its poison. The momentary visitation of the high spirit was over; departing, it had not even been followed by

446

the return of his dark powers. He no longer had the power to forge invisible chains, conjure up curses, command demons, control destinies. His blind-seeing eye no longer saw: blackness lay before it, eternal shadow. He had been uprooted from the nether world, where his force had lain; he had been lifted up to the highest heaven of vision. Now, cast forth, belonging neither to the heights nor the depths, he floated between the two, at the mercy of every wind.

He began to howl like a wounded animal: "Thou hast prevailed against me once more, Jacob! Again hast thou deceived me! Thou hast done with me as with thy brother, thou hast stolen away my birthright for a mess of pottage. Thou didst place a bridle on my mouth, thou hast compelled me to deliver up to thee the benedictions which I had reserved for thine enemies, for Moab and Midian and Amalek, and thou hast made me curse my friends. I have made thee inherit Edom, and thou hast broken the borders of Moab, and thou art become a ruler of nations. Thou didst wrestle with me, as once with the angel of God, and thou hast prevailed. Thou hast prevailed both against God and against the evil one. Thou hast swindled out of me the sheep of my spirit, as thou didst swindle away the best sheep from Laban. And now I am like a fig from which the honey has been sucked away. There is no portion for me in Israel and thou hast robbed me of my portion in the nether world."

And even as he wailed and lamented, he felt a sharp stab in his blind eye, and a shiver ran through his body. Something had darted into the field of his memory. He remembered that at a certain moment, when he had'looked down from the heights upon the encampment, he had seen a shadow resting on Israel, a thick, heavy shadow, a shadow laden with ashes and brimstone. He cried out suddenly: "I see now, I understand!" His body shook. "I perceive it now. I could see no sin in Israel. Therefore my powers were taken from me. Jacob must sin! Jacob must sin!"

He tugged at the reins, to make the ass turn round and take the road back to Moab. But the ass would not budge. She turned only her head, fixing her large eyes on him.

"Go whither I command thee," he shouted. "No angel of God will stand in the way now. I am free from the spirit of Jacob. With the power of the spirit of Esau, and by the authority of the unclean spirit, I bid thee obey me, without resistance or reluctance."

447

He made a magic sign over the ass, and the animal turned meekly, as he had commanded.

In the city of Moab, in the great house of the king, Balaam found Balak taking counsel against Israel with the lords of Moab and Midian. A horde of magicians had assembled, too, headed by the two sons of Balaam. In the full regalia of their craft these were conjuring up spirits and phrases for the overcoming of Israel.

When the assembled beheld Balaam standing before them, full of his ancient power even though stripped of all his magic instruments, they rose and made a path for him. And Balaam advanced between the lords of Moab and Midian, and turned his blind eye on Balak, the suppurating lids parted, and the red, wounded pupil was revealed, and Balaam spoke:

> "Thus says Balaam, the son of Beor,
> Thus speaks he of the open eye.
> Mine eye has opened and I have seen:
> Israel's end is destruction.
> The thundercloud of storm and anger
> Hangs over his head.
> Jehovah, laden with fire and brimstone,
> Advances now to destroy this people,
> The people which He brought forth from Egypt."

The lords of Moab and Midian were thrown into ecstasy; with violent gestures of praise and wonderment they called out to Balaam: "How is this?"

And he answered:

> "I saw no transgression in Israel,
> Therefore my powers left me,
> For Esau grows strong against Jacob
> Only when Jacob is weakly with God.
> Therefore in vain did I seek and spy,
> Till I saw the shadow on the tents of Israel.
> From the summit of Peor
> I saw the shadow fall,
> Making dark the heaven over Israel.
> I have found the opening, I have seen the finger,
> I have discovered the place
> Whereon to hang my curses.
> Israel must sin, Israel shall sin."

"How? Who shall persuade him to the wickedness?" asked Balak.

And Balaam answered:

> "Thou, O son of Zippor!
> For sin stood at thy cradle,
> Thou didst suck it in with thy mother's milk,
> Of father and daughter art thou born.
> The kid seethed in its mother's milk
> Shall be the poison for Israel."

"What shall I do? What shall I say?" asked Balak.

"Thou art the guardian of the sins. The wells of Sodom are in thy keeping. Come, lead me to them," said Balaam.

"At the opening of the first well lies the ancient serpent, the mother of sin. None may approach without serving her, or making obeisance to her."

"Lead me to her."

And Balak, accompanied by his lords, led Balaam to the wells of Sodom.

The wells and springs from which flowed the sins of Sodom were in a cavern to which the path led through dark ruins scattered among the lava hills. The lords of Moab and of Midian carried torches to illumine the way, and Balaam, clad once more in his tiara and mantle, followed the king. In one hand Balaam held his rod, in the other the carcass of a bird which had lived on carcasses. When they drew close to the cavern they were greeted by an evil stench, and a smoke of hidden brimstone fires wrapped them about. When the torchbearers stood at the entrance of the cavern, Balaam saw with his blind eye a gigantic serpent, wrapped in linens like a mummy, and only the head protruding, stretched across the threshold. Before the serpent was a stone altar, and on it burned the brimstone which sent out the coils of smoke and the vile stench.

"This is the ancient serpent, the mother of sin, to whom every living man must make obeisance before he can reach the wells of sin," said Balak.

Balaam knelt before the altar, buried his face in the lava ashes, placed the carcass of the bird of prey among the burning coals, and lifted up his voice in prayer:

> "Thou mother of all living things!
> Thou that art the beginning of creation!

Thou livest in the heart of man from his youth.
Open before me the springs of sin,
So that I may make a people to sin,
A people which would destroy sin."

Then Balak led Balaam into the inner chambers of the cavern, and they went on wrapped in fumes. They came to an opening in the earth from which steam poured as from a boiling well.

"This is the well of cruelty, from which the people of Sodom drank of old. Look down, and see what lies at the bottom."

Balaam looked down with his blind eye made seeing, and far below he saw a glimmer of waters. He saw a writhing of white snakes; and he saw all the abominations which the sons of Sodom had practiced.

"Whosoever drinks of this water is beset by the desire for cruelty. His nature is changed, and he longs to see man and beast in convulsions of pain."

And as he directed his gaze downward, Balaam saw more and more clearly. He distinguished faces of young people and old, of men and women and children. He saw the lips forming words which expressed the anguish of their hearts, he saw lips contorted in grimaces of pain and of hysterical laughter. But the faces of the children expressed only terror.

"These are the sacrifices and victims of the Bnai Sodom, reflected in the waters. On these the Bnai Sodom satisfied their lust for the sight of suffering."

"Lead me to the well of whoredom," cried Balaam, turning away his blind eye. Even for him this spectacle was too much.

At the bottom of the well of whoredom Balaam saw with his blind eye the corruptions of whoredom in all the forms, natural and unnatural, which the fantasy of man could conjure up, the whoredom of man with man, of man with beast, of incest, and of man with himself.

"Whosoever drinks of this well, his blood is transformed into blazing seedstuff; he is filled with lusts which he can never still."

"These are the burning waters which I seek. Come hither, lords of Moab, and you, chief men of Midian, stand about me and I will tell you what to do to make Israel sin, as I have learned it from offering on the altar of the ancient serpent, the mother of sin."

When the lords of Moab and Midian had ranged themselves

about the well of whoredom, Balaam began to chant in a choked voice:

"Thus speaks Balaam, the son of Beor,
He of the open eye:
Assemble your daughters,
The young ones, the comely ones,
Princesses for their princes,
Daughters of your people for their people.
Israel is young, like a leaping steer,
Like the unharnessed donkey braying for the ass.
Still uncircumcised he still lacks
The virtue of Abraham.
Put your daughters into booths, seat them there.
Booths of whoredom? Never!
Booths of provender and of stuffs,
Booths with the choicest merchandise.
Israel is rich
With the booty of the Amorites,
With the spoils of the cities and Bashan.
He is desirous of the linens of Bethshaan,
For sheets of leather and copper,
For sandals to guard his feet from the stones,
For morsels to eat, for rare drinks:
Insatiable are the desires of Israel.
But beware, I say, of making him drunk with wine,
Lest he find therein an excuse,
Lest he say afterward that he knew not his right hand
    from his left,
Like Lot, the father of your people, in the unforget-
    table night.
Only of the waters of this well,
Which turn the blood of man into blazing seed,
Only of the waters of this well
Let them be given to drink.
And let this warning be given to your daughters,
Let them remember and not forget:
Not for silver or gold shall they sell themselves,
Not for silver or gold shall they lie down on the couch,
But Israel shall be made to bend the knee

451

Before the Baal of Peor.
A handful of incense shall the son of Israel
Cast upon the altar of Baal-Peor.
Remember, not whoredom alone do I desire of Israel,
For God will forgive him whoredom:
I desire that Israel shall cleave to Baal-Peor.
And now, my brothers, be silent,
I have said nothing, I have done nothing,
But the word of God I have obeyed,
And I have returned to my own place."

"Balaam, son of Beor, thou meritest that Balak shall fill thee a house with silver and gold for thy counsel," cried the lords of Moab and Midian. And Balaam answered:

"I have not done this thing for a reward,
For we are one in this cause.
But if it shall be pleasing in your eyes,
The doors of my dwelling are ever open."

Outside the cavern, Balaam wrapped himself in his blue-striped mantle, and with the help of his two sons mounted the ass. "Why liftest thou thy pious face to me?" he asked. "Why starest thou at me with thy saint's eyes?" And he answered himself as he rode on:

"I have said nothing, I have done nothing
Against Jehovah, the great God.
But I have fulfilled my mission,
And I return to my own place."

CHAPTER EIGHT

AT the foot of the slope along which extended the city of Moab, in the Arnon valley which flowed into the Jordan valley of Shittim, where the Israelite encampment lay, there sprang up suddenly a gay bazaar of colored booths and tents. On the tables and trestles an infinite variety of merchandise attracted the eye with its dazzling brightness. There were saddles of motley wool, riding seats and blankets in crimson and violet, mantles and veils, robes and coverings, tunics and shirts of linen, lengths of cloth with blue and purple stripes—a vast, iridescent rainbow; and amid the stuffs and garments shimmered artificial stones set in bracelets, nose rings, and armbands.

From the midst of the bazaar the wind carried a savory odor of roast sheep's meat sharply spiced with cloves, cinnamon, bay, and ginger, so that the nostrils of a passerby distended of themselves, and the spittle dripped from his mouth.

There came forth from the camp of the Bnai Israel two young men, who directed their steps toward the little Mount of Peor. Partly they had come out to stroll in the radiance of the day, partly in the hope of finding the tracks of a hart or hare which had left the shady groves of the hill to seek the springs of Arnon, partly, also, to find the lair of a hyena which frightened the flocks nightly; and they were in gay spirits, as became their youth. Each of them wore at his girdle a dagger with a copper haft set with artificial jewels; their ears were ornamented with rings, in which flickered blue stones: these were booty taken from the Amorites. War plunder too were the bracelets on their arms, and the large-ringed chains about their necks, hammered of pure silver, taken from the bodies of giants of Bashan when they had stormed the hills. Their thick black hair fell forward over their shoulders in two heavy braids, into which were woven spangles of gold and silver, and which, reaching past the short, round beards, danced on their bosoms. Their bodies were naked save for the girdles which barely

453

covered their sex; their bellies, as of shining bronze, and their powerful thighs, as of chipped and polished granite, were exposed to the sun. They were altogether unembarrassed in their nakedness; for them the weave of sunlight on their muscles was covering enough. They held hands as they walked gaily, and their flashing eyes, keen as sword blades, darted from side to side as they looked for the track of a hart or the spoor of a hyena.

So walking, they fell into conversation. And what should the talk be between two young warriors who had just returned from victorious battles but of heroic deeds, and of the maidens which they had taken captive, the maidens they had brought back into the camp and which Moses had forbidden them to keep? Of these they talked, and of the latest gossip in the camp.

"It is more than four weeks since we overcame the Amorites and the king of Bashan. We took Yaazer and all the cities about it. We cleared the whole of this side of the Jordan, and now it has been settled by the Bnai Reuben and the Bnai Gad: but still Moses does not lead us across the Jordan, so that we may conquer our cities. Reuben, Gad, and half the tribe of Manassah—they have been given their heritage; they are rebuilding the ravaged cities, and settling there with wives and children. But us Moses keeps bound to the wilderness. Why does he not lead us across the Jordan?"

"They say, Jonadab, that he wants to have us circumcised first, before he leads us into our land."

"But I say that Moses will not bring us into the covenant of Abraham before we have taken Jericho. He is afraid that if we are circumcised before, the enemy will hear of it and will attack us when we are weak and unable to defend ourselves. But there's another reason, Osnath, and I'll tell it to thee. Moses knows that he will die on this side of the Jordan—for God has told him that he must be one with the Dead of the Wilderness. And before he dies he wants to leave us his last testament, which consists of nothing more than a great assortment of laws, statutes, and commandments. So he sits there in his tent and thinks up new ordinances and rules and laws. And until the whole list is ready we shall be kept here, on this side of the Jordan."

"Now hear what I have to say, Jonadab, and this I heard from none other than our own captain, Zimri, and surely he is right: 'Why can we not be like the other nations, like Moab and Edom? Are they not of the seed of Abraham? Why may we not intermarry

454

with the Bnai Moab and the Bnai Edom?' Dost thou remember the beautiful Amorite maiden whom I brought home from the war? An elder came into my tent and bade me send her home! The maiden herself wept bitterly. She did not want to leave the tent. I persuaded even my wife, Zipporah, to have the maiden with us. But it availed me nothing. She could not remain with us even as handmaid. We must have nothing to do with them. Zimri is right. Look at Moses—he was permitted to take to wife a woman of Midian, but for us it is forbidden."

"I, too, have heard our Zimri speak on these matters; and he says it is better for us to live at peace with our neighbors than to be forever at war with them. It would be well for us to take their daughters to wife, and to give them ours."

"But they have poisoned the ear of Moses against Zimri, and from that time forth Moses keeps him at a distance."

"True. Moses fears him. He knows that Zimri is a greater warrior than Joshua. The deeds of valor he performed in Bashan! Osnath—look, look! Seest thou that sand hillock? That must be the lair of our hyena. The howling comes at night from that quarter. Do thou go round by the right, and I will take the left, and we shall trap it."

But the instant they turned from one another, to separate, they halted, and stood stock-still. With a single gesture, they lifted their hands and pointed at the path which came round the hill into their valley.

The sharp odor of roast sheep's meat had been carried suddenly from that direction to their nostrils, so that they swung round simultaneously; and from this point they were able to perceive, beyond the hillock, the booths and tents of the bazaar and the multi-colored merchandise on display. They forgot the hyena and without a word hastened toward the gay panorama.

As they drew close to the first booth the odor of the roasting meat became overpoweringly provocative; but before they reached the booth an elderly, gray-haired, motherly woman, with a huge nose ring dangling before her veiled face, came toward them.

"Peace be unto you," she said in a sweet, friendly voice. "Peace unto you, children of Jacob, grandchildren of Abraham. Our eyes have longed for the sight of you ever since we heard how the God of our fathers drew you forth from bondage. Now that you have come unto our country, you are the dearest of guests. For we are close kin, you and we. One forefather we had, Terah, and of one family we are, the family of Abraham. Choose, then, what pleases you best of all the things you see, and be gracious to us, and accept it as a gift from us."

The young men stood still in a mixture of embarrassment and astonishment at this warm welcome. No suspicious thought crossed their minds. This was not a young woman who addressed them; the voice was motherly, the eyes that looked out from above the veil were motherly too. In hands no longer young, but webbed with thin blue veins, she held out to them two white mantle veils striped with purple.

"Your garments have rotted away on you during the long wandering in the desert. Jewels and adornments you surely do not lack, but you have no raiment for the body. Let these mantles, woven in Bethshaan of the finest linen, and edged with purest purple, cover your princely nakedness. A present from an aunt to her nephews," said the woman, and without waiting for their consent threw the two mantles over the shoulders of the young men.

One of them asked: "How many pieces of silver? Or perhaps a nose ring, or a bracelet?"

"What is gold or silver between thee and me? Did ye not destroy our enemy, the Amorite?"

"Moses commanded us, in the name of Jehovah, to do no evil unto you, the people of Moab, nor to rob you, and not even accept a gift, but to pay for everything with money."

"God be witness that you have borne yourselves toward us like the kinsmen you are. Come, children of a brother tribe, you shall break bread with us, and taste of the best that we can prepare. Likewise we have better goods than these, rarer merchandise, within the booth. Come nearer, dear kinsmen, we have waited for you. Yaldah! Sharfiah! Come out, and see what visitors we have. Our blood brothers, those that destroyed our enemy, the Amorite, who took vengeance for our shame. Receive them with singing and with playing on instruments, as they have merited."

The elderly, motherly woman pulled aside a curtain, and waved the two young heroes into the interior of the booth.

Yaldah was, in fact, but a child, a girl of ten or twelve, almost Eve-naked, with two little dovelike breasts which rose modestly rounded from her young body, on which she wore nothing more than a narrow girdle barely covering her sex. With her hair tumbling over her shoulders in thin rings, she sat on a carpet, a harp in her lap, and played before an image of a Baal in the likeness of a warrior with an uplifted fistful of thunderbolts; and as she played she sang, softly and harmoniously, the words of a hymn.

As against her, Sharfiah was—as her name indicated—a burst of fire. Her skin was tawny, her breasts and belly ripe, and her hair was like a weave of golden flames. She lay stretched out on a couch of washed sheep- and goatskins. Before her stood a statuette of an Ashtoreth, with parted legs, with a large belly from which protruded a navel shaped like the male member; in her hands she held a dove which she pressed to her breasts. On a table at her side was a fire pan with smoking incense, and near the fire pan a collection of good things—cakes, eggs, vegetables, cruses with milk, wine, beer, and water. Over a three-legged brazier heaped with burning coals hung an earthen pot in which a kid was seething in its mother's milk, spiced with cloves and other condiments.

The two young men stood there gaping, lost. They poked one another in the ribs, they laughed in their embarrassment, showing their sharp white teeth. Warm glances and friendly words were directed at them:

"Come in, good friends. Welcome guests are you, our kinsmen. You have wiped away our shame, taking vengeance for us on the Amorite. We have prepared food and drink for you—the best," and the two young girls rose, and led the young men to their couches.

In a little while the embarrassment was gone; the young men sat on the couches, they ate and drank. Sharfiah was already playing with one of Osnath's heavy-braided earlocks. If he would only let her cut it off, it would make a beautiful neckband for her, adorned with stones and gold spangles—to be worn, of course, only on holidays.

No, he could not give her his earlock. That was the badge of his people. How could he show himself in the camp without it? Was there nothing else with which he could purchase the key which opened the gate of her garden? Perhaps this armband, which he had taken from a warrior he had slain at the taking of the fortress of Bashan? It was hammered of pure silver and set with moonstones which would shine like stars in the night.

No, neither gold nor silver nor precious stones could open the gate of her garden; all that was needed was a little obeisance before the Ashtoreth goddess, and a pinch of incense thrown on to the fire

457

pan that smoked for her. The smoke would thicken, the smell of it would please the goddess; and she herself, Sharfiah, would feel her blood warmed by it.

How could he do such a thing? Moses, in the name of Jehovah, had strictly forbidden the worship of other gods. Four kinds of death awaited him if he committed such a sin.

But it was precisely the little Yaldah who succeeded in winning over the two strong men for the idol. She was a *kedeshah*, consecrated from childhood to the god—her mother had so consecrated her, she twittered in her birdlike voice. A virgin. Her womb was sealed with seven seals, and no one could break them until he had served the Baal, and paid him her price.

And what was her price?

Prostration on the ground before the mighty Baal, a pinch of incense on his altar, and a meal of kid's meat seethed in the mother's milk, eaten in the presence of the god. There was the fire pan with the coals, there was the kid, seething in its mother's milk. But first he must stand up naked before the Baal, and uncover his manhood to him; for her first acceptance of a man must be sanctified by Baal-Peor.

How could he do such a thing? Jehovah had forbidden it with the utmost severity.

But it was nothing to stand naked before the god. It would be only for a second; and he would be blessed with virility for all his life.

It was not the waters of the wells of Sodom which set on fire the senses of the young warriors, as Balaam had foretold. That was, simply enough, effected by the barley beer which they drank, and by the ointments, livened up with incense, which Yaldah and Sharfiah applied to breast and sex. The garden sealed with seven seals was opened. The two men of Israel, commanders of hundreds in the tribe of Simeon, stood naked side by side with the daughters of Moab, exposed themselves before the idol of Baal, bent the knee to him, smoked incense to him, and kissed the honey-besmeared navel of Ashtoreth.

Late that evening, under cover of night, the two men of Simeon stole back to the encampment, and into their tents. Their bodies were wrapped in mantles of Bethshaan linen; and under their mantles they now wore, suspended from their necks, little abominations: images of Baal with bundles of lightning in his fist; and

458

they believed that from these images they would derive endless virility.

There began, the next day, a stampede to the village of booths which had been set up under the city of Moab at the foot of the mountain. The plain people went, and the leaders went, commanders of hundreds and even commanders of thousands. First they went stealthily and returned stealthily, hoping to escape attention. But before long the stampede was in the open. Moreover, the abomination returned the visits. Soon there were seen in the encampment of Israel men and women of a strange kind: men whose eyes were ringed with blue, whose lips were smeared with crimson salve; women in men's attire, with sashes over their breasts and swords at their sides. A change came over the Israelitish women, too. There was a sudden blossoming of scarlet cloths and veils, of exposed breasts, of provocatively tumbled hair. And Israelitish men appeared with images of the Baal on their breasts. A singing and a playing of instruments went up from the tents of the Israelites, and in the encampment there was a mingled odor of various incenses.

Moses was withdrawn into his tent. Ever since Jehovah had revealed to him that because he had smitten the rock for water instead of speaking to it, as commanded, he would share the fate of the Dead of the Wilderness, he had been occupied with the laws of Israel: he was reviewing and revising the great complex of commandments and ordinances, the affirmative commandments and the prohibitions, which he had issued to Israel in the name of Jehovah during the forty years of wandering. This was to be his testament, a personal testament into which he would weave the record of his trials, ideas, temptations, and tribulations. He wanted to leave to the Bnai Israel an everlasting admonition, a code and guide for all time to come. He therefore labored at the systematization of the laws, and at the expression of his views, his warnings, his exhortations, as well as at the rehearsal of past events. "And now, Israel, what does Jehovah thy God desire of thee? Only that thou fear Him, and that thou go in His ways and love Him with all thy heart and with all thy soul." And he weighed and measured each law separately, examined it from the legal and the moral sides, and expressed it with an exactitude and economy of words that gave it precision and incisiveness of form. Often he modified and cor-

459

rected; he mitigated severities which had been born of a specific, critical situation. Not vengeance unto the second and third generation: "Thou shalt not punish the son for the sins of the father or the father for the sins of the son. He that has sinned, let him pay with his life." It was loving work, and Moses devoted to it every moment of his free time. It was not to be a dry list of laws; life was to be woven into it. And if he himself could not accompany the Bnai Israel into the promised land, then his love and devotion to Israel, incorporated in the laws and commandments, should accompany them, and not them alone, but all their generations to be, in the land which they would inherit and beyond: the seed of God for all lands where men lived, for all times. "And not with you alone do I make a covenant today, and swear an oath, but both with those that stand with us now before Jehovah our God, and with those that are not with us today."

Into the midst of this preoccupation they burst with the dreadful report of the abomination in the camp.

Now Moses stood in the night, and at his side were Joshua, his minister, and the young Phineas, his brother's grandson, the priest of the armed host, one of the generation born in the desert; he stood before his tent by the entrance to the place of assembly, and he looked into the night. He saw the lights shimmering at the foot of the hill where the image of Baal-Peor was erected. The Bnai Israel were there, with the daughters of Moab and of Midian, whom they had made into whores, and together with them they were sacrificing to the Baal. He could hear from afar the tumult, the human braying, as he had once heard the yelling and the howling of the desert generation round the golden calf. Was it to be the same story again, here on the threshold of the promised land, after forty years in the wilderness?

He looked away from the lights. But he did not turn his gaze across the starlit night toward the Salt Sea, shining in the valley, and toward Jericho beyond the Jordan, as he was so often wont to do, with deep longing for the land that had been forbidden him. He gazed instead toward the wilderness, beyond the springs of Arnon. The stars were big and luminous above the white-shimmering heights. Under the bright heavens a profound silence reigned; the silence of death reigning over the stretches of the desert. Yet even out of that silence voices broke through to his ears. He heard the wailing and lamenting of the hyena, he heard the triumphant cry

460

of the jackal, the long-drawn howl of triumph of the beast of prey which has found a carcass to feed on. Would this too be a generation of the wilderness, would these young bodies too become a prey to jackals and hyenas? How well he knew that howling! The beasts of the wilderness were hungry; they had caught the stench of carcasses.

No! No! He must avert the anger of Jehovah before it burst into a devouring fire.

"Go! Call me together the elders of Israel and their judges!"

In that same night he issued the command to the elders and judges of Israel, in the name of Jehovah:

"Bring together not the people, but the captains and the elders who should have set the example, and let judgment be executed on them without delay. Take all those that have bowed to the gods of Moab and have cleaved to the Baal of Peor, and hang them up in the light of the sun before God. And let this be a warning to the Bnai Israel not to go out to the daughters of Moab and Midian, whose fathers have sent them out to play the whore in order that Israel may be drawn away from the path of Jehovah."

The next morning the sun dawned on a row of loaded gallows ranged before the tent of assembly, and the swinging bodies of the captains who had served the idolatry of Baal were a warning to all Israel.

Among the swinging bodies were those of the two captains of hundreds of the tribe of Simeon, Jonadab and Osnath, with the images of the Baal given them by Yaldah and Shafriah, daughters of Moab, dangling on their bosoms.

461

CHAPTER NINE

BUT this did not close the incident of the Moabite temptation.

Zimri ben Sula was a "prince of a father's house" in the tribe of Simeon. He was also a captain of a thousand in the army of his tribe. The two executed warriors, Jonadab and Osnath, had served under him, like many other young warriors of the fruitful tribe of Simeon who had, like them, been condemned to the gallows. As prince of a father's house Zimri felt a special responsibility. He had long been embittered toward Moses. As a prince he had aspired to the chief command of the army of his tribe. But Joshua had kept an eye on him, knew of his dissolute habits, of his misconduct with women, and of his contemptuous attitude toward Israel's special position among the nations: for it was Zimri's opinion, which he did not conceal, that the Bnai Israel did wrong to irritate the surrounding peoples by their isolation, that it would be better for them to mingle with the others and to intermarry with them. On Joshua's advice Moses had recently relieved Zimri of his military duties and appointed in his place a prince of the family of Zerah.

But Zimri was beloved by his warriors. He was a valorous fighter and had distinguished himself greatly in the battles with the Amorites and the Bashanites. He had become a hero in the eyes of the young men of Simeon. Moreover, they found his dissolute ways attractive. He permitted the men under him many things which were forbidden and which no other captain of a thousand would countenance: he pretended not to hear when told that his warriors had raped daughters of the enemy; he considered it no duty of his to carry out the command of Moses which forbade the Israelites to take the women of the enemy to wife; and he was generous in the distribution of war plunder. It was to him that Jonadab and Osnath had first carried the report of the whoring booths which the daughters of Moab had set up opposite the encampment of Israel; and he had been the first of the leaders of distinguished families to go out to the daughters of Moab.

But for Zimri, captain of a thousand, no ordinary snare had waited. His trap was the rich tent of the princess Kozbi, daughter of Zur, prince of a father's house in Midian. This leader of the Midianites had like many another Midianite father given his daughter to be used as a temptation and a snare to lure away the Bnai Israel by whoredom from Jehovah. The father himself had adorned her tent in the valley, had supplied her with luxurious tapestries and divans, with a couch of costly skins, with woven curtains of purple and violet. Moreover, Kozbi was attended by a retinue of servants and entertainers: flute players, dancers, women hairdressers, anointers, and perfume mixers. She also kept by her a priestly eunuch whose duty it was to conduct the service before the stone image of the Baal which occupied the center of the large tent.

Such was the special bait prepared for an important catch. In person the princess was alluring of body and features, and her attractiveness was doubly heightened by the art of the wanton and the aura of nobility which clung to her name. Originally it had been hoped that she might even be used in some manner to tempt none other than Joshua ben Nun, or, failing him, then the young and fiery Phineas, the priest with the Egyptian name, of whom it was told that his prayers inspired Jehovah Himself with warlike feelings, while his addresses to the warriors before battle roused them to the highest pitch of valor. If Kozbi could but ensnare such a central figure and thereby destroy the fighting spirit of the Israelites, that would be a great victory. But none of the highest men of Israel was drawn to her tent, not Joshua ben Nun, and not the high priest of the armies, concerning whose manly beauty and valor many legends were told. And Kozbi had to be content with Zimri, though he was, to be sure, a prince of a father's house in the tribe of Simeon, and a captain of thousand.

The princess Kozbi was in the ripeness of her womanhood, with a body such as the men of Midian found particularly alluring—a body which split a fleshy fold on the ornamented bed where she half sat, half reclined, holding in her hand, after the Egyptian fashion, a lotus flower which she carried now and again to her nostrils. A heavy, gold-red peruke of artificial hair was set like a flat bonnet on her head. Her eyes were deep set in blue-painted sockets, her throat covered by a golden neckband from which a tassel hung—the only cover on her nakedness. Thus toying with the lotus she conversed with the richly dressed prince of Israel, who sat by her in his blue and red striped robe.

"Thou mayest think of me, prince," she said, "as an emissary of peace from my people, the Midianites, to our brothers, the Bnai Israel. Our fathers have sent us as it were into the camp of Israel to carry salutation and benediction to our kinsmen, returning to their land. I am a princess, and my embassy is therefore to a prince. I thought I would be received by the heroes of Israel; such was my belief and that of my sisters in Moab. We expected a joyous reception, a great welcome, in answer to our greetings and loving good wishes. But what did we find? The gates of the encampment were shut against us, and the valorous youth of Israel, who came out to us in goodness of heart, have been punished with death. Tell me, prince, what sort of people is this, what kind of priests, and what kind of customs are these?"

"These customs, princess, are the consequence of our too long sojourn in the wilderness. They have been imposed upon us by a little clique of priests, headed by Moses, who wish to keep us sundered and apart from our good neighbors. The people itself would gladly live in peace and friendship with you, knowing that we are all of one family; and this thou hast surely marked, princess, from the eagerness of the young warriors who came out to your tents against the express prohibition of Moses. Let me assure thee, princess, that wert thou but to appear with me in my chariot in the encampment of Israel, and the whole people would swarm out to greet thee, according to thy rank, and according to thy embassy as the bringer of greetings from the Midianites."

With a gesture which he strove to make elegant Zimri laid at the feet of the princess his belt, which was thickset with precious stones, and two woman's breast shields, trophies of war which he had taken from the most beloved concubine of the Amorite king.

"With thee, prince, into the encampment of Israel? Fearest thou not that Moses will do unto thee what he did with the other commanders? And will not my own life be endangered?"

"Moses do to me what he did with the other commanders?" repeated Zimri, haughtily. "I stand not a finger's breadth lower than Moses. I am a prince in Israel, the eldest of the foremost family in the tribe of Simeon. Our family numbers its warriors in the hundreds. And here, among the tents of the daughters of Moab, there are still hundreds of the most valorous young warriors in Israel, among them leaders and men of renown: and all of them are one with me in the belief that we must live in friendly union with our neighbors. At this moment they fear to return to the camp because of what Moses has done to the others. But let me gather them into a host, let them, with their swords and bows, form a guard for thee, princess; and let us burst into the camp of Israel. Then let us see who will dare to oppose us."

"For such a man I have waited!" exclaimed the princess, and nestling close to Zimri rewarded him with warm and subtle caresses. But when the Israelite prince, fired by the skilled and wanton touches, pressed for a fuller reward, she withdrew coyly from him, shook a warning finger, and twinkled at him with her blue-encircled eyes:

"Not here, prince. . . . In thine own tent, as becomes a warrior who returns from battle with the woman he has taken captive."

But the princess Kozbi did not rely solely on the power of her trained charm; while she went to prepare for the invasion of the Israelite camp, she sent to Zimri the priest of Baal whom the Midianites had attached to her service, so that reasoned argument might fortify the promptings of lust. And the priest of Baal did his work well:

"Be sure," he said, stroking his heavy black beard thoughtfully, "that Jehovah will not bring you into the land which He promised your forefathers, but that He will have you die in the wilderness, even as your fathers did."

"Why, then, did He bring us thus far, to the borders of the land and into the heart of Moab?"

"Thus far indeed He brought you, to the borders of the land and the heart of Moab, and this is the limit of His power. Now He will lead you back, as the ox is led by the nose ring, into the desert, and there He will keep you locked and imprisoned until your bones, like the bones of your fathers, shall mingle with the sand waves. For Jehovah is a God of the desert, and not a God of the settled and sown. If it is the desire of the Israelites to become a settled people, they must acknowledge the god of settlement, and that is Baal, even as we Midianites have done."

"Tell me," said Zimri eagerly, "what mean those words, that Jehovah is only a God of the desert? And what happened with the Midianites?"

"We Midianites, too, were once a people of the desert, and that not long since. We too lived under the power of the storm and of the cloud in which Jehovah conceals Himself. In the days of Jethro Moses came to us and he brought Jehovah with him, and Jethro served Him. Then, like you, we became dependent on Him for every morsel of food, for every mouthful of water: only by His grace could we eat or drink. And this went on until we slew Jethro, and freed ourselves from Jehovah, and acknowledged the god of the sown settlement, the god of Ammon and Moab, who is Baal. And we began to till our soil, and to dig wells, and we became a people of the sown settlement. For Baal is lord of tillage, and without him thou canst not bring forth the fruit of the earth, or draw forth its waters."

"Tell me more, priest of Baal."

"Jehovah, I told thee, is the God of the desert. Thou mayest know it thus: He is without form and image, even as the desert is without form and image. Jehovah is borne by a dark and threatening cloud across the face of the desert, and He rules by terror, by the thunder and lightning which He launches from the cloud. Thus He held in subjection many peoples descended from Abraham, and us too, of another seed, the Midianites. All of us dwelt in the desert until, one by one, we threw off his yoke; one by one we took to tillage, we dug wells, we pastured our flocks, and we turned to the god of the soil, to Baal. And Baal made fruitful for us the wilderness itself, so that we ate fruit and wheat instead of the watery manna of the wilderness; he gave us water in abundance, from the heart of the earth, not from the heart of a rock. He strengthens our loins, and makes fruitful the wombs of our wives; he increases our flocks and our herds. He gives us the fullness of the earth, for he is Baal, the lord of the soil. Without him no people can prosper in settled places, for he is the god of possession." And as the priest talked his eyes began to shine with ecstasy. "And if it is the desire of you Israelites to become a settled people, then you must forthwith renounce your Jehovah, and leave Him to His wilderness, even as Edom and Ammon and Moab have done, and even as we Midianites have done, to turn to the Baal of the soil."

"But how? In what manner shall it be done?" asked Zimri.

"Is not thy family one of the greatest in Israel? And art thou not the prince of a father's house? Art thou not a captain of thou-

466

sand? The people knows thee and will listen to thy voice. Go to thy people, then; say unto it: 'As long as we were in the wilderness, we, the Bnai Israel, needed Jehovah and Moses, His prophet and spokesman. Now that we have come out of the wilderness to a settled place, we must be like the other peoples, like Ammon and Moab. We must turn to the god of the settled places, to Baal!' And thou, Zimri, shalt be the prophet of Baal in the settled place of Israel, even as Moses was the prophet of Jehovah in the wilderness."

Now Zimri the prince stood in the midst of the multitude of renegades, the warriors and captains of Israel who had come out to the daughters of Moab and dared not go back to the camp lest they meet with the fate of the others. And Zimri spoke cunningly, avoiding all mention of Baal:

"What is it we have done that Moses himself has not done? Why was it permitted to him to take to wife a Midianitess, while to us it is forbidden? Wherein did Osnath and Jonadab and our other brothers merit death? Our friends came out to greet us, our neighbors, our kinsmen, whom Jehovah Himself bade us spare. We are strangers in this land. We cannot forever hold off our neighbors with the terror of the sword. We must make a covenant of peace with them. We are no longer isolated wanderers in the desert. We have come to our own land, and we must learn to live in peace with the peoples about us. Come, brothers; follow me into the camp of Israel. What have we to fear? There are spears in your hands; you are men of valor who overcame the Amorites and Og, king of Bashan. Come, let us show Moses and the priests that we are freemen in Israel, and do that which we find pleasing in our eyes."

So there advanced toward the camp of the Bnai Israel, by the city of Moab, a caravan of camels and asses, accompanied by many warriors—warriors of Israel, of Moab, and of Midian. At the head, immediately behind the heralds, Zimri rode on a lofty camel adorned with a rich and multicolored saddle. The hand which held the long spear was extended before him, and the bronze armbands flashed in the sun. His head was covered with a massive copper helm, with a large boss on top—the helm of Baal, worn by his warriors; a corselet of copper covered his chest. Behind the hero marched four Ethiopians, carrying on their shoulders the palanquin

with Midian's special gift to the conspiracy for the corruption of
Israel through whoredom and idolatry. The palanquin was open,
and the princess Kozbi half sat and half reclined in it in such
fashion as to exhibit her beauty and her wantonness: the heavy
gold peruke lay in flat folds on her head; her big round eyes
sparkled in the newly painted sockets; her lips were vermilion
bright; and the two cupolas of her breasts shone in their shields.
Countless were the golden ornaments which were suspended from
her ears, her locks, her neckband, and her breast shields, from her
armbands, her legbands, and her girdle. All the dangling ornaments
were linked with little chains and hooks, so that it seemed as if the
princess was caught in a golden net which the hero Zimri trailed
after him. In one hand the princess held a dove pressed to her
bosom, the symbol of Ashtoreth whose personification the princess
was. But if the princess herself was almost hidden under her ornaments, her cortege had decided to dispense with all covering. A
horde of women dancers, Eve-naked but for the wisp of lawn
which covered their sex, with bells tinkling on their feet, surrounded the palanquin, and danced to the music of flutes and
cymbals. Behind the dancers strutted a proud dwarf, carrying on
his huge head an ape, the princess's favorite pet. Then came a procession of women of various ages, matrons in heavy ornaments,
maidens and little girls, with slender bodies and delicate limbs;
nor were there wanting crippled and monstrous creatures, so that
every natural and unnatural caprice of lust might find its ministrant.

Thus, with a warrior guard, Zimri brought into the camp of
Israel Kozbi, princess of Midian, daughter of Zur. The heralds
with their staves led the pageant to the great place before the
sanctuary, where Israel was wont to assemble to receive the word
of God, where Moses and Eleazar, the high priest, and Phineas,
the priest of the fighting hosts, and many of the elders of Israel
were now taking counsel as to how to arrest the pestilence of corruption which the daughters of Moab and Midian had brought into
the camp of Israel.

Moses and the council had come forth from the tent; and a vast
multitude of the Bnai Israel had assembled. And Zimri, towering
on his camel, lifted up his voice and spoke:

"Men of Israel! Our brothers, the peoples of Moab and Midian,
have sent their daughters to us; not as to enemies, but as to friends,

468

to rejoice with us and to greet us with peace as we come to our land."

And turning to Moses, he said:

"Let not that be forbidden to the people which is permitted to thee"—and he laughed loudly. Then, turning back to the people, he went on:

"Men of Israel, we cannot put to shame the daughters of our friends. Show them that you are freemen." Therewith he stretched out his hand toward the princess of Midian. "See, the princess Kozbi, the daughter of the chieftain Zur, of Midian, has come to meet you and to greet you, men of Israel. It is a great festival, and large sacrifice will Zimri, chieftain of Israel, offer for the daughter of Zur. You are invited to the tent of Zimri. Let us show our friends that all we desire is peace, and there are no evil thoughts between us. Come and play with the daughters of our friends. We will see who will dare to forbid us. Freemen are the children of Israel."

And Zimri and the princess Kozbi turned toward the tent of Zimri, and many of the people followed them.

In that instant the great Moses lost himself and was overcome by weakness and indecision. What was he to answer? Should he pray that the earth open, and swallow this people, as Korah and his congregation had been swallowed—here, on the threshold of the promised land? A man of Israel, a prince and an elder, of a distinguished family, had dared to bring a Midianitess into the camp, in the presence of the assembled people, before the sanctuary and the presence of Jehovah, and not a word had been said, not a voice had been raised in protest—only because this was a prince in Israel, and he was surrounded by the men of his family. Would it not be well for God to send a pestilence now, to destroy this people which He had brought with so many wonders to the gates of its land?

And this, indeed, was what happened. The pestilence struck, and Moses had not the heart to implore Jehovah to arrest it. His lips were smitten with dumbness. He sat apart, speechless, stony; his long face was stone-white, too, and stonelike in their immobility were the hair of his head and his beard. Then those that watched him in awe suddenly perceived two great tears spilling over from his eyes and rolling down the deep folds of his face. They were followed by more tears, which ran steadily down the white, expressionless face. No word came from him. Like the rock which he had smitten in the desert, so he sat, the tears welling up and running over.

Then, outside the tent, a tumult and a lamenting were heard, and a cry for help. "Moses! Moses!" Many voices took up the cry. He did not move; he only sat, the tears coursing down his face. Those that stood about him—Eleazar, Phineas, the elders—knew the meaning of the cries. It was the smiting of the pestilence. But Moses was silent; he was silent like some monstrous hill which could give nothing forth but its locked waters.

"Shall I carry the fire of the altar among the people, in order to arrest the pestilence, as my father Aaron did?" asked Eleazar.

Moses stared at him with tear-dimmed eyes, and made no answer. Then, after a while he found words:

"Wouldst thou carry the fire of God into a house of whoredom? All is whoredom without in the camp. Commit not blasphemy against the fire of God."

Phineas, the young priest, stood leaning against the doorpost of the tent, staring at Moses. Moses was weeping! Through the eyes of Moses Phineas seemed to look into an abyss, a nethermost pit in which Israel was sunk. He understood well the answer which Moses had given his father. How could one carry the sanctity into the uncleanness? Israel was corrupt, unclean. The uncleanness had to be removed first, and only then could Israel be purified with the fire of the altar. The handsome young face of Phineas, framed in its thick, round young beard, was white. From his eyes, too—young, coal-black, gleaming eyes—the tears ran. His hands trembled; he clenched and unclenched them. In the first instant when he had seen the insolent Zimri approach on his camel, the impulse had flashed through him to take a spear and stab the renegade through. But he had mastered himself with a violent effort, knowing as he did that for a priest in Israel it was forbidden to touch the blood of man, or to come in contact with a corpse, or to intervene in a fight. The slightest defect of the body could unfit the priest for his holy office; and against such a defect the priest was always on his guard. And he, Phineas, was one of the small number of the Bnai Aaron—one of the handful of descendants of the first high priest. But now, when he heard the harsh answer of Moses, when he beheld the tears falling ceaselessly on the face of Moses, he knew what had to be done. It was another fire that had to be carried among the people, not the fire of sanctity, but the fire of uncleanness, as was fitting for them. And it was for him to do it. What if thereby he was unfitted for the priesthood? Let a hundred such as he perish, and let Israel be saved.

He started suddenly from his place, fled out into the camp, and made for Zimri's tent. The sentinel who challenged him he flung to the ground, wresting his spear from his hand. Like a fury he burst through the assembly of those who had come to rejoice with the daughters of Moab. A fury, an angel of fury, an angel with a blazing spear in his hand he was as he flung to right and left the drunken celebrants, smiting so that they fell dead at his feet. He burst open the door of Zimri's inner room and disappeared.

In a little while the angel of fury reappeared, an angel with a white face set in a young black beard: in his mighty hands he held a spear, and on the spear were impaled the bodies of the sinner in Israel, Zimri, and his whore, Kozbi: both of them thrust through and through. And Phineas carried this emblem of uncleanness through the camp, and threw the bloody carcasses at the feet of the people.

The pestilence was arrested in the camp when Phineas carried the uncleanness through it, as a pestilence had once been arrested when Aaron had carried through the camp the fire of the altar.

CHAPTER TEN

THERE were far-reaching and dreadful elements in the Zimri incident which accounted for the shattering effect it produced on Moses, for the momentary weakness into which it betrayed him, and for his failure—as it seemed to him—to respond as he should have done. He had yielded to tears; he had permitted the young, hot-blooded priest Phineas ben Eleazar to intervene with an act of violence instead of taking measures himself, as he had always done in the many years of trial in the wilderness. The Zimri affair had unveiled for Moses, with frightful suddenness, the abyss before the Bnai Israel. As long as they had sojourned and wandered in the wilderness they had had no contacts with other peoples. There had been no problem of keeping them in isolation while he trained them in the discipline which he had brought down from heaven, to fashion them into Jehovah's peculiar people. Now all this was drastically changed. Here they were in intimate contact with Edom, Ammon, Moab, Midian, and others. They were able to observe the manners and customs of other peoples—and they were attracted to their free, unburdened way of life: a life unoppressed by the yoke of commandments and prohibitions which forbade the indulgence of natural lusts, which denied the natural inclination to moral dissoluteness. The Bnai Israel of the new generation, born in the wilderness, bred in it, were children of nature: they were like a bursting fount which flows into the plain and is not kept in bounds by channels; or they could be likened to virgin soil, untouched by the plow, ready for any kind of seed. In the Zimri incident there was revealed to Moses the frightful dangers which now confronted the Bnai Israel—now and, even more, in the time to come when he would not longer be with them.

It was not that he believed in no one else and saw himself as the only one capable of maintaining the discipline of the people: he had complete faith in Joshua ben Nun, and he felt that God would confirm in the leadership the man he had trained for so many years.

What he did feel, however, was a special relationship to Jehovah in respect of Israel; no one else had his aptitude for softening the rages of Jehovah against the Bnai Israel, to none other would the Spirit of the forefathers yield as He did to Moses. And again, this was not because Jehovah was a respecter of persons; but God knew his heart, knew how ready he was at any moment to give up his life for the Bnai Israel, to take their sins upon himself, to interpose himself between Israel and the falling lash. There was something more: he had been given two tasks by Jehovah, and he had to complete them both. The first was to liberate the Bnai Israel from the fiery furnace of Egypt; this he had done. The second was to bring the Bnai Israel into the promised land; and he would not die, he would not leave the Bnai Israel, until he had seen this task fulfilled too.

With the Zimri incident new grounds were added to his fear of leaving the Bnai Israel. A new threat had been leveled against the peculiar destiny of Israel, against its character as the chosen people. And though he loved the Bnai Israel tenderly, and longed with all his soul to see them planted in their own land, happy under the sunlight which Jehovah poured out, their existence had no meaning for him except as the chosen people, peculiar, dedicated to the election. An Israel without this divine destiny, assigned to it through the covenant between Jehovah and Abraham, was for Moses—if conceivable at all—without content and without meaning.

And though Moses was a very old man by the reckoning of years, his inner feeling was one of health and youth. The hair on his head was like a shock of white snow; but beholding this giant one had the feeling that he had but to shake that head vigorously and the snow would be scattered from it, so that the head of a young man would be revealed. His eyes had not become dim; his teeth were like a complete set of giant pearls in his mouth; his movements were elastic and swift. He knew that he had in him both the physical and moral energy to complete his mission.

But not for a moment did he dismiss from his mind the recollection of the judgment which hung over him. He did not know when the judgment would be executed; he only permitted himself to hope that Jehovah would relent in His severity, would forgive him his sin as He had so often forgiven the sins of the Bnai Israel, would let him live long enough to complete his mission to the last detail.

Meanwhile he directed his energies toward curing the wounds which the Zimri incident had inflicted on the Bnai Israel, toward restoring normal conditions in the camp and making preparations for the crossing of the Jordan and the conquest of Canaan.

But first it was his purpose to punish those who were guilty in the catastrophe; and here he was confronted with a severe trial. When he inquired of God how he was to proceed against the people who had made this abominable conspiracy for the corruption of Israel he received the answer: "Smite the Midianites." He found it difficult in the extreme to send out a punitive expedition against that people. Had he not dwelt in their midst so many years? Had not Jethro concealed him from Pharaoh? Had not his own wife Zipporah, now long dead, been a Midianitess? He knew both the good and the evil qualities of the Midianites; he had understood the full worth of his father-in-law, Jethro, not only for his protective hospitality, but for the wise counsel he had received from him. But difficult or not, Moses was not the man to falter, for personal reasons, from the execution of a command which he knew to be as just as it was severe. And after a sharp inner struggle he overcame his reluctance. It became clear to him, indeed, that not the Moabites but the Midianites had been the prime movers in the foul strategy against Israel; at any rate, their guilt was deeper. There were reasonable grounds for Moab's uneasiness and fear; after all, Israel had taken up a strong position on the borders of his land, and his shadow fell heavily on Moabite territory. Moab might well be afraid, too, that Moses would take venegeance for the greedy and niggardly treatment which he had accorded the Israelites. No such motives had existed for the Midianites. The Bnai Israel had never sought to cross their borders; their land was not among those which Jehovah had promised the forefathers of Israel. Whenever Moses had found himself in their vicinity his attitude had been one of friendliness and consideration. Their hatred of Israel was an unprovoked hatred, like that of Amalek, and out of this unprovoked hatred they had sent their daughters—from the noblest as well as from common families—to play the whore with Israel. And precisely because on the one hand he felt close to the Midianites, and would have spared them, he was the more outraged, on reflection, by their behavior. Before his mind's eye rose the picture of his wife Zipporah, as she stood by the well with the other daughters of Jethro. Princesses they had been, all of them! And daughters of

474

Midian like these had been instructed in whoredom for the undoing of Israel. A Zipporah had perhaps been among the wretched temptresses! Such a people must be punished. Nor had Moab, after all, actually sent an ambassadress of corruption into the camp of Israel. That had been the hideous distinction of Midian, who had sent a princess into the heart of the camp, to debase the people and to provoke a rebellion against Moses and the elders. She had taken captive in her net a prince in Israel, and she had conspired with him to bring the cult of Baal-Peor among his people.

The incident had left behind it a mood of bitterness and resentment among the Bnai Israel. But Moses held off for a time with the punitive expedition until he had restored order; for while many were filled with anger against Midian, there were not wanting those —of the family of Zimri—who murmured against Phineas for his slaying of their kinsman.

On command from Jehovah Moses first carried out a census of the Bnai Israel, as a preliminary to the crossing of the Jordan; he reinstituted the hegemony of the elders of the tribes and made a strict gradation of tribes and families according to their number and importance for partition of the land when it would be conquered. During the forty-year sojourn in the desert many of the tribal customs and traditions had died out, and there had also been a degree of fusion between tribes and families. It was now the plan of Moses to reconstitute the old order before the Jordan was crossed. The Zimri incident had, moreover, brought out clearly the necessity of a revision in the list of leaders and the substitution of new men, responsible and reliable. Only through these could the tribes and families be disciplined, and thus order maintained and control exercised throughout the people as a whole.

When the census and the revision of leadership had been completed, the command came to Moses:

"Execute the vengeance of the Bnai Israel on the Midianites, and then thou wilt be gathered to thy people."

And because God had told him that this vengeance on the Midianites would be the last act of his life, Moses hastened to obey the command. He would not have it seem that he delayed action because of his impending death. He was clear in his mind now as to the justice and necessity of the act. The neighboring peoples had to learn that Israel was entering his land in order to live a special and separate life of his own, despising the others for their idolatries and their abominations and refusing forever to mingle with them. Israel, it must be demonstrated, had been destined by Jehovah to live according to His commandments, to be the peculiar people, not for its own sake alone, but as a model for mankind—for Jehovah was not only the God of Israel, but the Father of all that had been created.

For the expedition Moses chose a thousand warriors from each tribe, and he sent with them Phineas, the son of Eleazar, with holy vessels and trumpets, to rouse their fighting spirit. And the army of Israelites warred with Midian and slew all the men, including the princes. The Israelites also laid hands on Balaam, who had come to the princes of Midian to claim a reward for the subtle counsel he had given them, which had been responsible for the death of twenty-four thousand Israelites; and marvelous stories were told in after years concerning the capture of Balaam and his death.

Balaam, who had been born at about the same time as the patriarch Jacob, had attained to his fantastic old age by magic. He had been able repeatedly to elude the grasp of the Angel of Death. Whenever the Angel of Death had come for him Balaam had been able, with an incantation, to take on a new form—sometimes that of an animal, sometimes that of a plant. Once he had even transformed himself into a stone. The Angel of Death swept by him and around him and could not recognize him. Now, when he fell into the hands of the Israelites, he resorted to the same device, but he was betrayed by his ass. The ass denounced Balaam to Phineas for having repeatedly broken his promise to Jacob, and having but recently occasioned the death of twenty-four thousand of the Bnai Israel; and she appeared as an adverse witness at the trial of the magician. When the moment came for his execution, Balaam transformed himself into a stone pillar, and the swords were all blunted against him. When he had to abandon this likeness, he turned himself into a huge bird and tried to fly out of Midian. He could not be brought to justice until Phineas, with the help of the sacred vessels he had taken with him, overcame his magic. Phineas forced the huge bird down to earth and compelled Balaam to reassume his human shape; only then was it possible to behead him. And when that had been done, there remained of him only his ancient, gray locks, and his fingernails, for the rest of him dissolved completely into dust.

With vengeance executed on the Midianites, the expedition returned, bringing with it an immense quantity of booty, vessels, clothes, ornaments, gold, silver, sheep, and cattle, besides many women and children.

Moses was a son of his time. However sharply his eagle eyes pierced the remote future, glimpsing there a new world order, he was, in his wars against his enemies, who were also the enemies of Jehovah, like any other warrior leader of his time. No one will be found to excuse or to justify the action of Moses against the Midianites; but, without attempting an excuse or justification, there is something to be said concerning the war of annihilation against Midian in the light of that moral attitude which characterized Moses.

The faith which Moses reposed in Jehovah was blind, untouched by questioning or doubt. It was not on the ground of their justice in the light of human intelligence and human evaluation that he accepted the laws of God, but on the ground that they were, simply, the laws of God, the Creator of heaven and earth, the Creator of the laws of nature: they were just for that reason alone. He also believed that every inspiration which came to him from the Spirit was a revelation of His will, an aspect of the perfection which was planned for the world. For inasmuch as Jehovah was the Father of the individual spirit of each soul, His laws and commandments were the expression of a higher justice and an eternal truth not only for the single creature but for His whole creation. Moreover, the faith which Moses brought to his exclusive mission filled him with an iron determination and obstinacy which ignored the sacrifices which would have to be exacted from his own or from others: he saw his mission—the uplifting of the Bnai Israel to the condition of the chosen people—as the instrument of the ultimate purpose which God had set for man and the world.

He had become reconciled to the payment of high and bloody sacrifices for the fulfillment of the mission. Had not God rejected a whole generation, the generation of the exodus, because He had discovered that it was unfit to become the chosen people? How many times had not the wrath of Jehovah kindled a raging fire in the ranks of the Bnai Israel? With a mighty hand and an outstretched arm Jehovah had led the people forth from Egypt; with a mighty hand and an outstretched arm He had compelled it, through hunger and death, into the discipline of His commandments; and with a mighty hand and outstretched arm Jehovah

477

would thrust aside every stumbling block which lay on the path of His purpose.

The women of Midian were such a stumbling block. Their fathers and husbands had surrendered them to whoredom and had sent them into the camp of the Bnai Israel to corrupt them to the worship of Baal-Peor. They had brought disorder and ruin into the camp. Twenty-four thousand souls had perished in the pestilence because of them. Jehovah had bidden Moses take vengeance and to smite the Midianites, "for by their wiles they have beguiled you in the matter of Peor." Why, then, should he be more compassionate and considerate toward them than toward the children of Israel? They were a danger and a threat to the children of Israel, and therefore they were to be swept out of the way.

But that danger was not ended with the defeat and destruction of Midian.

Going forth from the camp with Eleazar the high priest to greet the returning warriors, Moses saw the horde of women which was part of the booty; nor were they old ones, but women in the fulness of womanhood, and many young ones, too, with lips painted scarlet, eyes ringed with blue, and adorned for their captivity. Here was defeat nesting in the very midst of victory, the evil which had caused the disaster and the war surviving both, to the undoing of the Bnai Israel. Were these emissaries of the whoredoms and idolatries of Midian to justify the counsel of Balaam after all, and to achieve in captivity what they had been incapable of achieving in freedom?

"Have ye let the women live?" cried Moses. "But was it not they who, guided by Balaam, caused Israel to sin with Baal-Peor, bringing the pestilence into the camp?"

And Moses issued a command which was in the spirit of the war customs of his day.

The punitive expedition against the Midianites was the only aggressive war undertaken by Moses. In all his other wars he had been on the defensive. To symbolize the fact that the taking of a life, even in battle, and the contact with a corpse were sins, he issued a command of purification to the warriors: "Encamp ye without the camp seven days; whosoever has killed a person, and whosoever has touched the slain, let him purify himself on the third day and on the seventh day, and the captives shall also be purified; and every garment, and all that is made of skin, and all work of goats' hair, and all things made of wool, shall be purified."

Moses also made use of this occasion to institute a system in the distribution of the booty brought back by a victorious army. The vessels, clothes, and ornaments, the sheep and cattle, and the young women who had been spared—those that had not known any man —were divided into two parts; one was distributed among the warriors who had fought Midian, and one among the entire congregation. The tribes in their turn had to surrender a portion to the Levites, and the tabernacle received its share from the part given to the warriors, "a tribute unto the Lord." But at the suggestion of the high priest, the captains of thousands and the captains of hundreds brought a "freewill" offering of thanks because not one man was missing among those they had sent forth to war. "We have brought the Lord's offering, what every man received of jewels, armlets, bracelets, signet rings, earrings, and girdles, to make atonement for our souls." This division of booty became the model for future wars. The surrender of gold and silver for the sanctuary was always to be voluntary. It was called *corban,* and it constituted the treasury of the people in the keeping of the sanctuary. And even though the offering of gold and silver and precious ornaments was considered voluntary—being accompanied by the corban vow —it turned into custom and law, and every evasion of it was, in later times, severely punished.

Moses also formulated a system for the distribution of the lands which the Bnai Israel were to conquer. Certain cities he set apart for the Levites, others he set apart as cities of refuge for such men as might take someone's life unintentionally and would flee from before the kinsman or avenger of the slain one. He set forth clearly, in the name of Jehovah, the boundaries of the promised land; and through Joshua he commanded the men of Reuben, Gad, and half the tribe of Manasseh, to leave their wives and children and flocks on the eastern side of the Jordan, which they had taken from the Amorites, and to cross the Jordan with the other tribes to help them conquer their portion: only thereafter could they settle in their own portions. The two and a half tribes heard the command and readily undertook their share in the conquest.

During the working out of the division of the land among the families of Israel, which was to be put into effect by Joshua, Moses issued, in the name of Jehovah, a ruling and judgment which was of profound importance for the status of woman in those days. Five maidens, daughters of a distinguished member of the tribe of Manasseh, Zelophehad by name, appeared before Moses and Eleazar the high priest and the princes of the congregation with a claim:

"Our father died in the wilderness, and he was not of the congregation of Korah, which rebelled against the Lord, but he died in his own sins. And he had no sons. Why should the name of our father be done away from among the family, because he had no son? Give us a possession among the brothers of our father."

It was so unheard-of a thing that the daughters of a man should lay claim, in the same manner as sons, to the lot and portion of God, that those who were in attendance with Moses would have driven the maidens away. But Moses said that he would bring their claim before God. And later Moses issued this judgment in the name of God:

"The claim of the daughters of Zelophehad is a just one, and they shall be given an inheritance among the brothers of their father, and their father's inheritance shall descend to them." And Moses reported in the name of Jehovah: "Speak thus to the children of Israel: If a man die, and have no son, then ye shall cause his inheritance to pass to his daughter."

CHAPTER ELEVEN

ABOVE the encampment of the Bnai Israel the clouds drifted steadily—massive purple and light blue—like ships laden with heavenly treasure to be delivered to the children of the earth. It was the time of the *malkosh*—the latter rain. The Israelites had never before witnessed the downpouring of God's benediction, and they rejoiced and marveled at the sight; and as the waters fructified the seed in the earth, so they fructified the spirit of the Bnai Israel, causing faith and trust to spring up in their hearts. They went out into the descending flood, they soaked themselves in it to the bone, and then they sat in their dripping tents, huddled happily to one another.

It was the hour of tranquillity in the encampment, the twilight hour when the curling smoke went up from the sanctuary, where Eleazar and his priests were offering up the evening sacrifice. Morning and evening, when the Bnai Israel saw the smoke ascending from the court of the tabernacle, they knelt at the doors of their tents, and stretched forth their hands in prayer. This the men were now doing, in the damp earth before their tents.

Within the sanctuary Eleazar tended the light of the *menorah;* from the delicately wrought golden ewer he poured the refined oil which had been pressed from the purest and rarest plants. In the court of the sanctuary the sons of Eleazar stood in their priestly raiment before the golden altar. They sprinkled incense on the altar fire and on the fires that glowed in the pans; they carried the flickering fire pans across the sanctuary court, and they let the curling smoke float out of the court toward the tents of the Bnai Israel, to purify them.

Within the sanctuary, in the sacred recess of the cherubim, reigned a profound stillness which seemed to flow from the radiant darkness surrounding the holy of holies. The light of the *menorah,* dimmed by the smoke ascending from the fire pans, glimmered faintly across the woven curtains. Here, in a fold of the curtains, face to earth, Moses lay in his white mantle. He had been called by Jehovah to present himself in the inmost sanctuary—for when an important revelation was impending, the holy of holies was the place chosen for it.

Lying thus on the threshold of the holy of holies, Moses listened to the voice of Jehovah issuing from the cloud of incense above the ark, where the two cherubim turned upon each other, across the dimness, their young, childlike faces:

"Go up upon this mountain of Abarim and behold the land which I have given to the children of Israel. And when thou hast seen it, thou shalt be gathered to thy people, even as thy brother Aaron was gathered to them; because ye rebelled against my commandment in the wilderness of Zin, in the strife of the congregation, to sanctify me at the waters before their eyes."

And Moses buried his face deep in his hands, so that light of the glory should not shine on him between his fingers, and he said:

"Let Jehovah, the God of the spirits of all flesh, set a man over the congregation, who may go out before them, and who may come in before them, and who may lead them out, and who may bring them in; that the congregation of God be not as sheep without a shepherd."

"Take thee Joshua, the son of Nun, a man in whom is spirit, and lay thy hands upon him; and set him before Eleazar the priest and before all the congregation, and give him thy testament in their sight. And thou shalt confer of thy glory upon him, so that all the congregation of the children of Israel shall hearken. And let him stand before Eleazar the priest, who shall make inquiry for him from the Urim before God. According to his word they shall go out, and according to his word they shall come in, both he and all the children of Israel with him, even the whole congregation."

But Moses did not stir from the place. His face buried in his hands, he broke into passionate supplication:

"O Father of all created things, into my hands didst Thou deliver this people, to bring it into the promised land. Now that Thou biddest me deliver it into other hands, cause me to know, O God of compassion, whether he that follows me will succeed in the mission wherein I have failed; and cause me to know the spirit of him that follows me. Will he be a true judge to Thy children? Will he understand them, each one apart? Will he feel within himself their wants and their needs? Will there be within

482

him the spirit of each and the spirit of all, so that he may be to them a true judge and their faithful leader?"

And the answer came: "Not only the spirit of him that follows thee shalt thou behold, but the spirits of all that will follow thee, the judges and the prophets that will come after thee until the day of the resurrection of the dead: open thy eyes, and behold!"

And Moses opened his eyes and beheld.

He beheld, arising from the cloud between the cherubim, multitudinous faces, faces not of the flesh but of the Spirit. He beheld their inmost being, their spiritual essences, the hierarchy of their souls, in an ascent which reached no final purpose. And he cried out:

"Father of all created things, I see spirits. Very mighty are those whom Thou hast elected as the leaders of Thy people; they ascend on the wings of prophecy and they carry the people with them, even to the throne of Thy glory; but the final purpose they do not attain. I see them doing battle with men and with demons for Thy dominion. Like giants they rise up from the depths of the sea of evil, lifting out of them the body of man. I see further: they bring closer, ever closer, the day of fulfillment and perfection, but they themselves do not partake of it. They go on forever, and never do they reach the goal." The voice of Moses became sorrowful: "Will they all fail of the end, even as I have failed?"

And the voice answered from between the cherubim:

"Know, concerning these spirits which I have shown thee, that each of them has his own separate spirit and his own separate knowledge; but such a one as thou desirest to have for thy successor, a man whose spirit shall embrace the spirit of all the Bnai Israel, such a one as will be able to speak for each of them according to his understanding, and for all of them—such a one shall not arise before the end of days. He alone will be possessed of that spirit which will embrace the spirits of all men."

"Who is he?" asked Moses.

"He is the Messiah," answered God.

The years of wandering in the wilderness, the battles with the enemies of Israel, had long since changed the young lad Joshua, who had ministered in the tent to Moses, into a powerful figure of a man, rock-firm of character and cunning in the craft of war. The locks of his mighty head, bronze streaked with gray, unkempt

—for unlike the other princes and commanders he begrudged himself the time for oiling and anointing—fell down on his nape and shoulders, and mingled with the thick tresses of his earlocks and his long, wire-hard beard. His wind-tanned face was deeply trenched, and in his gray eyes, set in a firm network of seams, rested a commanding light which overwhelmed every man upon whom it was turned.

Moses brought Joshua into his own tent, into the inner room which was his retreat when he meditated on God, and there revealed to him the command which he had received. Dismay filled the heart of Joshua.

True, he had often thought of the time when Moses would be gathered to his fathers, but he had not imagined that it would come so swiftly; and he had still considered it far off. He knew of the judgment which had been hanging over Moses ever since the day of the waters of Meribah; yet he had hoped and in part believed that God would withdraw the judgment and permit Moses to fulfill his mission. Moreover, Joshua could not conceive how the lands beyond the Jordan could ever be conquered without Moses, whose massive presence and undiminished spirit in no wise corresponded with the notion of a man whose time had run out. Hearing now the dread decision, Joshua mastered his alarm and at first spoke with Moses as one that takes council concerning events over which he has no control, but which must be weighed and measured and met in cool and considered judgment.

"Moses, my teacher"—it was so that he always addressed him —"who am I that I should say aught concerning the secret things that Jehovah entrusts to thee? But as the leader of the fighting hosts of Israel it is incumbent upon me to make this much clear: that withdrawing now from the congregation of Israel thou imperilest the safety of thy people. Thy name is linked with the liberation, from the day of the exodus until this day. The signs and wonders which Jehovah has vouchsafed us through thy hand have spread the terror of thy name among the peoples. They fall before thee like ripe ears, and like garnered wheat they are gathered into bundles and bound before thee. And still we are but at the beginning of our goal. The land lies untouched on the other side of the Jordan; it is inhabited by a powerful enemy with experienced hosts; and behind us we shall leave Moab and Ammon, unfought and still strong, and Edom who hates us not less than they. Now

484

if they will hear that thou hast been taken from us they will say: Assuredly Jehovah has abandoned them, has delivered them like sheep without a shepherd into our hands. And they will assemble and unite and fall upon us, to avenge the defeat of Midian. No, Moses, my teacher, thou canst not leave us now. Thou must strengthen thy prayers, thou must awaken the compassion of Jehovah, that He leave thee with us until thou hast conquered the land beyond the Jordan, which Jehovah promised to our forefathers."

A mournful light shone from the eyes of Moses while he meditated on the words of Joshua. Then, smiling sadly, he took Joshua's hand and said:

"Joshua ben Nun, thou knowest as well as I that without the will and help of Jehovah we would never have come thus far. We would have perished when the first threat of war was leveled at us by Amalek. It is not the enemy without that fills thee with alarm; something else weighs upon thy heart. Say now, what is it?"

Joshua knelt before Moses and raised his hands to him:

"My lord and my teacher, Moses, thou knowest the Bnai Israel better than I. Thou lovest them, too, more than I. Thou alone standest like a wall of iron between the sins of Israel and the wrath of Jehovah. O Israel's shield, and bow of Israel, who am I and what am I that I should bring my supplication for Israel before Jehovah? I possess not thy love, nor have I thy understanding, and it is not in my power to intervene for Israel. At his first sin Israel will be ground between the millstones of Jehovah's wrath as the ripe ear is ground between the stones of the miller. Without thee I am nought. Thou art all! Abandon me not, my teacher!" and the tears poured down Joshua's cheeks.

"Stand up, my son! It is unbecoming that the leader of Israel kneel before one of flesh and blood." And Moses lifted up Joshua's head. "Sit down here beside me. Diminish not thyself. Be comforted, and hear my words. All the nations that exist, wheresoever they be, are the creation of Jehovah, and we are one of them. But in us alone did Jehovah see the promise of understanding, and therefore he chose us to be His messenger to the other nations—from the beginning of creation until the end of days. Nothing has escaped His vision and preparation. He knows all, He foresees all that will happen. He has marked out the path, He has set the stages of the advance. He chose me to be the leader of

485

Israel, to plead for Israel when he sinned and failed. Not for my merit did He make this choice, but out of His grace and His compassion. Hear me, Joshua: not for Israel's sake, and not for Israel's merits and virtues will God subdue for thee the nations of Canaan and destroy the peoples that worship idols. It is for the sake of the path which He has laid down for all the peoples since the beginning of the world, as the aim and purpose of His creation. Be therefore of good cheer, and let thy heart be strong, for thou art a messenger of Jehovah, even as I am. He will speak through thy mouth, and He will act through thy hand. Destroy the enemies of Israel, reward the worthy in Israel, punish the sinners with a heavy rod; but of this be sure: howsoever harsh and heavy be God's visitation of enemies on Israel, He will not destroy him, for Israel is the destined instrument of God, designed for the fulfillment of His will. Go, therefore, and fear not; the angels of the Lord will accompany thee and will conquer the land which He promised to our forefathers."

Joshua, who had sat and listened, a strand of his graying beard held between his teeth, said now, in a tone of supplication:

"But wherefore me—me—the least worthy in Israel? I am a leader of fighting men, not of the people. Something I know of the art of war, nothing whatsoever of the art of government. I am a warrior, not a judge. There are wiser and more learned men without number in Israel."

"This question—Wherefore choosest Thou me?—I too asked of Jehovah when He appeared to me in the burning bush. Wherefore me? I cried. But Jehovah, like a mighty eagle, seeks out with piercing eye him whom He seeks out; and when He has sought him out, He comes upon him like an eagle upon his prey, and carries him away in His claws. Thus He did to me, and thus He does to thee, and thus He will do to each one whom He appoints for his mission, until the end of days. And we must be obedient, whether we desire it or not, for there is no other way for us."

Joshua let his head sink on his breast, and thought long. Suddenly he left his seat, sank once more on his knees before Moses, and implored him:

"My lord and my teacher, tell me, transmit the virtue and secret to me: how didst thou surmount all these obstacles? How didst thou remove all the stumbling blocks which were strewn upon thy path, how didst thou rescue the Bnai Israel from all the dangers which have threatened them until this day, how didst thou soften the wrath of Jehovah and bring Israel to go in His ways?"

"The secret virtue wherewith I surmounted all obstacles and overcame all dangers was—love: 'Thou shalt love the Lord thy God with all thy heart and with all thy soul and with all thy might'—and 'Thou shalt love thy neighbor as thyself.' These two loves were my shield and my bow; and these two loves I shall cause thee to inherit. Come, let us pray to Jehovah that these two loves become a unity in thy heart."

The Bnai Israel, who had so often murmured against Moses and uttered bitter things about him behind his back, became indeed like a flock which has lost its shepherd when they heard that Moses was about to be taken from them and Joshua would be put in his stead. They assembled in groups and asked quietly of each other: "Moses is being taken from us! What will happen to us now?" Their faces fell, their heads sank upon their bosoms, and uncertainty again peered out from their eyes. "Woe, woe unto us! Who will lead us across the Jordan? Who will do battle for us?"

And Moses felt how frightened and forlorn the people had become. He therefore planned to make of the induction of Joshua a great and impressive ceremony, which would lift up the heart of the people and fill it with confidence in the new leader.

On the day of the induction he assembled the entire congregation at the entrance to the sanctuary, and there he placed his judgment seat, covered with purple and gold, all prepared for the elevation of Joshua. A second throne, of like dignity, was occupied by the high priest, who wore for the occasion his robes of office, complete with ephod and breastplate. The sons of the high priest and the youngest scions of the dynasty, the blossoms of the priesthood, were ranged behind this second throne. On other thrones, of inferior dignity, were seated the seventy elders, the twelve princes of the tribes, and the captains of a thousand.

Then Moses himself, at the head of a delegation consisting of elders, captains of thousand, and the prince of the tribe of Benjamin, went in solemn procession to Joshua's tent, to conduct him to the ceremony, where he was to mount the judgment seat of Moses.

Moses entered the tent, where he found Joshua lying face to earth sunk in prayer. He called out:

"Joshua ben Nun, the time of thy service to Israel has come. Arise, go forth to thy mission."

Then Joshua, rising, his face bathed in tears, would have done obeisance to his teacher, but Moses prevented him, saying:

"From this time forth it is I who shall do obeisance to thee," and he did so, adding: "My teacher, Joshua." Then he took a basin of water from one of the accompanying heralds, and would have washed Joshua's hands; but now it was Joshua who would not permit it, for he said:

"Moses, my teacher, how can I let thee serve me?"

"It is thy duty to let me serve thee, as I have let thee serve me," answered Moses. "Rebel not against the commandment of God."

And Joshua permitted himself to be served by Moses.

Then Moses washed Joshua's face and hands, and took a white mantle, borne by another herald, and threw it over Joshua's shoulders; and he removed the white veil from his head and hung it over Joshua's head.

And when Joshua appeared on the threshold of his tent in the veil of Moses, with Moses following uncovered and unveiled, the elders and captains of a thousand and the prince of the tribe of Benjamin turned pale, and made as if to withdraw and hide themselves. But Moses compelled them with a glance to stand their ground; and he bade the heralds blow the trumpets for the approach of the new leader and teacher of Israel.

The banner of the tribe of Benjamin led the procession; behind the banner strode Joshua, and to the right and left of him, but somewhat to the rear, strode Moses and the prince of the tribe. Then came the delegation of elders and captains of a thousand. To the sound of trumpet peals the procession drew toward the place of the sanctuary, where the high priests, the general priesthood, the remaining elders, and the congregation waited.

When the people saw Joshua in the garb of Moses, and Moses himself, uncovered and unveiled, following him, as a pupil follows a teacher, many averted their eyes, and some threw themselves face downward to the ground that they might not see.

But Moses took Joshua by the hand and led him to the throne which stood side by side with the throne of the high priest, and made him mount and take his place in the midst of the elders; and himself he turned to the people and addressed them:

"Hear, children of Israel, the word of God. This day I am a

hundred and twenty years old. I can no more come in and go out to serve you. Moreover, God has said to me: 'Thou shalt not cross the Jordan.' Jehovah, your God, shall cross before you. He will destroy these peoples before you, and ye shall inherit them. Joshua shall lead you, even as God has spoken. . . . Be strong and stout of heart, and fear not the inhabitants of the land, for it is Jehovah your God Who goes before you, and He will not abandon or forsake you."

Then Moses drew near to Joshua and made him rise and approach the people. And Moses spoke to Joshua in the hearing of the people:

"Be strong and stout of heart, for thou wilt come with this people into the land which God swore unto them through their forefathers, and thou wilt cause them to inherit it. The Lord God shall be He that goes before thee. He will be with thee and He will not forsake or abandon thee. Thou shalt not fear, and thy heart shall not tremble."

Then Joshua knelt, and Moses placed his hands upon his head and called out:

"The spirit which God put into me, I put into thee. Go in strength, and let thy might increase."

And Moses knelt by the side of Joshua, and lifted his hands to heaven and prayed aloud:

"I thank thee, O God, the God of our fathers, that Thou hast granted it to me to see the leader of Israel before Thou didst close mine eyes. And I implore Thee, God of our fathers, to strengthen his hands and to be with him as Thou hast been with me until this day."

Then he rose from his knees and called out to the people:

"See your leader, Joshua! Him shall ye obey!"

But among the people there was a heavyhearted silence. No tumult was raised, and no voice was heard save that of Joshua, which lamented:

"My lord, my teacher, my father!"

Then Moses led Joshua before the high priest, and thence to the judgment seat; and having made Joshua take his place upon it, Moses withdrew and went into his tent.

Four heralds, one for each of the threefold hosts, sounded their trumpets and called out:

"Israel! Israel! Moses comes before the threshold of Joshua

declaring: 'Whosoever would hear the word of God, let him come to Joshua, for he is the elder and leader of Israel, according to the command of Jehovah."

But the people did not stir from their places. No one came for judgment to Joshua, and there was only a quiet weeping in corners.

CHAPTER TWELVE

MOSES had become ripe for death like a fruit about to fall from the tree in its season. Yet he rebelled against death like a mother whom death calls while her child is at her breast: she opposes her will to God and the destroying angel, she will not surrender until the child is taken from her. Thus it was with Moses. Israel was his suckling child, still unweaned, and the child would not turn to the new nourisher whom God had prepared for it— Joshua. In vain did the heralds go through the encampment each morning with the message of Moses: "Whosoever would hear the word of God, let him come to Joshua, for he is the elder and leader of Israel, according to the command of Jehovah." The people did not come to Joshua; nor did the leaders, the elders of Israel, the representatives of the tribes and the judges. Orphaned and forlorn, they wandered about near the tent of Moses.

Meanwhile Moses sat alone within, writing out his testament. He hastened now, knowing that while he yet lived Israel could not cross the Jordan, and time, precious time, would be lost. Yet the task on which he was engaged was important, too; it had been laid upon him by Jehovah—the uttering of a great warning and admonition to Israel, for all the coming generations.

And while he wrote his restatement of the law he was visited by a shattering experience. God unfolded before him not only the long martyr road of Israel, but also the endless vicissitudes of Israel's spirit, the alternations of exaltation and degradation, the agonizing aspirations toward the heights, toward the abode of God, the hideous lapses into the abyss. That which Balaam had sought in vain, the vulnerable spot in the soul of Israel, the wound into which he would have poured the poison of his curse, that which was denied to Balaam was revealed to Moses in all its fullness. Moses saw the long, long exile and dispersion across which Israel would leave the trace of his blood, footstep by footstep. And with a pen steeped in terrified mother love, in malediction and benediction, in terror and warning, he wrote:

"And it shall come to pass that if ye hearken not to the voice of Jehovah, your God, to do all His laws and commandments which I command you this day, that all these curses shall come upon you and overtake you. . . .

"The Lord will cause you to be smitten before your enemies; ye shall go out one way against them, and shall flee seven ways before them. . . . Ye shall grope at noonday, as the blind grope in darkness, and ye shall not make your ways prosperous, and ye shall only be oppressed and robbed always, and there shall be none to save you. . . . Your sons and daughters shall be given unto another people, and your eyes shall look and fail with longing for them all the day, and there shall be no power in your hand. . . ."

With fury and terror the pen went on to the frightful words:

"Ye shall go mad because of what your eyes shall see. . . . Ye shall become an astonishment, a proverb, and a byword among all the peoples whither the Lord shall lead you away. . . ."

He sat on the ground in his tent; before him was stretched a ruled parchment, and he wrote on it with a rush dipped in blue fish ink. His white hairs bristled and stood up like needles on his mighty head, and his face was pallid and yellow and lustrous; and great tears poured from his eyes. His body was drenched through and through with the sweat of his anguish, and he sat there like a beast trapped and held down in a net. He could not stir from this place. Jehovah had fastened him down and was compelling him to look into the sealed future while He guided his hand over the parchment. And he wrote further:

"Because ye did not serve the Lord your God with joyfulness, and with gladness of heart, by reason of the abundance of things, therefore shall ye serve your enemies whom the Lord shall send against you, in hunger, and in thirst, and in nakedness, and in want of all things; and they shall put a yoke of iron upon your neck. . . ."

"I can no more, I can no more!" shrieked Moses. "I am but flesh and blood! How much can I endure? Pierce mine eyes through and let me not see! Make powerless my hand, and let me not write. I can no more, Jehovah, my God!" And he threw himself face to earth.

But the Spirit of Jehovah compelled him to lift his tear-drenched face from the ground, compelled him to see and hear, to look into the abyss, and to echo with his pen the angry thunder of the Lord:

"And the Lord shall scatter you among all peoples, from end to end of the earth, and there ye shall serve other gods, which ye have not known, and which your fathers have not known, gods of wood and stone. And among these nations ye shall have no repose, and there shall be no rest for the soles of your feet. . . . And your life shall hang in doubt before you, and you shall fear night and day, and you shall have no assurance of your life. In the morning you will say, 'Would it were even!' and at even you will say, 'Would it were morning!' For the fear of your heart which you shall fear, and for the sight of your eyes which you shall see . . ."

"Wherefore hast Thou cursed us with the curse of Thy election?" cried Moses to God. "Other peoples, too, sin, and do not Thy will. Why must it be the children of Thy friend who are chosen to pay the full measure? Why hast Thou laid down this bloody road for them, for them alone?"

"You, and you alone, have I chosen from among all the peoples to be a people holy unto Me. And it is because I loved your fathers that I have chosen their children to be My people, elected from among all peoples, My peculiar people, belonging to Me. For your fathers have sold you unto Me by the covenant which I made with them. And should ye not desire it, I will compel you, and break your obstinacy. And for your election you must pay in full measure. . . ." Thus Moses heard the voice of God in his heart.

"God of my fathers, God of Abraham, Isaac, and Jacob, Thou camest to me in the wilderness, and Thou chosest me to be Thy messenger to Thy people. And I strove against the mission, but Thou didst compel me to it. Thou didst show Thy servant Thy greatness and Thy mighty hand. Where is a god in heaven or on the earth who shall do what Thou hast done? I pray Thee, let me see the good land which is on the other side of the Jordan, the delectable mountain in Lebanon."

"Wherefore, and to what end? Have I not told thee that thou wouldst not cross the Jordan, but that I would send Joshua, and through him would I make the Bnai Israel inherit their land?"

"Jehovah, God of mercy, Thou that art compassionate to all Thy creatures, be Thou compassionate to Thy servant, too. My heart trembles in me, I melt with fear. I am terrified lest Israel depart from Thy path, and fail to obey the commandment which Thou hast laid upon him, and Thou bring upon them all the curses which Thou hast shown me."

"Wouldst thou be with them through all the generations, and be their guide until the end of days? Knowest thou not that I have been gracious unto man in that I created death? Through death I have given him life, and through mortality I have made him eternal. Only those live that have died. Wouldst thou be with Me through all the eternities? Thinkest thou that without thee I cannot bring Israel into his inheritance, and without thee Israel will perish?" Thus Moses heard the angry voice of God in his heart.

"In Thee I believe," answered Moses; "in Thee is my trust. But I believe not in Israel, and my trust is not in him."

"I demand of thee that thou believe not only in Me, and that thy trust be not only in Me, but that thou believe in My creation, and trust in it. Therefore have I decreed that man shall die with closed eyes. I have raised up a fiery wall between life and death, and none shall break through it. And to man I have given nothing to take with him into death save faith and trust. Thus too it shall be with thee. Go with closed eyes to thy rest, and nought shall accompany thee save faith and trust; faith and trust not only in Me, but in Israel too, whom thou leavest behind thee."

But Moses still kneeled in his place and would not withdraw:

"Give me a sign and a presage that Thou wilt never destroy Israel," implored Moses.

God's voice answered in his heart: "That sign and presage I gave thee when I first appeared unto thee."

"O God of compassion, mighty Jehovah, open my heart, that I may understand Thee."

"Did I not appear to thee in a burning bush? And the bush burned, and burned, and was not consumed. This will be the destiny of Israel."

"Shall Israel forever burn on the altar, an eternal offering?" cried Moses in terror. "God of compassion, let me tear up Thy decree. Let me be near them, to warn them. I know them, I know their heart, and I know how to speak to them."

"I have appointed prophets, generation by generation. They will exhort and admonish. And some shall be scourged for their words.

Their bodies shall be drenched in the anguish of their blood and suffering. They will run before the people, and their bones shall be strewn on the path. Thy lot is better. Thy body has not received their lash nor thy head their stones. What more wouldst thou?"

"O Father of all creation, let my body be given to the lash, let me be a helper to Joshua, his servant and pupil, if only I might be with them and keep my eye on them, if only I might serve Joshua."

"Thou hast been granted enough. I appointed for thee, as for every man, a time and a generation. Thou belongest to thy generation, and thou must share its destiny. Thou must die on this side of the Jordan, in order that thy generation may rise with thee to eternal life. Thy time is fulfilled. Wherefore holdest thou back Israel from coming into his land? Joshua cannot take over the rule while thou livest."

"O God of Israel, let a hundred such as I perish rather than that the redemption of Israel be delayed one day, one hour. Tell me what I must do."

"Thy days run out. Call Joshua, and let him stand side by side with thee in the innermost chamber of thy tent, and I will deliver My message."

All night long Moses remained locked with Joshua in the innermost chamber of his tent, and he delivered to Joshua the secrets of the unrevealed Torah; and he presented Joshua to his friends, the angels, and he required of them that they stand by him as they had stood beside himself. And when the morning star rose he led Joshua out of the tent, and pointed to the place of the rising sun, and said:

"If thou wilt teach Israel to hearken to God and to obey His commandments, He shall make subject to thee not only men and peoples, but even the stars in heaven, and the sun, and the moon. They will obey thy command, for they are God's creatures even as we are, and He will give thee authority over them, that they serve thee."

Then he washed Joshua's hands, and robed him in white, and purified him, and led him back into the inmost chamber. And there God appeared to them as a pillar of cloud. And God spoke to Joshua, and He spoke to Moses, to each of them separately. And Moses did not hear the words that God spoke to Joshua, but heard only the words that God spoke to him.

And God comforted him, and gave him the promise which He had withheld until this moment, for He said:

"Behold, thou goest to lie with thy fathers, and this people will rise against Me and will turn to the idols and false gods of the land into which I bring it; and it will transgress against the covenant which I have made with it. And My anger will be kindled against it, and I will withdraw from it and hide My face from it, and it will be delivered as to destruction, and many sufferings shall come upon it, and it will repent, saying: 'Surely it is because God is not in my midst that this evil has come upon me.' And My face will be concealed from it in the day of evil, because it has followed false gods. And now, write down this song, and teach it to the children of Israel; and put this song into the mouth of Israel, that it may be an eternal witness between us."

And to Joshua God said: "Be strong and stout of heart, for thou wilt bring the children of Israel into the land which I swore unto them and I will be with thee."

Now it remained for Moses only to complete the book of the testament which he had been writing for all the future generations of Israel. And when he had completed the testament, or song, as God had named it, he handed it over to the Levites, who were the carriers of the ark and the tables of the commandments, and he bade them place it by the side of the ark, by the covenant, and it was to remain there as a warning and admonition to Israel through all the generations. And he commanded the Levites:

"Gather to me all the elders of the tribes and their officers, and I will speak these words in their ears, and I will call heaven and earth to be witnesses against them."

And when the people were assembled before the sanctuary, Moses came out accompanied by the new leader, Joshua ben Nun, who wore the white veil of his office. And as the two of them stood before the people, Moses repeated for the Bnai Israel the ten commandments, and added:

"See, I have this day placed before you life and the good, and death and evil, and the commandment to love Jehovah, your God, and to go in His ways, that you may live, and multiply, and be blessed of God. . . .

"For now, O Israel, what does Jehovah thy God demand of thee? Only that thou fear Him, and love Him, and serve Him with all thy heart and with all thy soul. . . . For a holy people art thou to Jehovah, thy God. Thee has Jehovah chosen to be His own people. And not because you were greater in number than other peoples did Jehovah desire you, but because He loves you, and because He will keep the covenant which He made with your fathers. And when He chastises you, it is as a father chastises his son, for the children of God are you. And what people is there with a god as close to it as Jehovah our God is to us when we call upon Him? What great people is there with laws and commandments as just as the laws and commandments of this, our Torah? Do justice to the fatherless and the widow, and love the stranger, and give him bread and a garment. And love the stranger because ye were strangers in the land of Egypt. And thou shalt love thy neighbor as thyself, and be merciful to him, for thy God is a God of mercy and forgiveness. Therefore has He given you laws that are just and compassionate. For this commandment which I give thee today, it is not in heaven, that thou shalt say: 'Who will go into heaven for us, and take it for us, and let us hear it?' But the word is close to thee, in thy mouth and in thy heart. It is the way of life and the good, and do thou live with it, for only thereby canst thou prosper in the life which awaits thee in thy land."

And he foretold the Prophet, saying: "The Lord thy God will raise up unto thee a Prophet from the midst of thy brethren like unto me. And to him ye shall hearken."

And Moses chanted to them his testament song:

> "Give ear, ye heavens, and I will speak,
> And let the earth hear the words of my mouth.
> My doctrine shall drop as the rain,
> My speech shall distil as the dew."

> "For I will proclaim the name of Jehovah,
> Ascribe ye greatness unto our God.
> The Rock, His work is perfect,
> For all His ways are justice."

And he foretold that they would rebel against God after He had brought them into the land of milk and honey:

> "And he forsook the God who made him."

He admonished them to remember who they were, and what God had done for them:

497

"For the portion of the Lord is His people,
Jacob the lot of His inheritance.
He found him in a desert land,
And in the waste, a howling wilderness.
He compassed him about, he cared for him,
He kept him as the apple of His eye.
As an eagle that stirs up her nest,
And hovers over her young,
Spreads abroad her wings, takes them,
Bears them on her pinions."

"And He made him to suck honey out of the crag,
And oil out of the flinty rock."

And after he had stricken them with terror, revealing what
would be their lot when they had abandoned Jehovah—"the sword
shall bereave them without, and terror within the chambers"—he
lifted them to supreme heights, comforting them with the promise
which God had given him:

"For the Lord will judge His people,
And repent Himself for His servants,
When He sees that their force is spent,
And they are abandoned and forlorn;
And the peoples ask: 'Where are their gods,
The rock in whom they trusted?'
For He avenges the blood of His servants. . . ."

And after he had blessed each of the tribes by name, he turned
to all Israel with a triumphant cry of hope and comfort:

"Happy art thou, O Israel, who is like unto thee?
A people saved by the Lord,
The shield of thy help,
The sword of thy greatness.
Thine enemies shall melt before thee,
And thou shalt tread upon their high places."

And Moses lifted his hands and called out to the people:

"Hear, O Israel, the Lord our God, the Lord is One."

And these words were his farewell to the children of Israel.

CHAPTER THIRTEEN

IN stony immobility the entire congregation watched as Moses withdrew toward Mount Pisgah, whose slopes were visible from every part of the encampment. Not a limb stirred, not a tear was visible, not a word was spoken; no sound disturbed the stillness save the heavy breathing of the vast assembly.

It was in the full tide of glorious daylight that Moses left the Bnai Israel: not in the late evening, nor in the predawn twilight, when a dewy mist covered the earth; thus the people might see with their own eyes that Moses was not being taken from them to be bestowed elsewhere; he was not going to another land. He was not evading God's command, but in conformity with it he was ascending the slope in order to die on the heights. He went alone, a solitary, unaccompanied figure. The command had been: "Thou shalt go up the mountain alone." Joshua, Eleazar, the high priest, in his robes of office, the princes of Israel and the elders, the captains of the army and the officers of the people, ranged in order, with the tribe of Levi—the tribe of Moses—at the front, and in its midst the two sons of Moses, Gershom and Eliezer, to whom he had said a separate farewell—all these, and the congregation with them, stood rooted to the spot. There was no weeping, there was not even a murmur; the white faces were frozen on the white figure which, leaning upon the immense staff, moved with tranquil and measured step in the direction of the mountain. No sign of weakness or of lamentation. The figure was outlined with majestic massiveness under the white robe which concealed it; a kingly giant in flashing white raiment. The rays of the magnificent noonday sun turned into a blazing crown the locks of his head, and the locks which fell on his neck and shoulders were like a cascade of living waters. Only once he turned, to bestow a last look on those whom he was leaving. Then he resumed his journey. All that he had been bidden to do, he had done; all that he had been bidden to say, he had said. Now he was going, alone, to his God, Who had called him.

499

A long, long time the people remained assembled, watching. And even afterward they lingered in groups, about the leaders, or at the doors of their tents, fathers and mothers with children on their arms, still catching the shimmer of the remote and diminishing white figure. This was their last glimpse of the man Moses.

That which happened with Moses on the mountain remains a secret between him and God. But the love of Israel, which went with him on his last journey, and accompanied him in the spirit when he was lost to the sight, persuaded itself that it had penetrated the secret and could reveal the details of the encounter on the mystery mountain.

The mountain of Abarim, which is Pisgah, lay on the border between two worlds. The lower part of the mountain belonged to this world, the upper part belonged to the higher world. Midway on the slopes was the boundary between the two worlds.

It was early spring, the beginning of the month of Adar. The rains still fell in that month, but the sun was asserting itself against them. Winter and summer still contested the field. On this day, too, when Moses was on his way to the heights, the struggle was on between light and darkness. The rays of the sun shot like fiery lances through the thick weave of the rain clouds which hovered over the mountain, and alighted on the drenched grasses. From the overhanging branches of trees drops of rain and dew fell on the locks of Moses. The oleanders had broken into a thick blossoming of leaf and bud, and the white and red flowers shone like candle flames amid the laurel branches. The higher Moses ascended, the freer the landscape became of weeds, thorns, and tangles, so that it seemed to be emerging from an obstructing cloud until it lay clear and open before him. He could see the Jordan threading its way through the green valley and descending to the Salt Sea; he could see the mists rising from green-embowered little valleys; he could make out tiny, shifting patches of gray which were flocks of sheep. And it seemed to him that his ear could catch the far-off echo of human voices. And God endowed him with the power to perceive things that were to come, so that his eyes beheld the forms of the unborn times, and the sound of them came to his ears. He saw "the tents of Israel," the cities and settlements in the land which God had promised the patriarchs, he beheld each of the Bnai Israel sitting "under his vine and under his fig tree"; he heard the song of tran-

500

quillity and grace, his heart was filled with happiness, and on his face was the light of love and compassion.

But as long as Moses was on the lower half of the mountain he could see and hear only the things which pertained to the life of this world. He saw the city of Jericho, on the other side of the Jordan, he saw the mountains heaped up beyond the city, rolling downward on the other side toward the Great Sea. He saw fig trees and vineyards forming a green belt about the city, he saw towns and villages spread on the slopes of hills, and settlements nestling in valleys.

Then suddenly the entire landscape on the other side of the Jordan vanished from before his eyes. A thick, milky cloud had descended, filling all space and concealing from him everything above and below.

He walked in the cloud. Cloud rolls floated above him and drifted beneath him. He no longer knew where his feet trod, no longer knew whether he had passed the boundary between life and death, whether he had left this world and intruded into the next. And in this perplexity he saw the thick milkiness divide before him, and an island floated out from the heart of the cloud; it hung in the air, torn from the navel of the earth, suspended in the midst of cloud smoke, a crystallized image. On the island nothing was to be seen but a building in the form of the sanctuary: blue-gleaming curtains suspended before golden pillars fluttered and swayed round the sanctuary. Then the curtains parted. Moses beheld his brother Aaron, robed in priestly garb, standing before the golden *menorah* and trimming the lights. But there was another figure: someone kingly, in a silver mantle which flashed the reflections of a thousand colors; someone wearing a royal crown. And though he was in the likeness of a man of flesh and blood, his face was irradiated with the light of the divine indwelling. And Moses had already directed his footsteps toward the Temple which rose out of the milky cloud, when he heard the voice of his brother Aaron raised in warning:

"Moses ben Amram, draw not nigh. This is the place where rests the *Shekhinah,* the divine indwelling; and no man of flesh and blood may enter before surrendering his soul to the Angel of Death. Thou art now within the precincts of the Holy Temple which will be built here, on earth, by the Bnai Israel."

But Moses threw himself on the earth at his feet, concealed by the mist, and prayed:

501

"Father of all mercies, I know that he who is now with Aaron in the Holy Temple is none other than the King Messiah. Let me speak with the son of David before I surrender up my soul."

Then God revealed to Moses the Ineffable Name, saying:

"With the power of the Name thou wilt be saved from destruction by flames."

The moment Moses thus received from God permission to enter, as a living mortal, the Holy Temple which the Bnai Israel were yet to build on this earth, a wind lifted him and carried him beyond the Jordan to the gate of the sanctuary. Then Aaron and the Messiah came to meet him, and greeted him with these words:

"Blessed be he that comes in the name of the Lord."

Moses turned to the Messiah and said:

"See, God has told me that the Bnai Israel will build a Holy Temple for Him. Now I praise and thank the Lord of all the worlds that He has granted it to me to behold this Temple—and thee in it —with mine own eyes, and while I yet live on this earth."

"To thy forefather Jacob, too, it was granted to see with his own eyes the Holy Temple which his descendants were to build: this was in the dream which he dreamt when he slept in the field with a stone for a pillow, and the angels ascended and descended on the ladder. But this shalt thou know: the Holy Temple which is to be built on this earth is a temporal and fleeting thing. Eternally enduring is the Holy Temple which God has built with His hands in heaven. The Holy Temple of the upper world, and the Jerusalem of the upper world, shall live and shall be forever."

When Moses heard these words of the King Messiah he turned to the Lord of the world with this imploring prayer:

"O Thou that rulest the world, tell me when Thou wilt bring down upon earth the eternal Holy Temple which Thou hast built in heaven with Thine own hands?"

"This is the secret of the end of time; and this secret I have not revealed to any man of flesh and blood, and shall not reveal to one. But so much of a sign will I give thee: it will not come to pass before I shall have scattered the Bnai Israel, as with a shovel, upon all the face of the earth, before they shall be scattered and sown among all the peoples, bringing the Torah which I gave them on Mount Sinai to all the four corners of the world. For the End cannot come, and the Kingdom of Heaven cannot begin, until the

502

Law of Mount Sinai shall have been accepted by all the peoples of the earth."

Then the curtains of the heavenly white clouds closed before Moses, and the island with the structure of the Holy Temple vanished behind the heavenly gates. He found himself again on the mountain path, ascending, ever ascending. And an angel swathed in black, an angel with two mighty, black wings, followed him, step by step, accompanying him all the way.

Then, when they reached a certain point in the ascent, the black angel suddenly stepped forth, turned, and with drawn sword barred the way to Moses.

"Son of Amram, thou hast reached the boundary of thy world. No man born of woman may pass the threshold of the other world before he delivers to me his body and his soul. Thy soul too belongs to me."

"My Creator and thine has called me to the summit of the mountain. I have never failed to obey His command even in the face of death, and I shall not fail now."

Therewith Moses advanced his foot to pass the boundary of the worlds. But the angel interposed his sword and held him back.

"I too obey the command of my Lord. Either thou wilt slay me, or I thee."

"Thy command is for death, mine is for life," cried Moses, and he uttered the Ineffable Name which God had revealed to him.

At sound of the Name the sword fell from the hand of the angel, and Moses was about to destroy death by slaying the Angel of Death. At that instant a voice sounded from the heights:

"Do it not, Moses, let him live, for the world needs him."

And Moses obeyed the command, and he passed, body and soul intact, across the boundary between this world and the other.

Beyond the boundary which he had crossed he could perceive nothing. He was steeped in a sea of clouds black as night. He felt himself becoming light; it was as if wings had sprouted under his garment; he felt himself able to fly. And almost before he was aware of it he was indeed flying and had risen above the night-black cloud.

Suddenly he heard voices calling to him out of the cloud:

"Moses, our teacher, Moses, our teacher, has come to us."

He looked down on the surface of the cloud, and he saw lean, fleshless hands reaching out of the smoke. Then faces and beards of all but skeletons rose, crying:

"Moses, our teacher, take us with you."

He recognized them. They were the dead he had left in the wilderness.

"Your time is not yet come."

"Moses, our teacher, stay with us!" And the hands made as if to clutch at his white garment.

"I must go, in obedience to the command," answered Moses. "I cannot stay with you."

"Moses, our teacher, we would be with thee!" the voices implored and lamented.

"You will be with me at the resurrection," Moses comforted them, and swept onward beyond the cloud which covered the valley of death.

When Moses had passed beyond the cloud and the valley of death, he was set down on a broad, shining road which curved through dewy fields to the foot of a hill. The summit of the hill reached into heaven, and became one with heaven in a flaming amber brightness. The landscape was without sound or motion, and the only living thing in that world was Moses. The radiance of the amber brightness lay on the summit of the hill, but a strange, blue-shining cloud lay on the slopes, here concealing and here revealing green-blue fields. Moses marched a solitary figure in the landscape, hearing no voice and seeing no motion. But as he drew nearer to the hill he caught, across the circling blue clouds playing round the slopes, a golden glimmer of cupolas and palaces towering above each other. Before long he could discern a city of white-shining edifices with golden cupolas nestling in dewy recesses of the hill; and coming still closer he saw that the walls and towers rose beyond the recesses, climbed the heights, and reached toward the summit, where the amber radiance rested on them like a dazzling canopy. And now a quiet singing floated toward him from the hill, a prayer-like melody and outpouring of the soul which was wafted outward toward the horizon as if to fill all creation. But about him all was still as he strode along the white road toward the summit of the hill. Around the flickering summit seraphs flew, entering the fire and issuing from it, and a great singing pealed from the midst of the fire. And when Moses came to the border of the shining city he kneeled down and stretched his hands out to the light which shone from the Holy Temple of the upper world, on the summit of the hill, and he cried:

"Father of all spirits, in love hast Thou created Thy world, with love Thou guidest it. Do Thou therefore apply to me Thy attribute of love. Deliver me not to the pit of Sheol, but be compassionate unto me and take me to Thee."

And when Moses rose to his feet, and stood on the spot where he had been kneeling, he beheld three angels: Michael, the angel of Israel, Gabriel, the angel of peace, and Zagzagel, the angel who had been his instructor in heaven. They greeted him with these words:

"Blessed be he that comes in the name of God. Thy righteousness goes before thee, and the grace of God shall be thy recompense."

And they took Moses and led him into a hall. Gabriel set down a couch before him, Michael stretched out upon it a covering of purple, and Zagzagel placed at the head a white pillow, which was Jacob's stone. Then Michael stationed himself on the right, and Gabriel on the left, and Zagzagel at the foot of the bed.

And the voice of Jehovah was heard at the death of Moses as it had been heard during his life.

"Stretch out thy feet."

And Moses obeyed.

"Fold thy arms upon thy breast."

And Moses obeyed.

"Close thine eyes."

And Moses obeyed.

Then Moses felt as it were a wind breathing over him. And a flame touched his lips.

A smile rested on Moses' face, for on his lips hovered the kiss of Jehovah, the kiss wherewith God had taken the soul of Moses, our teacher, to rest with Him.

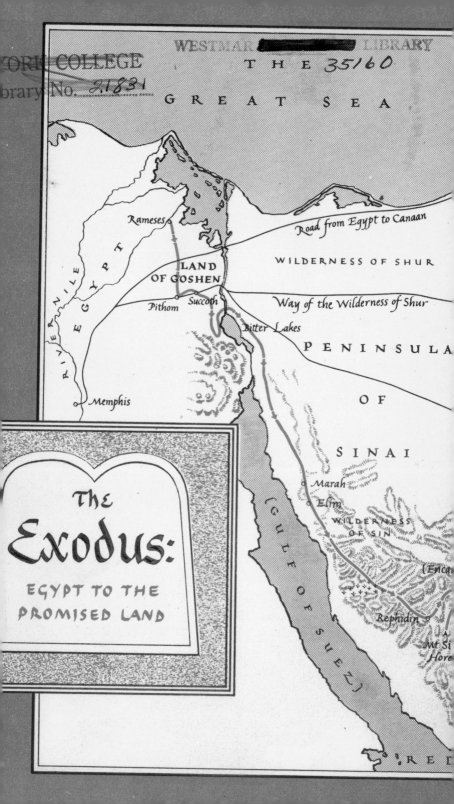

RIVER NILE

E G Y P T

Rameses

LAND
OF GOSHEN

Pithom   Succoth

Memphis

Road from Egypt to Canaan

WILDERNESS OF SHUR

Way of the Wilderness of Shur

Bitter Lakes

P E N I N S U L A

O F

S I N A I

Marah

Elim

WILDERNESS
OF SIN

[Enca

Rephidin

Mt Si
Hore

(GULF OF SUEZ)

RED

The
Exodus:
EGYPT TO THE
PROMISED LAND